Statics and Strength of Structures

Prentice-Hall International Series in Architecture

Mario Salvadori, Editor

SALVADORI AND HELLER *Structure in Architecture*
SALVADORI AND LEVY *Structural Design in Architecture*
SALVADORI *Mathematics in Architecture*
SALVADORI *Statics and Strength of Structures*

PRENTICE-HALL INTERNATIONAL, INC., *London*
PRENTICE-HALL OF AUSTRALIA, PTY. LTD., *Sydney*
PRENTICE-HALL OF CANADA, LTD., *Toronto*
PRENTICE-HALL OF INDIA PRIVATE LIMITED, *New Delhi*
PRENTICE-HALL OF JAPAN, INC., *Tokyo*

Statics and Strength of Structures

MARIO SALVADORI

Chairman, Architectural Technology Division
Columbia University

In collaboration with

JEREMIAH ECK
Columbia University

and

GIUSEPPE de CAMPOLI
The City College of New York and Columbia University

Prentice-Hall, Inc., Englewood Cliffs, N. J.

Current printing (last digit):
10 9 8 7 6 5 4 3 2 1

13-844548-61

Library of Congress Catalog Card Number 70-138821
Printed in the United States of America

Preface

This book has been written for those students and practitioners of engineering and architecture who are interested in designing structures, but do not want to loose sight of the physical woods because of the mathematical trees.

A careful reader of the following pages, without recourse to the calculus, will be able to dimension and check most of the structures he will encounter in his professional life, all the way from simple beams to space frames and thin shells. Moreover, the student will find in it relevant applications of statics and strength to real life situations and the professional the most basic information for preliminary design.

I have verified these two claims through the collaboration of Jeremiah Eck, one of my first-year students in the School of Architecture at Columbia University, and of Giuseppe de Campoli, a structural designer formerly with the office of Paul Weidlinger, Cons. Eng. in which I am a partner, who is on the staff of the Schools of Architecture at both The City College and Columbia University in New York. Mr. Eck criticized the manuscript and drew the figures; Mr. de Campoli taught students at The City College and at Columbia using the preliminary notes for this book.

The presentation of the material follows closely the intuitive, non-mathematical treatment of structures to be found in my book *Structure in Architecture* (written in collaboration with Dr. Robert A. Heller). This book is also a logical prerequisite for the more advanced material in *Structural Design in Architecture* by Matthys Levy and myself.

The answers to all the problems, gathered at the end of the book, and the availability of a complete handbook of carefully worked out solutions should enhance the usefulness of this book to the student, the self-teaching professional, and the instructor.

With her usual unusual skill, Miss Amy Bergvelt typed the manuscript of this book from the mimeograph notes produced by Miss Regina Tetens. Mrs. Isabelle Ruch typed with particular care the answers and the solution handbook.

MARIO SALVADORI

Contents

LIST OF MATHEMATICAL FORMULAS

The following formulas represent the entire mathematical knowledge required by the reader for an understanding of the subject matter covered in this book.

1. $(a \pm b)^2 = a \pm 2ab + b^2$ **2.** $a^2 - b^2 = (a + b)(a - b)$

3. $\dfrac{1}{1 + x} \approx 1 - x \quad (x \ll 1)$ **4.** $\sqrt{1 + x} \approx 1 + \tfrac{1}{2}x \quad (x \ll 1)$

5. $\dfrac{1}{\sqrt{1 + x}} \approx 1 - \tfrac{1}{2}x \quad (x \ll 1)$

6. $x^2 + bx + c = 0; \quad x_{1,2} = -\dfrac{b}{2} \pm \sqrt{\left(\dfrac{b}{2}\right)^2 - c}$

7. $\begin{aligned} ax + by &= c \\ dx + ey &= f \end{aligned} \quad x = (ce - bf)/(ae - bd); \quad y = (af - cd)/(ae - bd)$

8. $\sin(\alpha + 90°) = \cos \alpha$ **9.** $\cos(\alpha + 90°) = -\sin \alpha$

10. $2 \sin \alpha \cos \alpha = \sin 2\alpha$ **11.** $\sin \alpha \approx \alpha - \alpha^3/6 \quad (\alpha \ll 1)$

12. $\cos \alpha \approx 1 - \alpha^2/2 \quad (\alpha \ll 1)$

Note: The following new notation for steel sections used in the 1970 edition of the *Steel Construction Manual of the American Institute of Steel Construction* should be substituted for the old notation:

W 14 × 60 for 14 WF 60,
W 14 × 22 for 14 *B* 22,
S 8 × 25 for 8 *I* 25,
[for ,
L for .

LIST OF MATHEMATICAL SYMBOLS

$=$	equal to
$\equiv$	equal by definition to
$\approx$	approximately equal to
$\neq$	unequal to
$<$	less than
$>$	greater than
$\ll$	much less than
$\gg$	much greater than
$\therefore$	therefore
$\lvert \; \rvert$	absolute value (positive value of a number)

LIST OF ABBREVIATIONS

1. in. = inch
2. ft = feet
3. yd = yard (3 ft)
4. mi = mile (5,280 ft)
5. in.^{2} or sq in. = square inches
6. ft^2 or sq ft = square feet
7. in.^{3} or cu in. = cubic inches
8. ft^3 or cu ft = cubic feet
9. cu yd = cubic yards (27 cu ft)
10. lb = pounds
11. k = kips (1,000 lb)
12. t = tons (2,000 lb)
13. pli = pounds per lineal inch
14. plf = pounds per lineal foot
15. klf = kips per lineal foot
16. psi = pounds per square inch
17. psf = pounds per square foot
18. ksi = kips per square inch
19. ksf = kips per square foot
20. lb/cu in. = pounds per cubic inch
21. lb/cu ft = pounds per cubic foot
22. k/cu yd = kips per cubic yard
23. in.-lb = inch-pounds
24. ft-lb = foot-pounds
25. ft-k = foot-kips
26. sec = seconds (of time)
27. °F = degrees Fahrenheit
28. ′ = minutes of a degree (angle)
29. ″ = seconds of a degree (angle)
30. o.c. = on center

Statics and Strength of Structures

Chapter One

1.1 Statically Determinate Structures

The structure of a building must withstand the action of a variety of forces: the pull of the earth on the building itself and on its contents; the pressures and suctions due to the wind; the thrust of retained earth and that of contained or underground water; the shaking forces due to earthquakes; the impact forces due to waves (and, at times, to man-made explosions); the internal forces due to uneven foundation settlements and to temperature differences between the several parts of the building. For functional reasons, buildings are designed to undergo such minute displacements under the action of these forces that, for all practical purposes, they may be assumed to be at rest. When a building is at rest under the action of all the forces applied to it, we say that it is *in equilibrium.*

It may be thought that the determination of the conditions which guarantee the equilibrium of a whole building, and of each of its component parts, must be an extremely complicated task. And, indeed, it would be were it not for Isaac Newton's assertion that all problems involving the equilibrium as well as the motion of bodies can be solved by the application of three simple statements, now known as *Newton's laws.*

The Laws of Statics

Newton's statements may be paraphrased as follows:

1. If, while under the action of certain forces, a body moves at a constant speed in a certain direction, its speed will not change in direction or magnitude unless the forces change.
2. If a force is applied to a body, its speed in the direction of the applied force will change, and the larger the force the greater the change in speed.*
3. If a body is in equilibrium, for each force acting on the body there must be a corresponding equal and opposite force, or *reaction.*

Newton's statements are not mathematically provable. They are basic physical assumptions to be tested by experiment. Since to this day no experiment has proved them incorrect, they are accepted as the basic laws of mechanics.

In studying the action of forces on buildings and other structures, we are

*The change in speed is called the *acceleration* and Newton's second law simply states that the acceleration produced by a force is proportional to the force.

often concerned with structures at rest. The speed in any particular direction of a body at rest is and remains zero, i.e., *it does not change.* Hence, by Newton's second law, the force applied to the body in that direction is zero. Thus, if we limit our considerations to bodies at rest, Newton's laws may be reduced to the following two statements:

A. If a body is in equilibrium in a given direction (i.e., does not move in that direction), the total force acting on the body in that direction is zero.

B. To each force there corresponds an equal and opposite force, or reaction.

The practical importance of these two statements rests on the fact that a large number of architectural and other structures (e.g., certain beams, trusses, cables and shells) can be analyzed *without having to appeal to any other principle.* Since the study of equilibrium is called *statics*, such structures are called *statically determinate* (determined by statics only).

Statically determinate structures will be shown to present other advantageous characteristics. Since their behavior under load is independent of the material they are made of, such structures can be designed *without previous choice of material or size* (except, of course, when their own weight is of importance); moreover, they are not subject to the internal forces due to temperature differences and foundation settlements.

It must be recognized that many modern architectural structures are not statically determinate; their analysis cannot be performed without first choosing a material and establishing sizes on the basis of experience. For example, such is the case for the framed skeletons of modern high-rise buildings and for the structures of most large-span roofs. A structure that cannot be analyzed by statics alone is called *statically indeterminate.*

Since most modern structures are statically indeterminate, you may wonder whether one is justified in giving time to the application of statics to structures. There are, however, at least four reasons why modern architects and engineers must thoroughly understand the behavior of statically determinate structures: (1) all structures, both statically determinate and indeterminate, obey the laws of statics; (2) statically determinate structures are still widely used; (3) the behavior of statically indeterminate structures may often be excellently approximated by that of simpler statically determinate structures; (4) the behavior of statically determinate structures can be so easily grasped on the basis of purely physical considerations that *statics is the best introduction to the behavior of all structures.*

The main purpose of this book is to show the reader how, through the application of Newton's laws of statics, he can learn to design a large variety of architectural structures, using a minimum of mathematics and an elementary knowledge of materials behavior.

1.2 Degrees of Freedom

We shall say that a structure is *in equilibrium* if it does not move. In this definition of equilibrium we ignore the displacements which are a consequence of the minute changes in shape induced by the forces acting on the structure, since in a well designed structure these are extremely small in comparison with the dimensions of the structure. For example, the top of a steel skyscraper 1,500 ft high sways less than 1 ft under the action of the strongest wind; a horizontal displacement of 1 ft in a 1,500 ft high building is not detectable by the naked eye. Once the skyscraper is built, its top will move down by 1 or 2 in. under the action of all the weights put into it, a vertical displacement of only 1 or 2 in. in 18,000 in.

If minor changes in a structure's shape are negligible, the structure behaves as an undeformable or *rigid body*. We now need to inquire into the geometrical conditions of rigid body equilibrium.

Consider the building in Fig. 1.2.1, the sides of which are oriented in the east-west and north-south directions. Indicate these directions, for short, as the x- and y-directions, and the vertical direction as the z-direction. If the building were not tied to the ground, a west wind would move it in the x-direction and a south wind in the y-direction; moreover, if the soil were not sufficiently strong, the building would sink, i.e., move in the z-direction, under its own weight. We say in this case that the building has 3 *degrees of translational freedom*, in the x-, y- and z-directions. ("To translate," from the Latin *translare*, means to move a body in a straight line.)

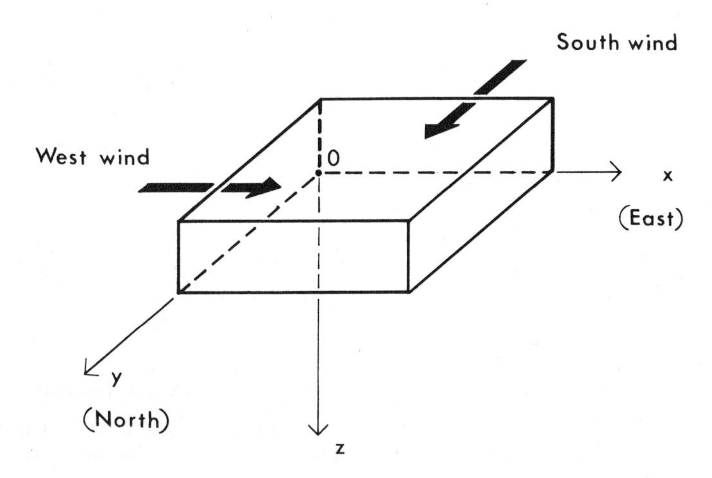

Fig. 1.2.1

When the soil is strong enough to prevent vertical motion, the untied building still has 2 degrees of translational freedom, in the x- and y-directions, but is *in equilibrium in the z-direction* since all of its points have zero displacements d_z (do not move) in the z-direction. Thus, a structure may be in equilibrium in one of 3 perpendicular directions, but not in the other 2.

To prevent motion in the y-direction, so that all points in the building have zero displacements d_y, we may set the building between two buttresses, placed along the two sides parallel to x (Fig. 1.2.2). The building then has only

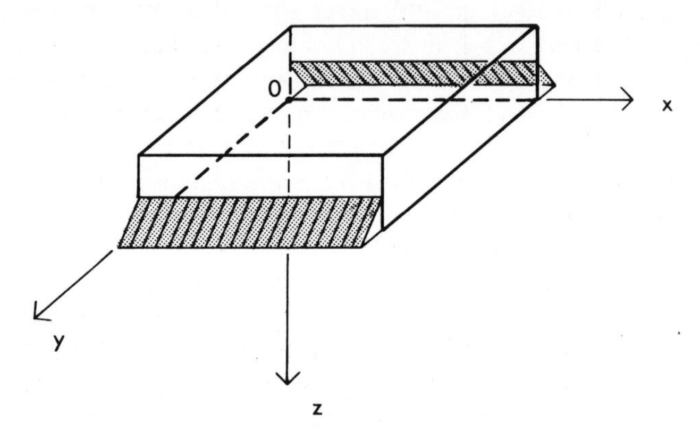

Fig. 1.2.2

one degree of translational freedom, in the x-direction; it is in equilibrium in the y- and z-directions, but not in the x-direction. Finally, if the building has buttresses along its four sides, so that it cannot move in the x-, y- or z-directions (i.e., so that it is in equilibrium along x, y and z), the building has *no* degrees of translational freedom. But since the building behaves as a rigid body, to guarantee that it will be in equilibrium in the three directions x, y, z, it is sufficient to restrain the motion of *one* of its points, say 0. Hence, translational equilibrium of a rigid body is guaranteed if *for one point* in the body:

$$d_x = 0, \qquad d_y = 0, \qquad d_z = 0. \tag{1.2.1}$$

On the other hand, the 3 conditions (1.2.1) are not sufficient to guarantee that a building will *not* move at all, because, even if we restrain the point 0 at its bottom (Fig. 1.2.3), an east wind could topple the building by rotating it around its edge along the y-axis, a north wind could rotate it around its edge along the x-axis and, moreover, the building could be twisted around the z-axis by any wind. Therefore, we say that the building also has 3 *degrees of rotational freedom* around the x-, y- and z-axes. To guarantee its total equilibrium, we must prevent (besides the displacements d_x, d_y, d_z of one of

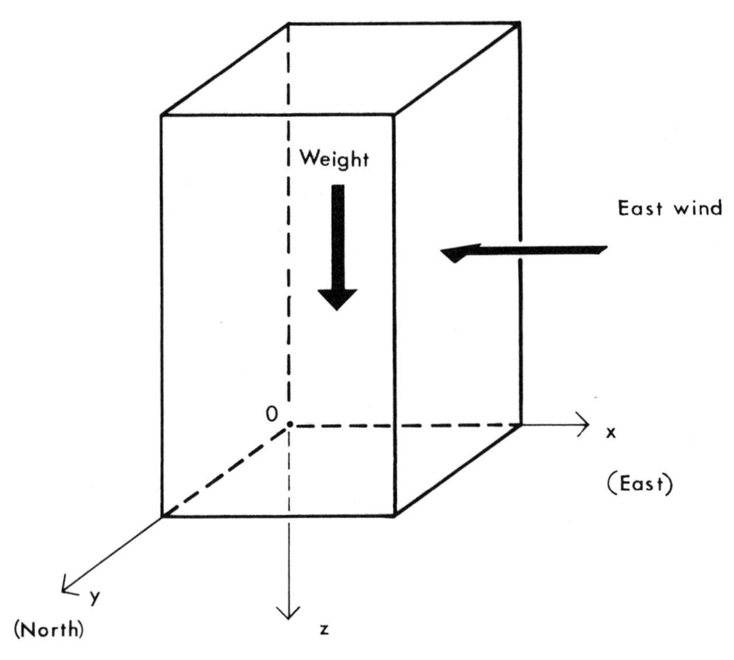

Fig. 1.2.3

its points *along* the 3 axes) the rotations r_x, r_y, r_z of the building *around* the 3 axes. Hence, the 3 conditions of *rotational equilibrium* are:

$$r_x = 0, \qquad r_y = 0, \qquad r_z = 0. \tag{1.2.2}$$

It is thus seen that, since a rigid body has 6 degrees of freedom, all 6 equations of (1.2.1) and (1.2.2) must be satisfied to guarantee its equilibrium.

We now wish to notice that *under certain conditions* the building in Fig. 1.2.3 may be seen *beforehand* to satisfy some of the 6 conditions of equilibrium. For example, if the building were completely unrestrained but were acted upon only by its weight and by a *uniform* wind from the east, the building would have no cause to move in the y-direction, nor to rotate about the x- or z-axes, so that the conditions:

$$d_y = 0, \qquad r_x = 0, \qquad r_z = 0 \tag{a}$$

would always be satisfied. The building would tend to move only in the x-, z-plane, i.e., to have displacements d_x and d_z and a rotation r_y. This example shows that, when a body is known beforehand to have its motion restrained to a plane, say the x, z-plane, because *all* the forces on it act in this plane, only

3 conditions are needed to guarantee its *plane equilibrium:*

$$d_x = 0, \qquad d_z = 0, \qquad r_y = 0, \tag{1.2.3}$$

since the other 3 conditions are always satisfied.

We finally wish to notice that for an entire building to be in equilibrium, each of its parts (columns, beams, floors, stairs, etc.) must also be in equilibrium. Hence, when a building is in equilibrium, *each* of its parts also satisfies the set of equations (1.2.1), (1.2.2) or (1.2.3). A part of a structure isolated from the structure itself ("freed" from it) and acted upon by the loads directly applied to it and by the reactions exerted on it by the rest of the structure, is called a *free body.* Thus, the previous remark states that, if a structure is in equilibrium, *any* free body cut out of it must also be in equilibrium. You will find that this fairly obvious statement is most useful in structural analysis.

PROBLEMS

1.2.1 A locomotive runs on a straight horizontal track parallel to x. Which of the 6 conditions of equilibrium are satisfied by the body of the locomotive?

1.2.2 A wheel rotates about a fixed axle parallel to y. What condition of equilibrium is not satisfied by the wheel?

1.2.3 The two ends of a ladder slide, respectively, on the floor of a room in a direction x perpendicular to a wall, and on the wall in a vertical direction z. What conditions of equilibrium are satisfied by the ladder?

1.2.4 What condition of equilibrium is satisfied by a marble moving on a horizontal x, y-plane?

1.2.5 A fire ladder is lowered vertically along the face of a building. Which condition of equilibrium is not satisfied by the ladder?

1.2.6 What conditions of equilibrium are satisfied by a moving elevator?

1.2.7 What conditions of equilibrium are satisfied by an escalator moving at a 30° angle to the x-axis in the x, z-plane?

1.3 Forces and Translational Equilibrium

In the preceding section we have considered equilibrium from a purely geometrical viewpoint, i.e., as the prevention of displacement. By means of Newton's laws, the geometrical conditions (1.2.1), (1.2.2) or (1.2.3) can be changed into equations dealing with forces which are directly useful in structural design.

Let us consider first the 3 translational equilibrium conditions (1.2.1). By statement A on p.4, if $d_x = 0$, the *total* force acting on the body in the x-direction must be zero. Let us indicate a force acting in the x-direction by F_x and give it a plus or minus sign depending on whether it acts in the direction of the positive or negative x-axis, and let us introduce the symbol $\sum F_x$ to indicate the algebraic sum, or *resultant*, of all the F_x forces acting on the body.* The condition for translational equilibrium in the x-direction can then be written as:

$$\sum F_x = 0. \tag{a}$$

Generalizing equation (a), we see that the 3 conditions for the *translational equilibrium* of a rigid body are:

$$\sum F_x = 0, \qquad \sum F_y = 0, \qquad \sum F_z = 0, \tag{1.3.1}$$

and that from (1.2.3) the 2 conditions for translational *plane* equilibrium in the x, z-plane are:

$$\sum F_x = 0, \qquad \sum F_z = 0. \tag{1.3.2}$$

For example, if a wind pressure of 30 psf acts on the west face of a building 100 ft × 100 ft in plan and 250 ft high (Fig. 1.3.1), the wind exerts on that face a force:

$$F_x = 30 \times 100 \times 250 = 750{,}000 \text{ lb} = 750 \text{ k},$$

which is positive because directed along the positive x-axis. For the building to be in equilibrium in the x-direction, the soil must exert on it a force or reaction R_x, given by the first of equations (1.3.1):

$$750 + R_x = 0 \quad \therefore \quad R_x = -750 \text{ k}.$$

We assumed R_x to be positive, *as one does with all unknown quantities*, but instead it is negative; this means that R_x acts in the direction of the negative x-axis, as indicated in Fig. 1.3.1.†

Similarly, if the building has 25 stories and weighs 0.25 ksf per story, its total weight is $W = 25 \times 0.25 \times 100 \times 100 = 62{,}500$ k and by the third of equations (1.3.1) the soil reaction in the z-direction is given by:

*The Greek letter $\sum$ (capital sigma) is equivalent to our letter S and stands for "sum." Hence, $\sum F_x$ is read "sum of all the forces acting in the x-direction."

†This result may also be derived from statement B on p. 4: to the force $F_x = +750$ k there corresponds an equal and opposite force $R_x = -750$ k, since the building is in equilibrium in the x-direction.

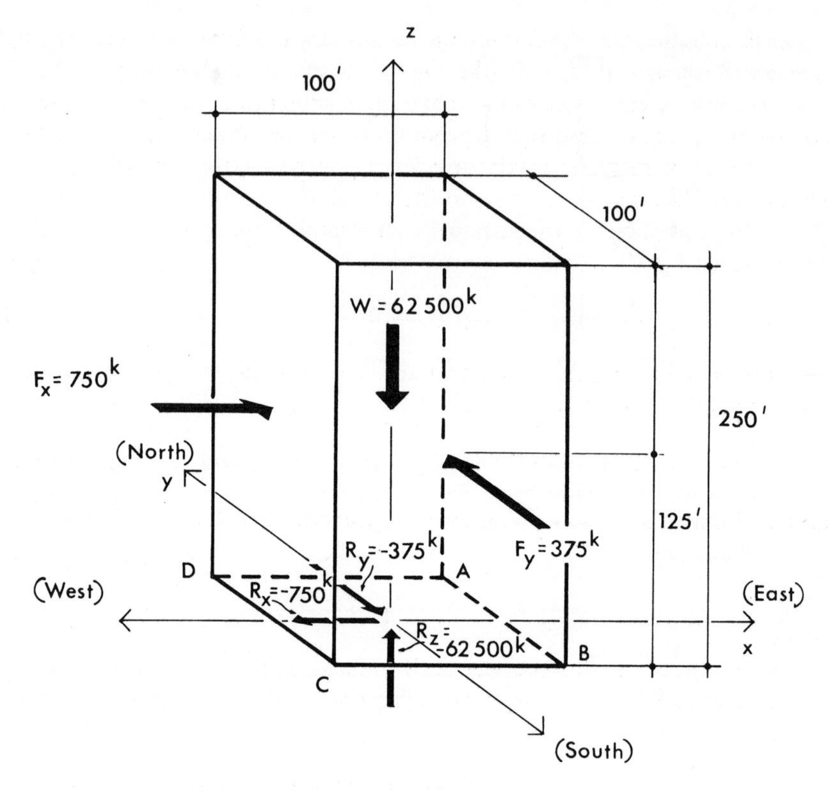

Fig. 1.3.1

$$-62{,}500 + R_z = 0 \quad \therefore \quad R_z = 62{,}500 \text{ k.}$$

The positive sign of R_z shows that R_z acts along the positive z-axis, i.e., upward.

Finally, if the wind also exerted a pressure of 15 psf = 0.015 ksf on the south face of the building, the soil reaction in the y-direction would be given by:

$$0.015 \times 100 \times 250 + R_y = 0 \quad \therefore \quad R_y = -375 \text{ k}$$

and would act in the negative y-direction.*

As an example of plane equilibrium, consider the beam of Fig. 1.3.2, which carries the three loads shown and is supported by end walls. We wish to determine its support reactions. All the loads on the beam, and hence, also

*The rotational equilibrium of the building will be checked in Section 1.4.

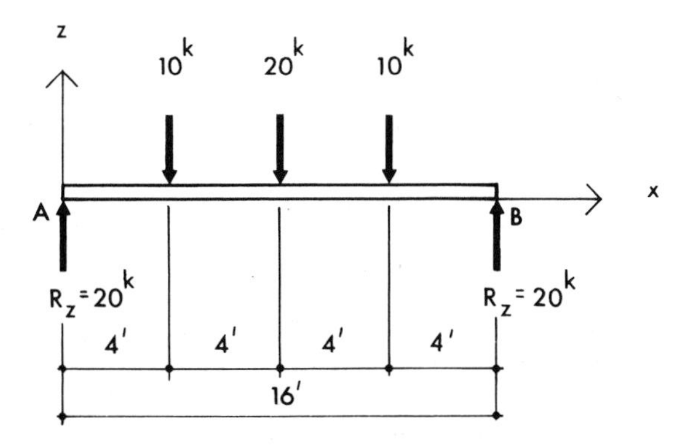

Fig. 1.3.2

its reactions, act in a vertical plane, so that equations (1.3.2) are sufficient to establish the translational equilibrium of the beam. Since there are no applied forces in the x-direction, by the first of (1.3.2) there is no reaction R_x.

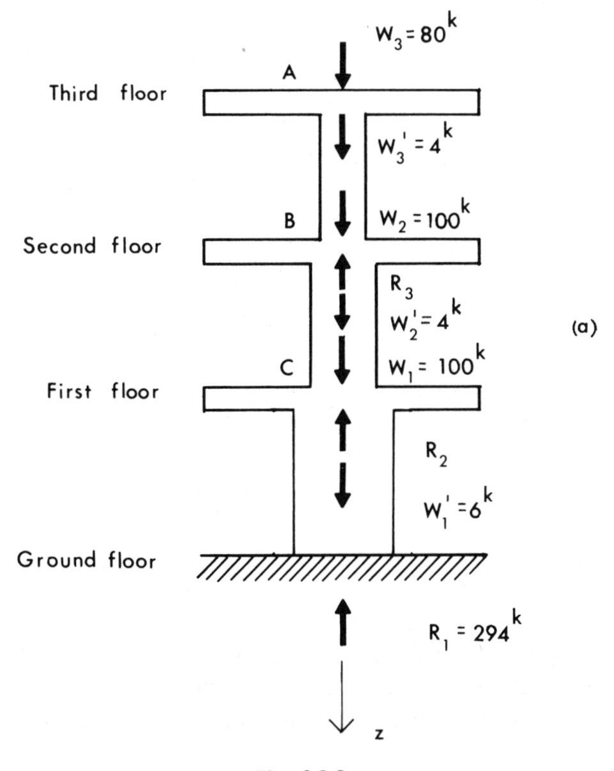

Fig. 1.3.3a

We now notice that the two walls are capable of exerting vertical reactions on the beam at A and B, but that, because of the symmetrical values of the loads and their symmetrical locations, the 2 reactions must be equal. Hence, by the second of equations (1.3.2):

$$R_z - 10 - 20 - 10 + R_z = 0, \qquad 2R_z = 40 \quad \therefore \quad R_z = 20 \text{ k}.$$

As an example of the use of "free bodies," consider the three columns of Fig. 1.3.3a, which carry the indicated floor loads W and their own weights W'. We wish to determine the reaction R_1 of the ground on the first column, the reaction R_2 of the first floor on the second column and the reaction R_3 of the second floor on the third column. The vertical equilibrium of the entire structural system gives:

$$80 + 4 + 100 + 4 + 100 + 6 - R_1 = 0 \quad \therefore \quad R_1 = 294 \text{ k}.$$

To obtain R_2, cut a free body consisting of the part of the system *above* the first floor (Fig. 1.3.3b), and apply to it the equation for vertical equilibrium:

$$80 + 4 + 100 + 4 - R_2 = 0 \quad \therefore \quad R_2 = 188 \text{ k}.$$

Similarly, by means of a free body consisting of the part of the structure *above* the second floor (Fig. 1.3.3c), we obtain:

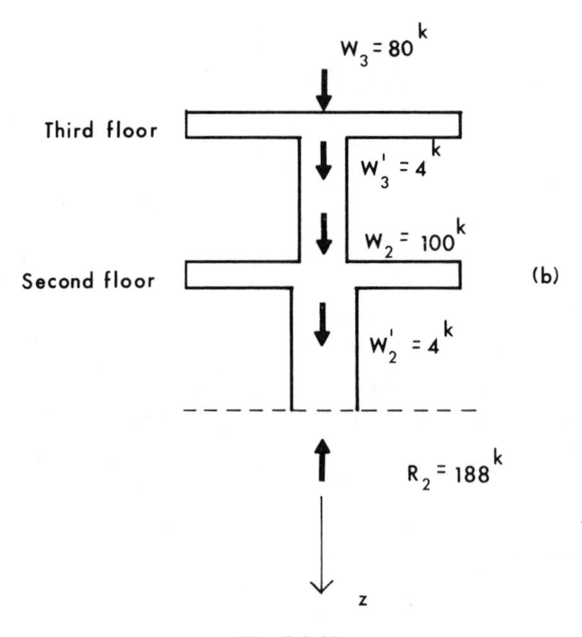

Fig. 1.3.3b

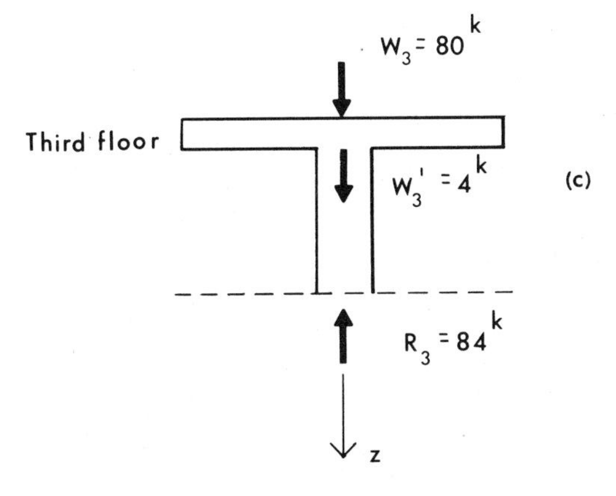

Fig. 1.3.3c

PROBLEMS

1.3.1 A cantilever beam carries the downward loads shown in Fig. 1.3.4 and is also supported by an upward cable pull of 25 k. Determine the reaction R_z.

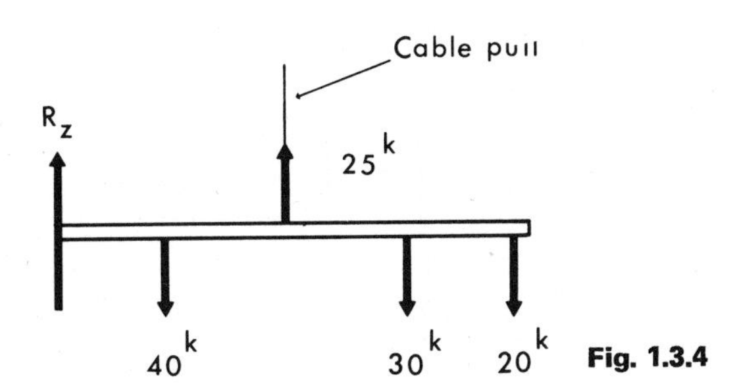

Fig. 1.3.4

1.3.2 A beam supported at its ends on two walls carries the loads shown in Fig. 1.3.5. Determine the reactions of the two walls.

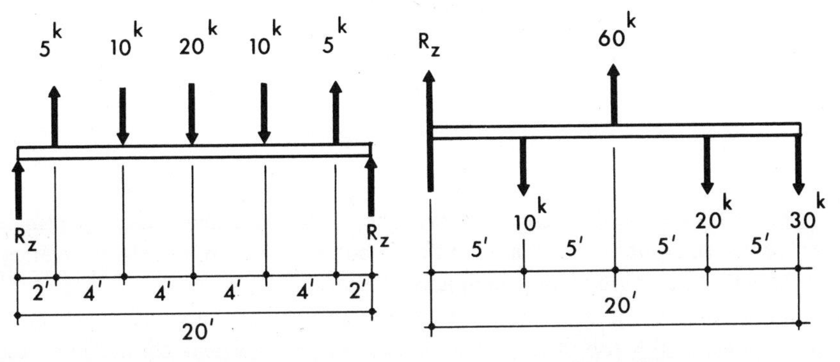

Fig. 1.3.5

Fig. 1.3.6

1.3.3 A cantilever beam carries upward and downward loads as shown in Fig. 1.3.6. Determine the reaction R_z.

1.3.4 A 20 story building weighs 0.2 ksf per floor including columns. Its columns are spaced on a square grid 20 ft on center so that each column carries the load on $20 \times 20 = 400$ sq ft of building. Determine the reaction R_z on a column at the bottom of the building and on a column right above the 12th story.

1.3.5 A 20 story tower, 30 ft $\times$ 30 ft in plan, is 250 ft high and weighs 0.2 ksf per floor. The soil is capable of developing (through friction) a horizontal force equal to 1/10 of the building's weight. What is the largest wind pressure p (in psf) the building can withstand before it slides on the ground, assuming the wind does not topple it?

1.3.6 A vertical dike made out of concrete and h ft high (Fig. 1.3.7) rests on a soil which can develop a horizontal frictional reaction R_h equal to one-half of the wall's weight. The total horizontal force exerted by the water on the dike is $H = 32\,h^2$ lb per horizontal foot of dike. If the concrete weighs 150 lb/cu ft, determine in terms of h the minimum width b of the dike required for horizontal equilibrium.

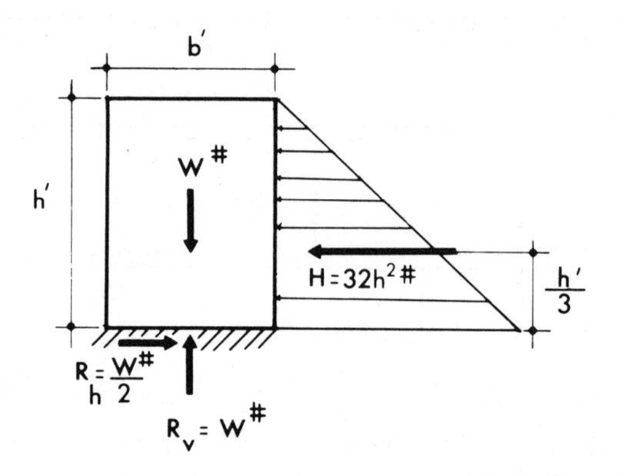

Fig. 1.3.7

1.4 Moments and Rotational Equilibrium

Newton's laws can be used to derive the force conditions which guarantee the *rotational* equilibrium of a rigid body, but these are more easily obtained by the well known physical principle of the lever.

If two boys of equal weight W sit at the ends of a seesaw with equal arms l (Fig. 1.4.1a), the seesaw does not rotate, and for vertical equilibrium, the upward reaction R at the seesaw pivot equals $2W$. If the two boys have different weights W_a and W_b (Fig. 1.4.1b), the upward reaction at the pivot, for

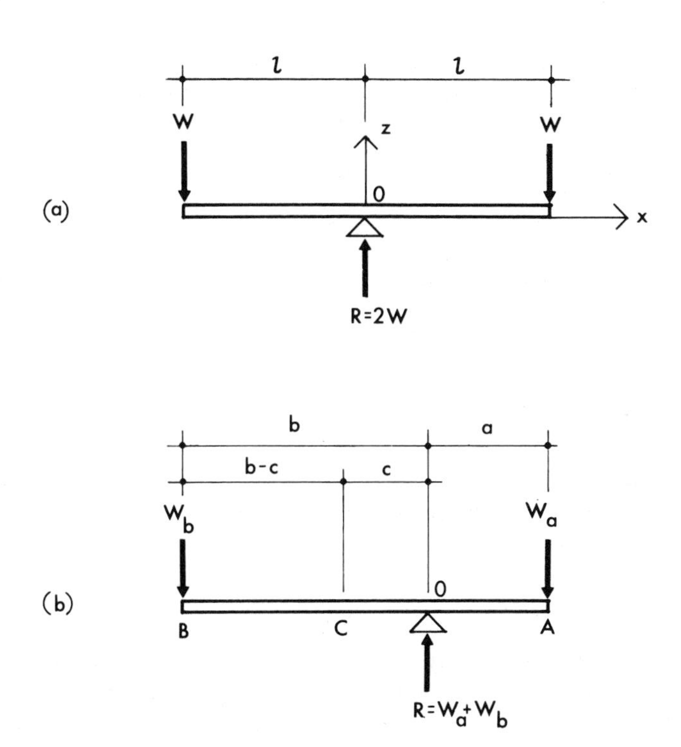

Fig. 1.4.1

vertical equilibrium, equals $W_a + W_b$, but the arms a and b cannot be equal if the seesaw is not to rotate. In this case, by the *lever principle*, rotational equilibrium will subsist only if:

$$W_a a = W_b b. \tag{a}$$

In words, rotational equilibrium is obtained if and only if the products of the 2 weights times the length of their respective lever arms are equal.

The product of a force F times the perpendicular distance between a point 0 and the line along which the force acts is called *the moment M_O of F about* 0. Moments are measured in foot-pounds, kip-feet or similar appropriate units and are usually given a plus or minus sign depending on whether the force tends to rotate counterclockwise or clockwise around 0. Thus, in Fig. 1.4.1b the moment of W_a about 0 is clockwise, i.e., negative, and the moment of W_b about 0 is counterclockwise, i.e., positive. Rewriting (a) as:

$$-W_a a + W_b b = 0, \tag{a'}$$

we see that the *algebraic* sum of the moments about 0 of all the forces applied to the seesaw is zero. (The reaction R has zero lever arm about 0 and hence zero moment about 0.) We now notice that the algebraic sum of the moments of the three forces W_a, W_b and $R = W_a + W_b$ about *any other point* is also zero. For example, the sum of the moments about B is:

$$\begin{aligned} &-W_a(a + b) + (W_a + W_b)\, b + W_b \times 0 \\ &= -W_a a - W_a b + W_a b + W_b b = -W_a a + W_b b = 0, \end{aligned} \tag{a''}$$

and the sum of the moments about a point C a distance c from 0 is:

$$\begin{aligned} &-W_a(a + c) + (W_a + W_b)\, c + W_a(b - c) \\ &= -W_a a - W_a c + W_a c + W_b c + W_b b - W_b c \\ &= -W_a a + W_b b = 0. \end{aligned} \tag{a'''}$$

We see from this example that the condition which guarantees the rotational equilibrium of the seesaw around its pivotal axis (i.e., around a y-axis through 0 perpendicular to the plane of the paper) is:

$$\sum M_y = 0, \tag{b}$$

where the moments M_y may be taken about 0 or any other point in the plane of the seesaw. Generalizing condition (b), we see that the three conditions which guarantee that a rigid body will not rotate about three perpendicular axes x, y, z are:

$$\sum M_x = 0, \qquad \sum M_y = 0, \qquad \sum M_z = 0. \tag{1.4.1}$$

For complete equilibrium of a rigid body, both the translational and the rotational equilibrium conditions must be satisfied. Hence, all 6 equations (1.3.1), (1.4.1) are necessary to guarantee the *space equilibrium* of a rigid body.

When all the forces applied to a body are known to lie in a plane, say the x, z-plane, the body has no cause to move in the y-direction or to rotate around the x- and z-axes [see equation (a) of Section 1.2]. Hence, the only rotational condition to be satisfied is (b), and, by (1.3.2), only the following 3 equations must be satisfied for complete (translational and rotational) *plane equilibrium* of a body:

$$\sum F_x = 0, \qquad \sum F_z = 0, \qquad \sum M_y = 0. \tag{1.4.2}$$

Let us first consider a few examples of plane equilibrium. The beam of

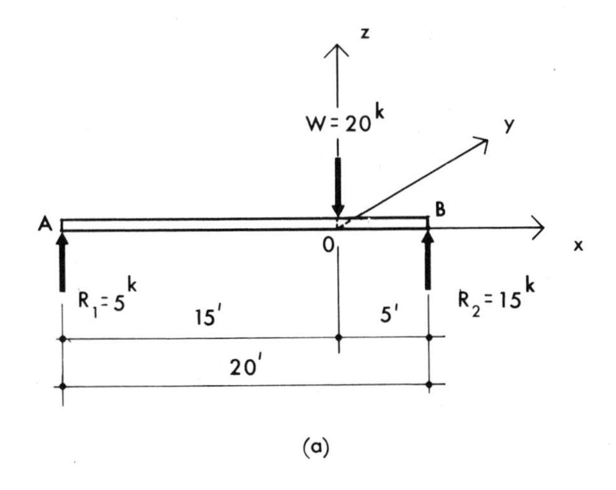

(a)

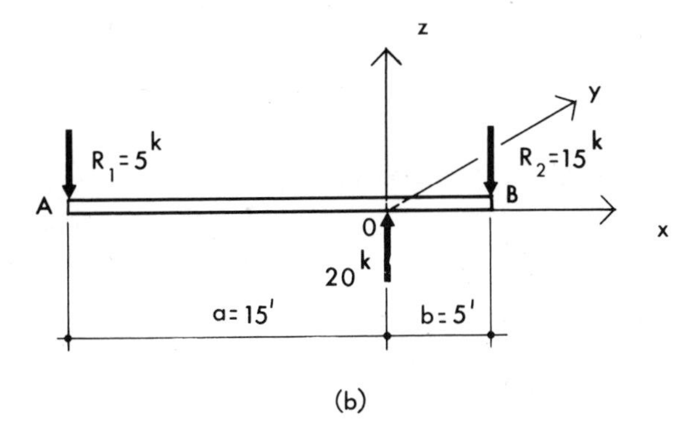

(b)

Fig. 1.4.2

Fig. 1.4.2 carries a vertical load as shown and is supported by two end walls.* To evaluate the wall reactions, let us notice first that, since there are no horizontal forces applied to the beam, and $\sum F_x = 0$, the supports need not develop any horizontal reactions. Therefore, the wall reactions R_1 and R_2 are vertical, and $\sum F_z = 0$ gives:

$$R_1 + R_2 - 20 = 0. \tag{c}$$

*In all the examples of this section, the weight of the beam is assumed to be negligible.

Taking moments about 0 (i.e., about the y-axis), one obtains:

$$\sum M_y = +R_2 \times 5 - R_1 \times 15 = 0 \quad \text{or} \quad R_2 = 3R_1, \tag{d}$$

from which, substituting $R_2 = 3R_1$ in (c):

$$R_1 + 3R_1 = 4R_1 = 20 \quad \therefore \quad R_1 = 5 \text{ k},$$

and, by (d):

$$R_2 = 3R_1 = 15 \text{ k}.$$

If we turn the beam upside down (Fig. 1.4.2b), we see that it behaves like a seesaw supported at 0 with loads R_1 and R_2 at the ends. It is then obvious that, since $b = 5$ ft and $a = 15$ ft $= 3b$, $R_2 = 3R_1$, so that $R_1 = 5$ k and $R_2 =$ 15 k.

Since the resultant moment of all the forces is zero about any point in the x, z-plane, one may obtain the same result [and avoid the solution of the 2 simultaneous equations (c) and (d) for the unknowns R_1 and R_2] by writing moment equations about 2 judiciously chosen points. Thus, taking moments about B, one obtains directly R_1:

$$-R_1 \times 20 + 20 \times 5 + R_2 \times 0 = 0 \quad \therefore \quad R_1 = 5 \text{ k},$$

and, taking moments about A, one obtains directly R_2:

$$+R_2 \times 20 - 20 \times 15 + R_1 \times 0 = 0 \quad \therefore \quad R_2 = 15 \text{ k}.$$

One may then check the vertical equilibrium of the beam:

$$R_1 + R_2 - W = 5 + 15 - 20 = 0.$$

As a second example of plane equilibrium, consider the ladder AB of Fig. 1.4.3, which carries a man weighing 150 lb as shown. The frictionless wall exerts a horizontal reaction R_1 on the ladder, while the floor reacts both with a vertical reaction R_2 and a horizontal reaction R_3 due to friction. We wish to determine R_1, R_2 and R_3.

For vertical equilibrium:

$$R_2 - 150 = 0 \quad \therefore \quad R_2 = 150 \text{ lb}.$$

For horizontal equilibrium:

$$R_3 - R_1 = 0 \quad \therefore \quad R_3 = R_1.$$

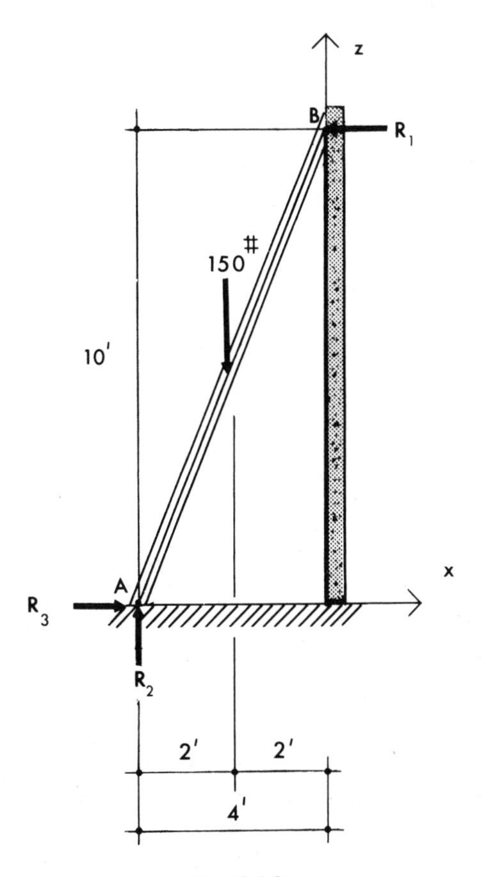

Fig. 1.4.3

For rotational equilibrium about A:

$$-150 \times 2 + R_1 \times 10 = 0 \quad \therefore \quad R_1 = 30 \text{ lb}, \quad R_3 = R_1 = 30 \text{ lb}.$$

The ratio of the horizontal to the vertical reaction at A is $R_3/R_2 = 30/150 = 0.2$. Physically, the horizontal reaction due to friction is always a fraction f (called the *coefficient of friction*) of the vertical reaction. If the coefficient of friction of the floor is less than 0.2, R_2 is less than $0.2 \times 150 = 30$ lb and equilibrium cannot subsist: the ladder slides on the floor.

As a last example of plane equilibrium, let us determine the wall reactions of a beam supported on two walls 10 ft apart and carrying a load of 10 k on a

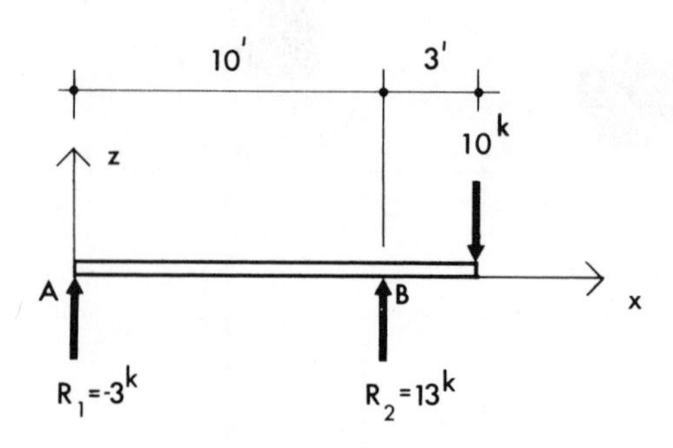

Fig. 1.4.4

cantilevered portion 3 ft long (Fig. 1.4.4). For rotational equilibrium about B:

$$-R_1 \times 10 - 10 \times 3 = 0 \quad \therefore \quad R_1 = -3\text{ k}.$$

The negative sign of R_1 shows that R_1 is directed downward (as one might have guessed by considering the beam as a lever pivoted at B). Since the action of the beam on the wall A is equal and opposite to the reaction of the wall A on the beam, the beam will pull up on the wall and must be anchored to it.

For vertical equilibrium,

$$-3 + R_2 - 10 = 0 \quad \therefore \quad R_2 = 13\text{ k}.$$

Notice that the reaction R_2 is directed upward and is greater than the load.

Let us now check the rotational equilibrium around the x-, y- and z-axes of the building in Fig. 1.3.1. The wind force, $F_y = 375$ k, is applied at mid-height of the building, since the wind pressure is uniform (see Section 2.4), and its lever arm about the x-axis is 125 ft. The weight of the building is 62,500 k and acts along the axis of the building, i.e., 50 ft from the x-axis. For equilibrium around the x-axis, the *overturning* wind moment must be less than the *stabilizing* moment of the weight. Since:

$$F_y \times \frac{h}{2} = 375 \times 125 = 46{,}875\text{ k ft}$$

is less than:

$$W \times \frac{a}{2} = 62{,}500 \times 50 = 3{,}125{,}000\text{ k ft},$$

the building will not topple over by rotating around its edge parallel to the x-axis. Similarly, since:

$$F_x \times \frac{h}{2} = 750 \times 125 = 93{,}750\text{ k ft}$$

is less than:

$$W \times \frac{a}{2} = 3{,}125{,}000\text{ k ft},$$

the building will not topple over by rotating around its edge parallel to the y-axis. In fact, the weight moment is 3,125,000/93,750 or 35 times the wind moment. We say in this case that there is a *coefficient of safety* of 35 to overturning about the y-axis. This means that it would take a wind pressure 35 times larger ($p = 35 \times 30 = 1{,}050$ psf) to overturn the building about the y-axis. Such wind pressures have never been measured; hurricane winds may produce pressures of at most 100 psf.

The moment M_z of all the applied forces is obviously zero since, by symmetry, F_x and R_x, and F_y and R_y have zero lever arms about the z-axis, and W and F_z have zero moment about the z-axis *because they are parallel to it.* Thus, there is equilibrium in rotation about the z-axis, and the building does not tend to "twist" about its vertical axis.

As a last example of space equilibrium, consider the triangular table ABC of Fig. 1.4.5, which carries a vertical load P of 100 lb at O and is supported

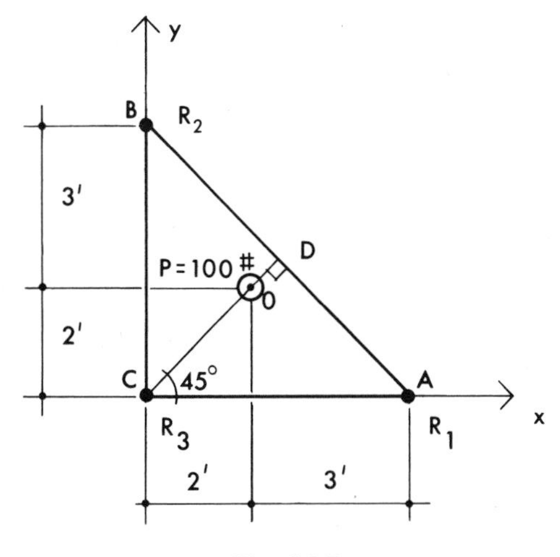

Fig. 1.4.5

by three corner legs. Since P is vertical and $\sum F_x$ and $\sum F_y$ must be zero, the legs do not react horizontally. To evaluate the vertical leg reactions R_1, R_2, R_3, we may use 2 moment equations about the x- and y-axis and one vertical equilibrium equation, or 3 moment equations. For rotational equilibrium about the x-axis:

$$-100 \times 2 + R_2 \times 5 = 0 \quad \therefore \quad R_2 = 40 \text{ lb.}$$

For rotational equilibrium about the y-axis:

$$-100 \times 2 + R_1 \times 5 = 0 \quad \therefore \quad R_1 = 40 \text{ lb.}$$

(R_1, of course, equals R_2 by symmetry.)

For vertical equilibrium:

$$40 + 40 + R_3 - 100 = 0 \quad \therefore \quad R_3 = 20 \text{ lb.}$$

As a check, R_3 may be computed by means of a third moment equation about the line AB, noticing that:

$$CO = \sqrt{2^2 + 2^2} = 2\sqrt{2} \text{ ft,}$$

$$AC = \sqrt{CD^2 + AD^2} = \sqrt{2CD^2} = 5 \quad \therefore \quad CD = \frac{5}{\sqrt{2}} \text{ ft,}$$

$$OD = CD - CO = \frac{5}{\sqrt{2}} - 2\sqrt{2} = \frac{5-4}{\sqrt{2}} = \frac{1}{\sqrt{2}},$$

$$-100 \times \frac{1}{\sqrt{2}} + R_3 \times \frac{5}{\sqrt{2}} = 0 \quad \therefore \quad R_3 = \frac{100}{\sqrt{2}} \bigg/ \frac{5}{\sqrt{2}} = 20 \text{ lb.}$$

PROBLEMS

1.4.1 Determine the reactions of the beam of Fig. 1.4.6.

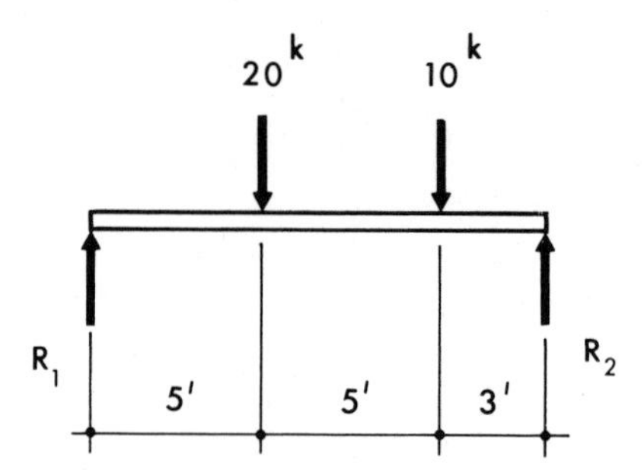

Fig. 1.4.6

1.4.2 Determine the reactions of the beam of Fig. 1.4.7.

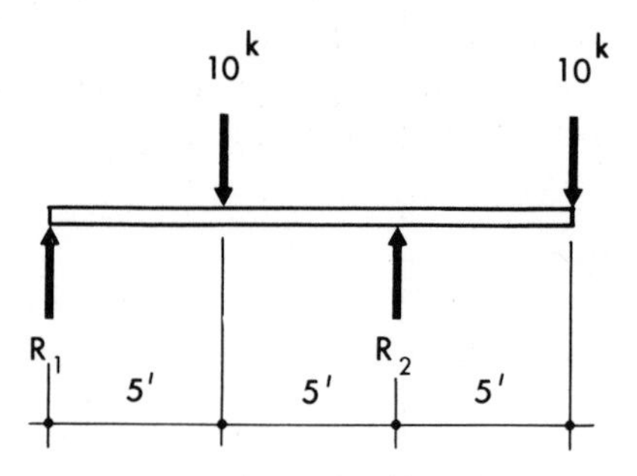

Fig. 1.4.7

1.4.3 Determine the reactions of the beam of Fig. 1.4.8.

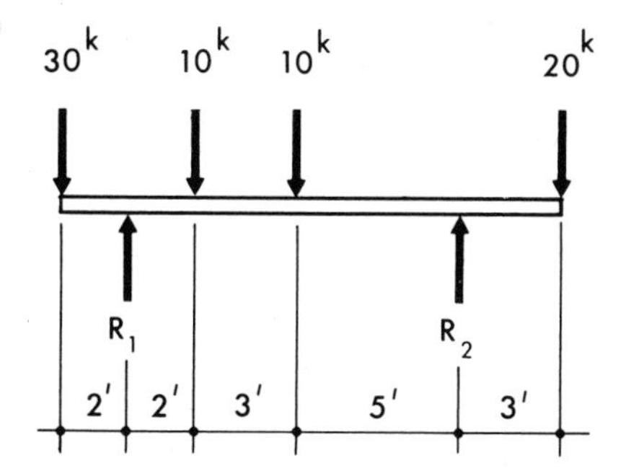

Fig. 1.4.8

1.4.4 Determine the reactions of the beam of Fig. 1.4.9.

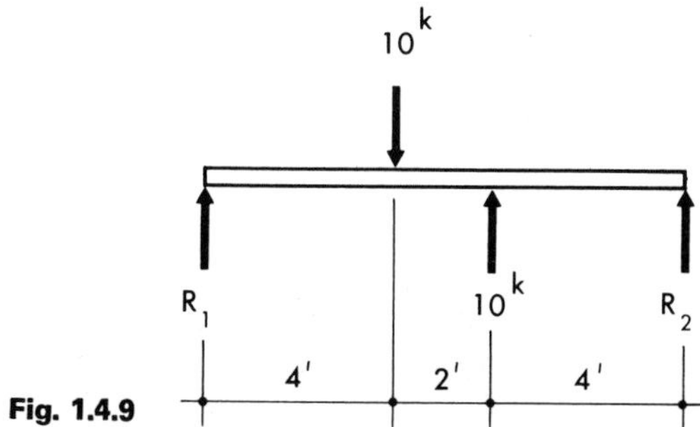

Fig. 1.4.9

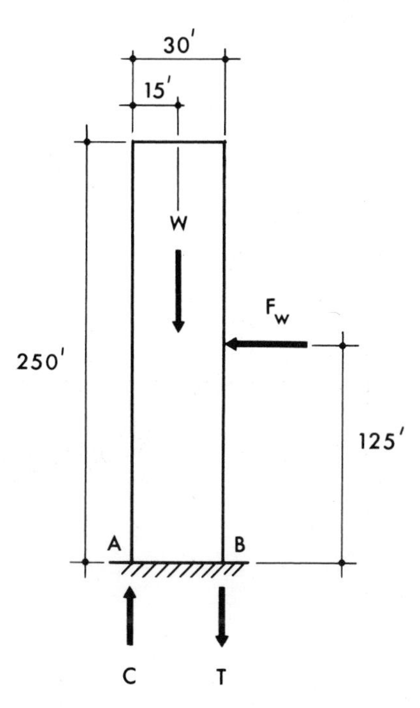

Fig. 1.4.10

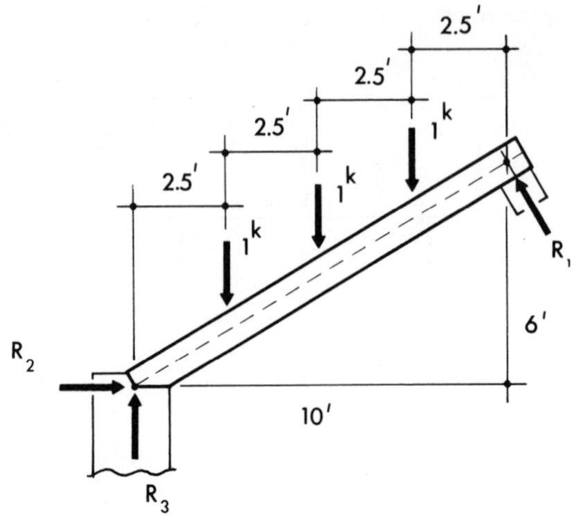

Fig. 1.4.11

1.4.5 Determine the minimum value of b, in terms of h, for rotational stability of the dike in Problem 1.3.6.

1.4.6 What is the highest wind pressure on one face of the square tower in Problem 1.3.5 that could be resisted by the tower without tipping?

1.4.7 The square tower in Problem 1.3.5 supports a wind pressure of 70 psf. It is stabilized by piles capable of tension on the wind side (Fig. 1.4.10). Determine the minimum tensile force T on the piles along B and the minimum compressive force C on the piles along A needed to maintain the tower in equilibrium.

1.4.8 The inclined roof joist of Fig 1.4.11 carries the loads shown. Its left support reacts both horizontally and vertically. Its right support reacts at right angles to the joist. Determine R_1.

1.4.9 A construction worker slowly lifts a bucket of sand weighing 50 lb by pulling on a vertical rope going over a pulley. What vertical pull T does he exert on the rope and what vertical load W acts on the pulley axle?

1.4.10 A staircase Z-beam rests on two end walls (Fig. 1.4.12). The loads on the staircase are vertical. Are the walls acted upon by horizontal loads?

1.4.11 The flag pole of Fig. 1.4.13 is supported in a socket by a horizontal cable. The total weight of the pole and flag is shown in the figure. Determine the tension T in the cable and the socket reactions R_1 and R_2.

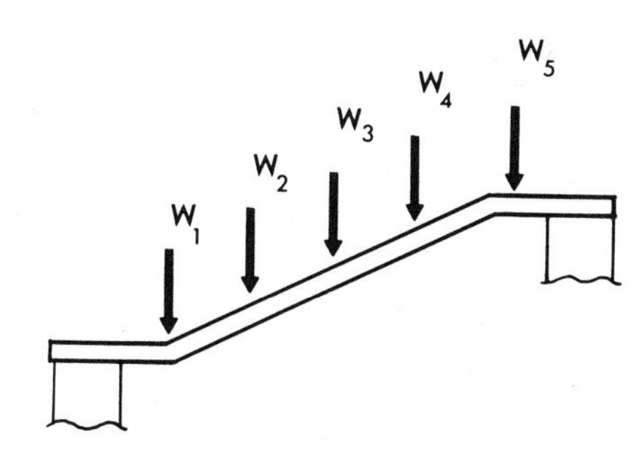

Fig. 1.4.12

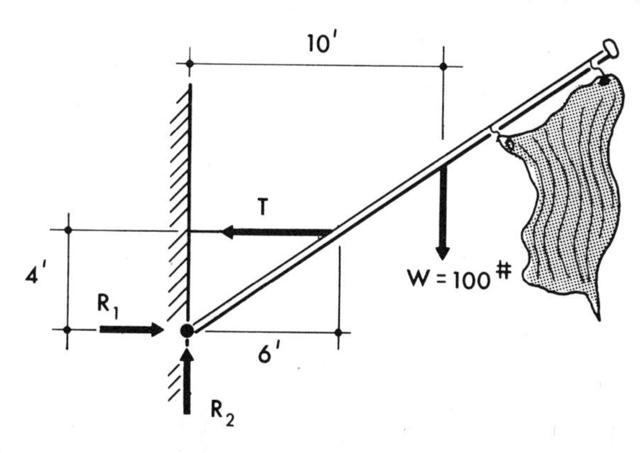

Fig. 1.4.13

1.4.12 The three-legged table of Fig. 1.4.14 carries a load P a distance x from the line AB. Show in a diagram how the leg reaction at C, and the equal reactions at A and B, vary with x.

1.4.13 The table of Fig. 1.4.15 carries a load P, which can be located at A', B' or C'. Evaluate the 3 leg reactions at A, B, C for each of the 3 positions of the load.

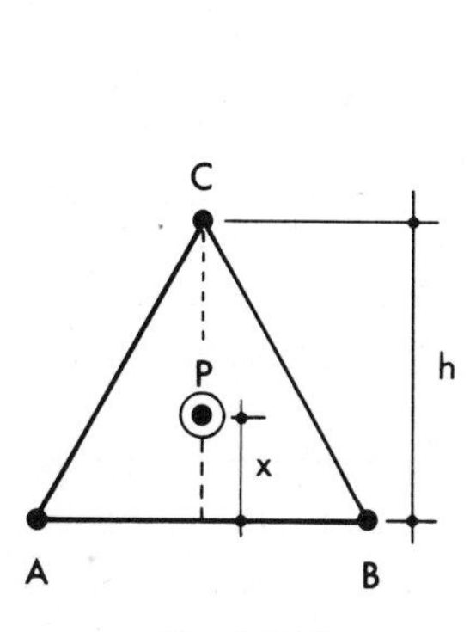

Fig. 1.4.14

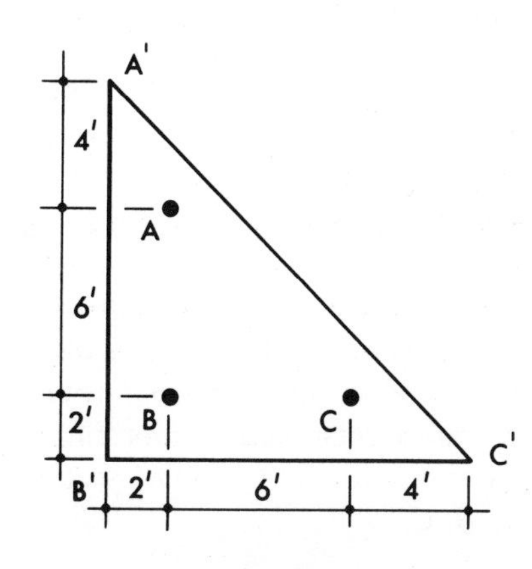

Fig. 1.4.15

1.5 Statically Indeterminate Structures

In a number of problems of the preceding sections the laws of statics were used to determine the reactions exerted by the supporting elements on the structure. The capacity of the structure to withstand the applied forces and consequent reactions (i.e., its strength) was taken for granted. The investigation of such capacity, which will be considered in later sections, is the task of *strength of materials* and presupposes the knowledge of all forces and reactions. In all the problems considered, once the loads were given, we were able to determine the reactions by the laws of statics alone. This means that, by definition, all the structures considered so far were *statically determinate* externally. On the other hand, it is easy to give examples of simple structures which cannot be analyzed by statics alone, and hence, are said to develop *statically indeterminate reactions.*

Consider, for example, the beam of Fig. 1.5.1, loaded by a vertical load P

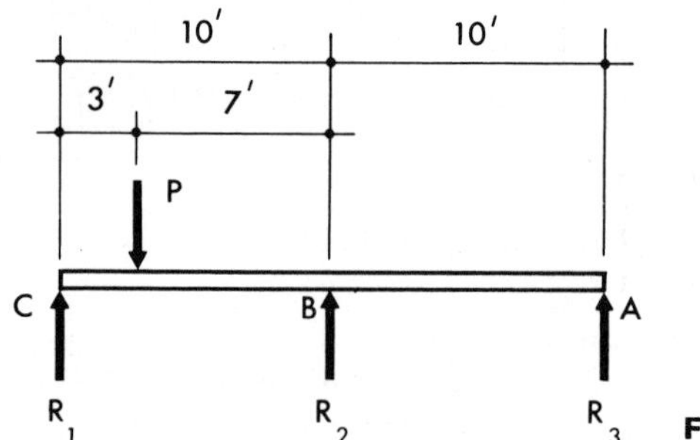

Fig. 1.5.1

and supported by three walls. We wish to evaluate its 3 unknown reactions R_1, R_2, R_3. Since the load and the reactions act in a vertical plane, and since there are no applied horizontal forces, only the last 2 equations of plane equilibrium (1.4.2) are available for this task, which give:

$$\begin{aligned} \sum F_z &= R_1 + R_2 + R_3 - P = 0, \\ \sum M_A &= + P \times 17 - R_1 \times 20 - R_2 \times 10 = 0. \end{aligned} \tag{a}$$

Since 3 equations are needed to evaluate 3 unknowns, the 2 equations (a) are insufficient to determine the 3 reactions.

Lest it be felt that an additional useful equation could be obtained by, say, taking moments about C, it is essential to notice that any such equation would not introduce any *additional* physical information about the problem, since to guarantee rotational equilibrium, one may take moments about *any* point [see equations (a′), (a″), (a‴) of Section 1.4].* To prove this, the moment equation about C:

*Such additional equations are not *mathematically independent* from the previous equations, and hence, are useless.

$$-3P + 10R_2 + 20R_3 = 0,$$

may be subtracted from the equation $\sum M_A = 0$, obtaining:

$$+\,20P - 20R_1 - 20R_2 - 20R_3 = 0,$$

which, when divided by -20, is seen to be identical with the first of equations (a). Therefore, the beam on three supports is statically indeterminate, and its analysis requires a knowledge of its material properties.

Similarly, the four-legged table of Fig. 1.5.2 carrying an eccentric vertical

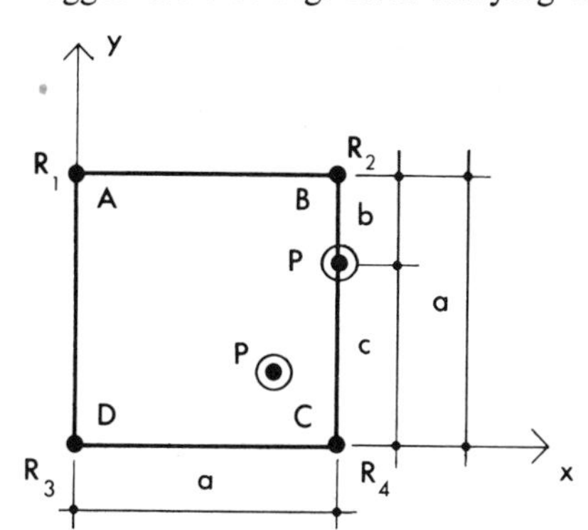

Fig. 1.5.2

load P is statically indeterminate, since only 3 equilibrium equations, say $\sum F_z = 0$, $\sum M_x = 0$, $\sum M_y = 0$, may be written involving the 4 unknown reactions. (Moment equations about the lines AB or BC lead to nonindependent equations and do not add any physical information about the problem.)

It must now be noticed that the location and values of the loads may, *in special cases*, transform a statically indeterminate problem into a statically determinate one. For example, if the load on the beam in Fig. 1.5.1 is located at B, it is obvious that the load P is carried by support B, $R_2 = P$ and $R_1 = R_3 = 0$. Similarly, if the load on the table of Fig. 1.5.2 is centered, the 4 reactions must be equal, and, for vertical equilibrium:

$$\sum F_z = 4R - P = 0 \quad \therefore \quad R = \frac{P}{4}.$$

Another such situation occurs when the load P acts along the support line BC, in which case, for rotational equilibrium about BC, we obtain $(R_1 + R_3)\,a = 0$ and either $R_1 = -R_3$, which is physically absurd (one of reactions due to an internal *downward* load would be a pull downward), or both R_1 and R_3 must be zero. The reactions R_2 and R_4 can then be determined by statics, since the problem becoms a plane problem:

$$R_2 = \frac{c}{a}P, \qquad R_4 = \frac{b}{a}P.$$

In the following chapters we shall consider a variety of structures which can be completely analyzed by the laws of statics.

Chapter Two

2.1 Force Characteristics

We have seen in Chapter 1 that a force tends to accelerate a body *in translation* in the direction in which it acts and to accelerate a body *in rotation* about a point 0 if the force has a lever arm with respect to 0. Hence, to determine the action of a force on a body we need to specify the following *force characteristics*: (a) the *direction* along which it acts, e.g., the horizontal direction; (b) the *sense* in which it acts, e.g., to the right or to the left; (c) its magnitude, e.g., 20 lb or 5 k;*(d) its *point of application*, e.g., the foot of a column or the midspan point of a beam. The direction and the point of application of a force define together its *line of action*, which in turn determines the lever arm of the force with respect to a point 0, and hence, its moment about 0.

It is convenient to represent the characteristics of a force, as we have already done in Chapter 1, by means of an arrow drawn in the direction of the force

*A quantity characterized by direction, sense and magnitude is called a *vectorial quantity* or a *vector*. A vector is represented by an arrow in the direction of the vector and with the head pointing in is sense.

Plane Force Systems

through its point of application, pointing in its sense and labeled with a number representing its magnitude in a given unit. A 10 k force acting through a point A at 45° to the horizontal is represented in Fig. 2.1.1a, while Fig. 2.1.1b represents the 100 lb weight of a body B, i.e., the vertical force downward exerted by the earth on the body and acting through the "center of gravity" 0 of the body.

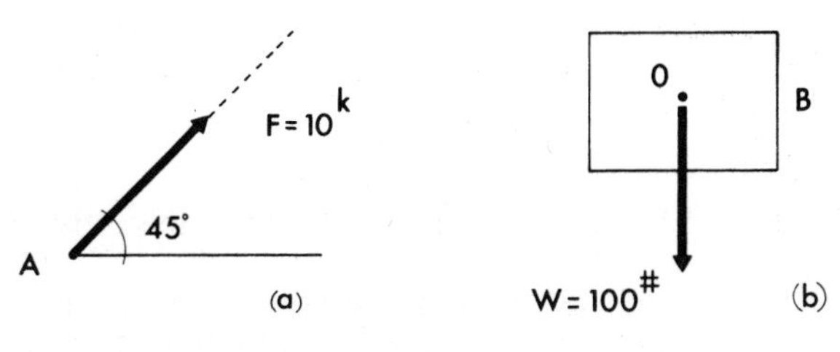

Fig. 2.1.1

2.2 Colinear Force Systems

A system of forces is called *colinear* when all the forces of the system act along the same line. The loads carried by a series of superimposed columns, like those in Fig. 1.3.3, are colinear.

It is convenient to choose (arbitrarily) a *positive sense* along the line of action of a system of colinear forces and to label the force magnitudes + or − depending on whether the forces act in the positive or in the opposite sense. The colinear forces in Fig. 2.2.1a, b are labeled according to this convention.

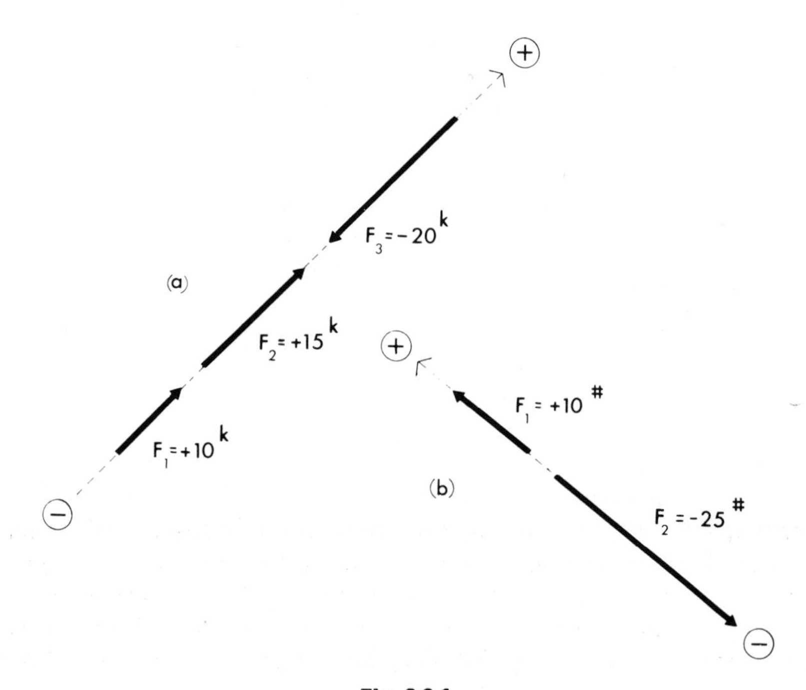

Fig. 2.2.1

The *resultant* R of a colinear force system is a single force, colinear with the forces of the system and of magnitude equal to the algebraic sum of the magnitudes of the forces of the system. The resultants of the force systems in Figs. 2.2.1a, b are forces of +5 k and −15 lb, respectively. Let us notice that since all the forces of a colinear system have the same lever arm about a point 0, the moment about 0 of the resultant equals the algebraic sum of the moments about 0 of the forces. For example, in Fig. 2.2.2:

$$R = 2 - 4 + 10 = 8 \text{ k}, \qquad M_0 = 2 \times 2 - 4 \times 2 + 10 \times 2$$

$$= (2 - 4 + 10) \times 2 = 8 \times 2 = 16 \text{ k ft}.$$

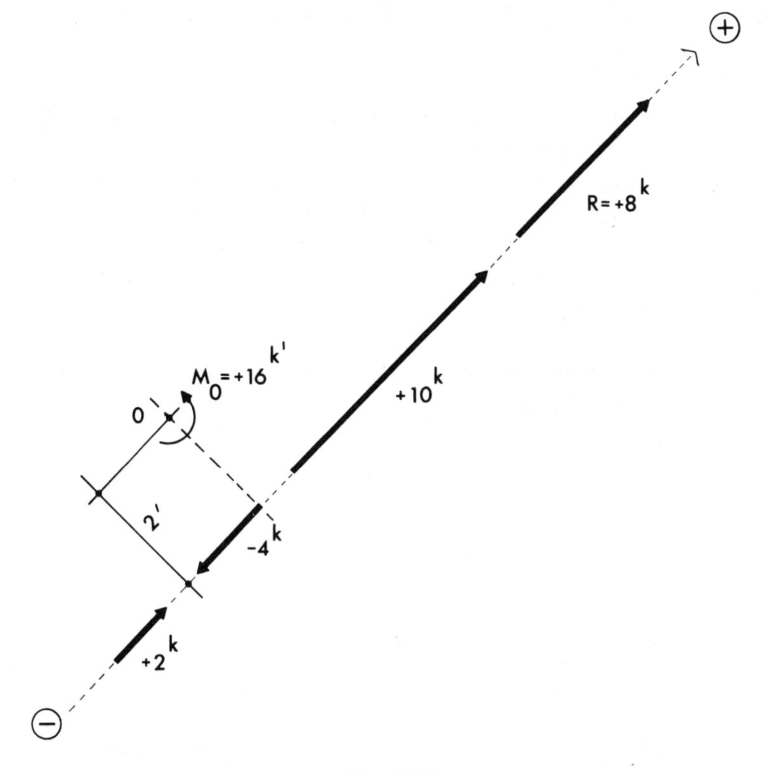

Fig. 2.2.2

Therefore, we can also say that the resultant is *statically equivalent* to the force system, since R will exert on a body the same action in translation and in rotation as the forces of the system.

PROBLEMS

2.2.1 Represent a horizontal force of -10 lb, having a moment of $+20$ ft lb about 0, with reference to the x-axis of Fig. 2.2.3.

2.2.2 Represent a 50 lb weight with reference to the z-axis of Fig. 2.2.3.

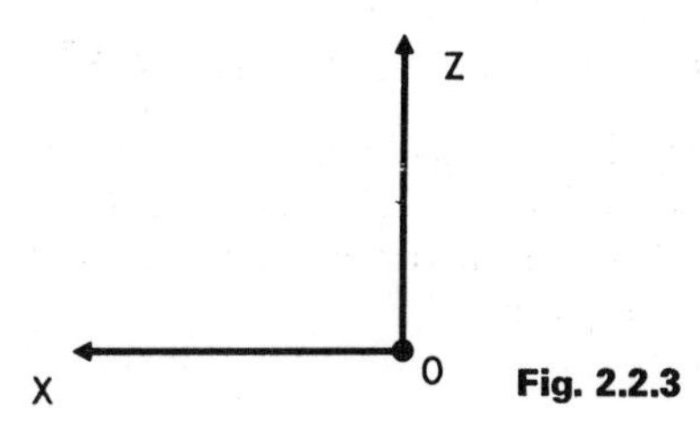

Fig. 2.2.3

2.2.3 A magnet attracts a piece of iron with a force of 10 lb. The magnet is to the right of the piece of iron. Represent the attractive force on the piece of iron with reference to the x-axis of Fig. 2.2.3.

2.2.4 A marble weighs 1 oz. Represent the reaction of the floor on the marble with respect to the z-axis of Fig. 2.2.3.

2.2.5 A wind exerts a pressure of 20 psf on the west face of a building 130 ft high and 40 ft wide. Represent the wind force with respect to the axes of Fig. 2.2.3, if the x-axis is in the west-east direction.

2.2.6 Determine the resultant of the forces in: (a) Fig. 2.2.4, (b) Fig. 2.2.5, (c) Fig. 2.2.6, (d) Fig. 2.2.7.

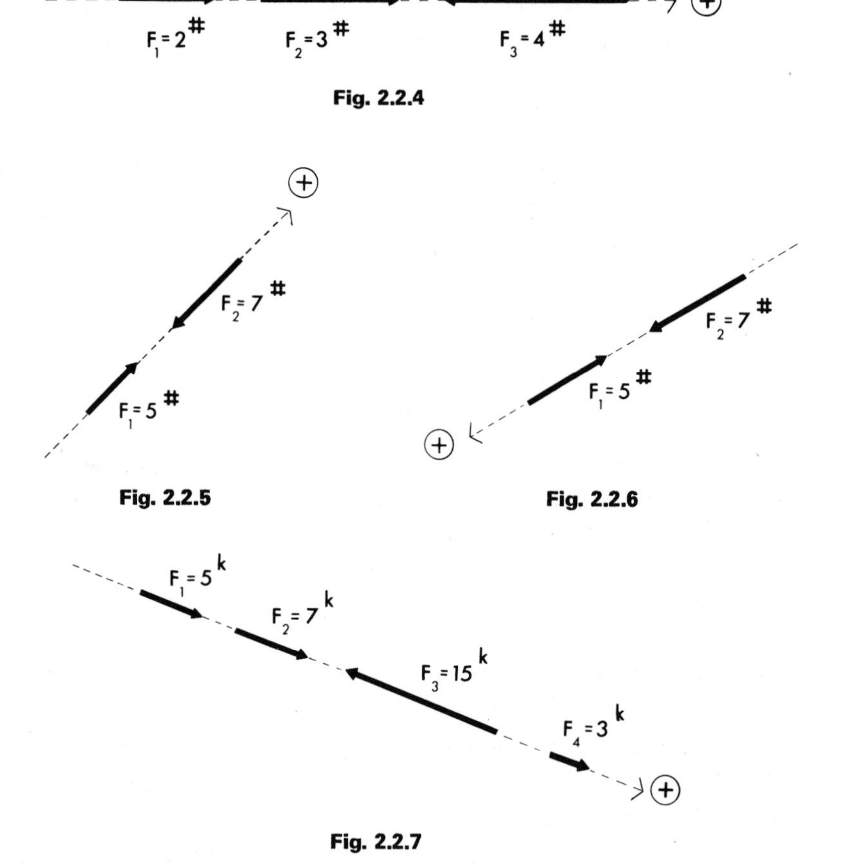

Fig. 2.2.4

Fig. 2.2.5

Fig. 2.2.6

Fig. 2.2.7

2.2.7 The cabin of an elevator is at rest at the 10th floor of a building. The elevator cable exerts on the cabin an upward force of 750 lb. The cabin weighs 500 lb and the friction against the rails is 50 lb. Will the cabin start moving up or down?

2.2.8 A concrete foundation slab is 3 ft thick and is subjected to the upward hydrostatic pressure of 20 ft of water. Before the building to be supported by the slab is completed, what resultant force acts on each square foot of slab? (Concrete weighs 150 lb/cu ft and water 63 lb/cu ft). Does the slab have to be anchored to the ground? Assume downward forces as positive. *Note*: The hydrostatic pressure equals the weight of a 1 sq ft column of water.

2.2.9 The foundation slab of Problem 2.2.8 supports a 15 story building weighing 250 psf per filloor. What resultant force acts on each square foot of ground after completion of the building?

2.2.10 To lift a weight W by means of a tackle, the weight is attached to a lower sheave, and a rope, anchored to a fixed point, goes over an upper sheave, under the lower sheave, over the upper sheave again and is pulled by a vertical force T (Fig. 2.2.8). Determine the magnitude of T and the reaction R on the upper sheave.

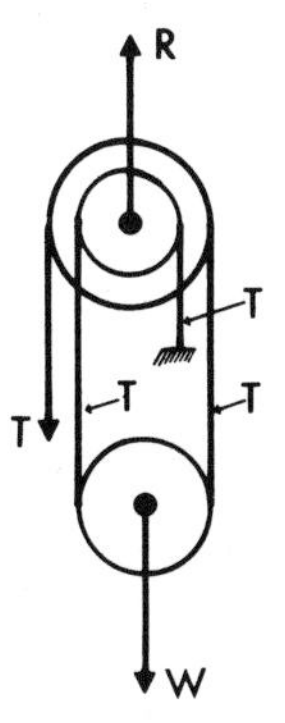

Fig. 2.2.8

2.2.11 A man can pull on a rope with a force of 100 lb. How many times must the rope go over the upper sheave and how many times under the lower sheave of a tackle for the man to lift 400 lb?

2.3 Parallel Force Systems

The beam of Fig. 2.3.1 picks up the column loads shown and is supported by two end walls, which exert on it vertical reactions. All the forces on the beam are vertical and constitute an example of a *parallel force system*, in which all the forces have the same direction.

In the solution of problems involving a parallel force system, it is convenient to use its resultant R, a single force *statically equivalent* to the forces of the system, i.e., capable of exerting on a body the same translational and rotational actions as the forces of the system.

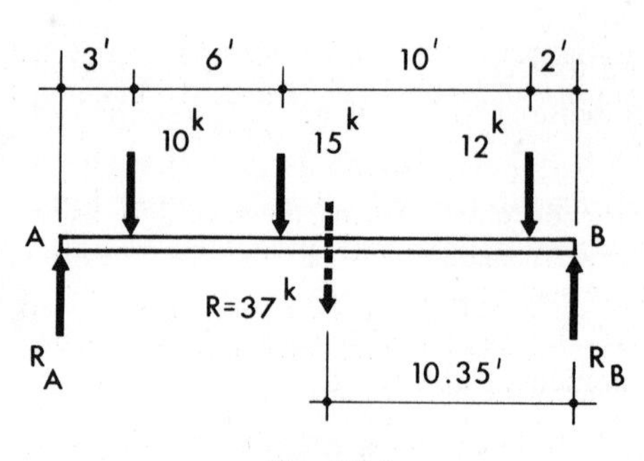

Fig. 2.3.1

To this purpose let us first consider the following simple problem, which involves a particular but highly significant parallel force system. In order to turn our car, say, to the left, we often apply to the rim of the steering wheel a pull F with our left arm and a parallel push F with our right arm (Fig. 2.3.2).

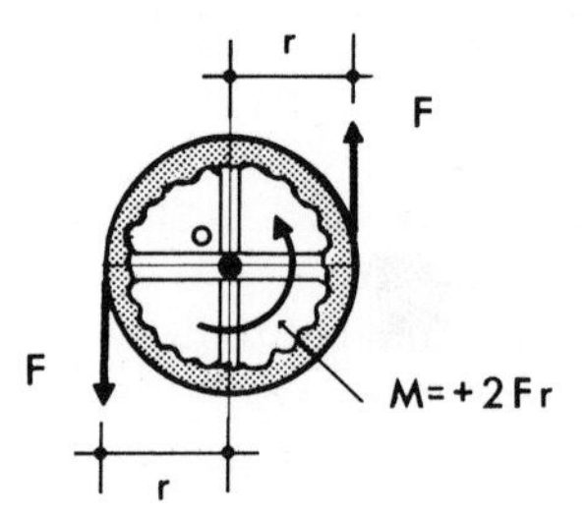

Fig. 2.3.2

The translational action of this force system is zero, since the two forces tend to accelerate the wheel *in translation* by the same amount in opposite directions. The magnitude of its resultant is zero:

$$R = F - F = 0.$$

But the rotational action of the system is not zero, since, taking moments, for example, about 0, we obtain:

$$M = F \times r + F \times r = +2Fr.$$

Thus, this parallel system has *zero resultant force*, but a *resultant moment* of magnitude $M = +2Fr$. Such a system is called a *couple of moment M.** A

*A moment is also a vectorial quantity, which is represented by an arrow perpendicular to the plane of the couple with the head pointing in the sense in which a right-handed screw would move if rotated in the sense of the moment.

couple does not tend to accelerate a body in translation but tends to accelerate it in rotation in the sense of its moment. It is customary to represent the moment of a couple by a curved arrow rotating in the sense of the moment, with a label indicating its magnitude M (in kip-feet, pound-inches or other appropriate units). A $+$ or $-$ sign is used to indicate whether the moment rotates in the chosen positive sense (usually the *counterclockwise* sense) or in the opposite sense (Fig. 2.3.2). The moment of a couple is independent of the point about which the moment is computed, since a couple has the same moment about any point in the plane of its forces, as shown by Fig. 2.3.3, in which, for example:

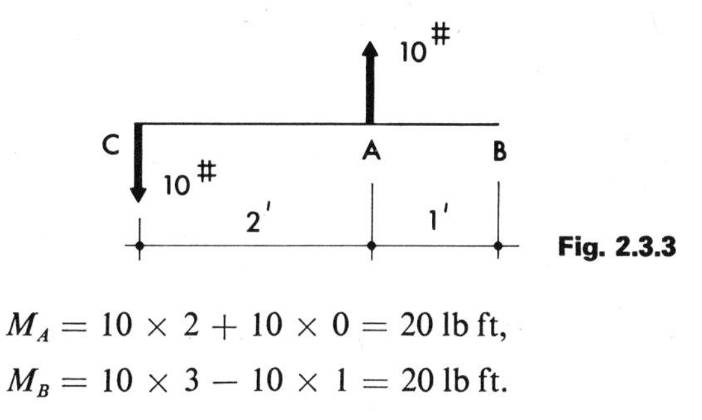

Fig. 2.3.3

$$M_A = 10 \times 2 + 10 \times 0 = 20 \text{ lb ft},$$
$$M_B = 10 \times 3 - 10 \times 1 = 20 \text{ lb ft}.$$

It is obvious that all couples having the same moment M are statically equivalent, since they have the same $R = 0$ and the same M.

Let us now consider another force system we often use to turn our car, say, to the left: a single pull F applied to the rim of the steering wheel with our left arm (Fig. 2.3.4). The action of F is not changed if we add at the center 0 of the wheel 2 equal and opposite forces $F_1 = +F$ and $F_2 = -F$ parallel to F, i.e., a system with zero resultant and zero moment. But we can now look at the system of the forces F, F_1 and F_2, which is statically equivalent to F, as consisting of: (a) the force $F_1 = F$ applied at 0, and (b) the couple of the 2

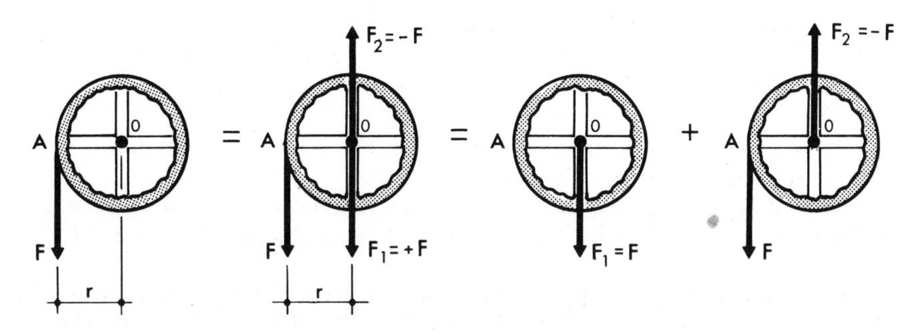

Fig. 2.3.4

equal and opposite forces F at A and $F_2 = -F$ at 0, whose moment is $M = +Fr$. The force F at 0 tends to accelerate the wheel in translation, while the couple of moment $M = +Fr$ tends to accelerate it in rotation.

This result shows that *a force F may be shifted at right angles to its line of action to a point O, provided the moment of F about O be added to the system.**

We are now in a position to find the resultant of a parallel force system, as that of the loads on the beam of Fig. 2.3.5, by means of the following 3 steps:

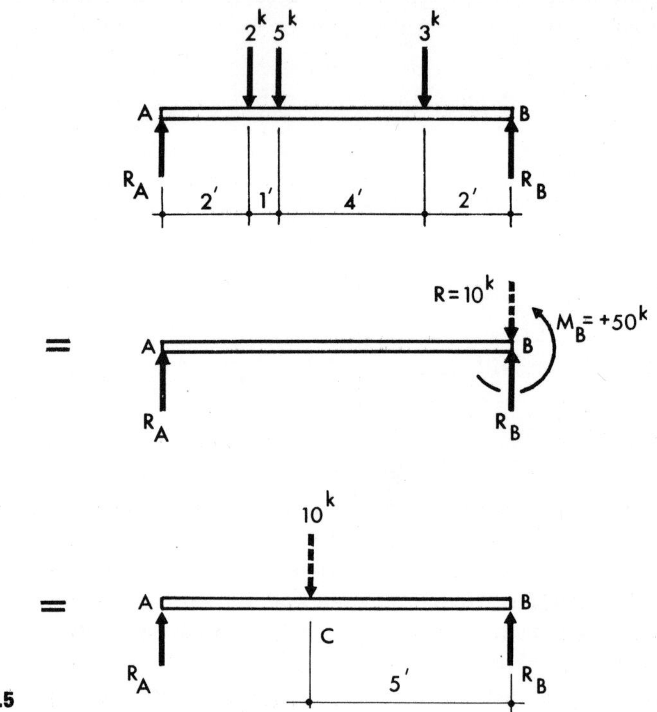

Fig. 2.3.5

a. Transfer all the forces to the point B, by adding the corresponding moments of the forces about B:

$$M_B = 3 \times 2 + 5 \times 6 + 2 \times 7 = +50 \text{ k ft.}$$

b. Evaluate the resultant R of the *colinear* system of vertical forces at B, by adding them up algebraically:

$$R = 2 + 5 + 3 = 10 \text{ k.}$$

c. Transfer R to a point C a distance x from B such that $Rx = M_B$:

*We shall often use the words "a moment . . . " to signify a "a couple of moment . . . ."

$$10x = 50, \qquad x = 5 \text{ ft.}$$

The example shows that the resultant R of a parallel force system has a magnitude equal to the algebraic sum of the force magnitudes and a moment about any point equal to the moment of the forces of the system about the point. For example, the resultant of the forces in the system of Fig. 2.3.6 is a force $R = 10 + 20 - 5 = +25$ k acting down at a distance x from A given by:

$$10 \times 10 + 20 \times 5 = 25x \quad \therefore \quad x = 8 \text{ ft.}$$

The forces in Fig. 2.3.7 constitute a parallel system with a resultant $R = 10 + 5 - 3 - 12 = 0$, but with a resultant moment:

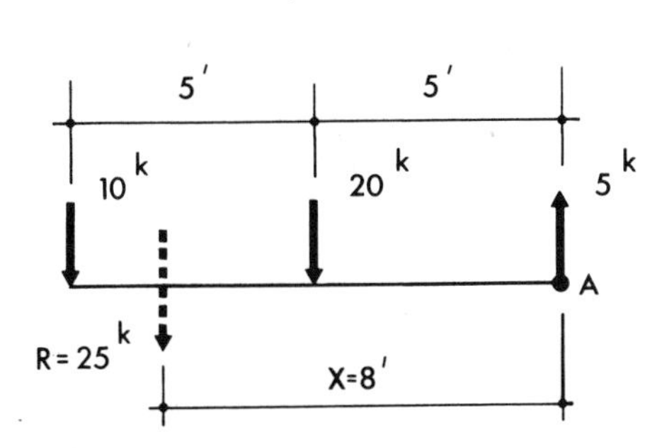

Fig. 2.3.6

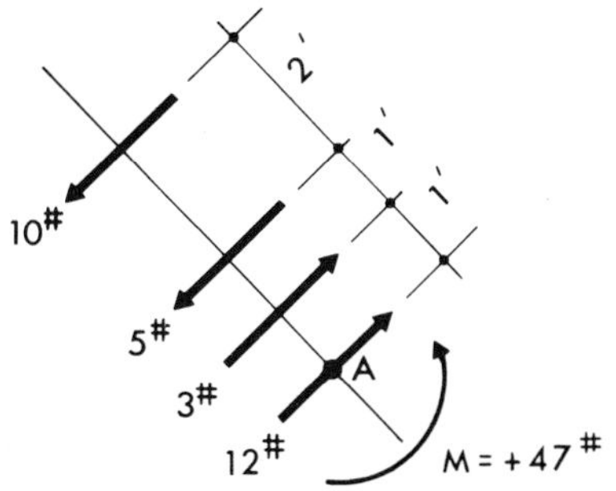

Fig. 2.3.7

$$M_A = 10 \times 4 + 5 \times 2 - 3 \times 1 = 47 \text{ lb ft.}$$

The system is equivalent to a couple of moment 47 lb ft, but in this case it would be impossible to specify the equal and opposite forces of the couple. The system is equivalent to *any* of the statically equivalent couples of moment 47 lb ft.

PROBLEMS

2.3.1 Evaluate and locate the resultant of the force system of Fig. 2.3.8.

2.3.2 Evaluate and locate the resultant of the force system of Fig. 2.3.9.

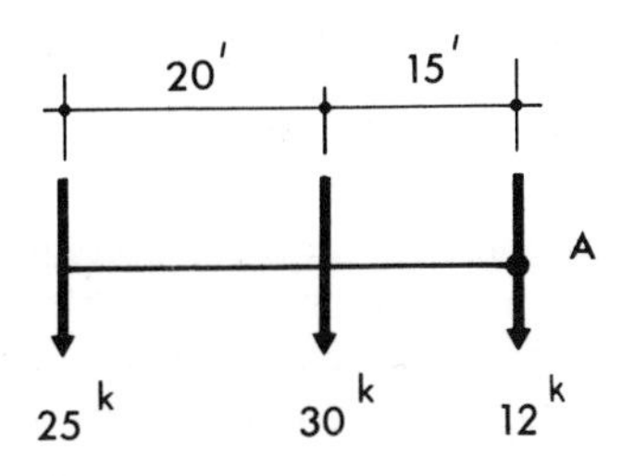

Fig. 2.3.8

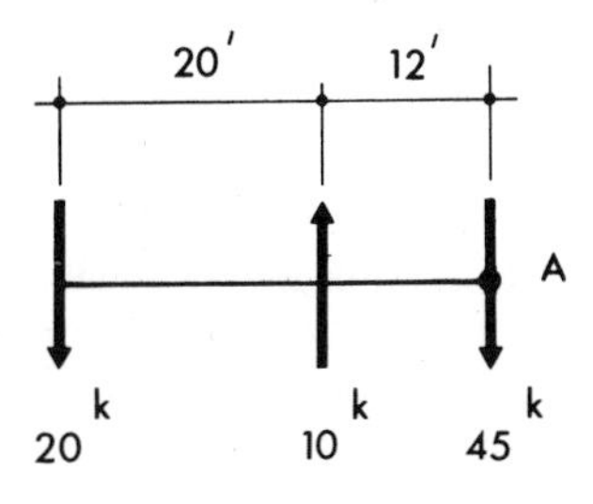

Fig. 2.3.9

2.3.3 The beam of Fig. 2.3.10 picks up three columns, which exert on the beam the loads shown. Evaluate and locate the resultant of the load system.

2.3.4 The beam of Fig. 2.3.11 is rigidly connected to the column and carries loads as shown. Evaluate the compressive force and the couple exerted by the loads on the column, by shifting the forces to B and adding suitable moments.

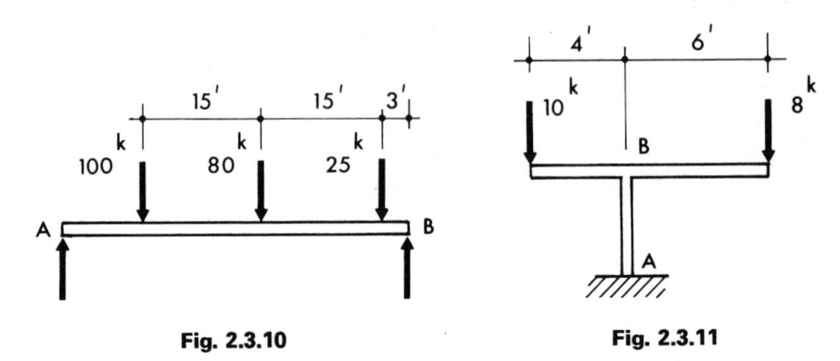

Fig. 2.3.10

Fig. 2.3.11

2.3.5 The columns along one side of a building carry the loads shown in Fig. 2.3.12 to a pick-up girder. Evaluate and locate their resultant.

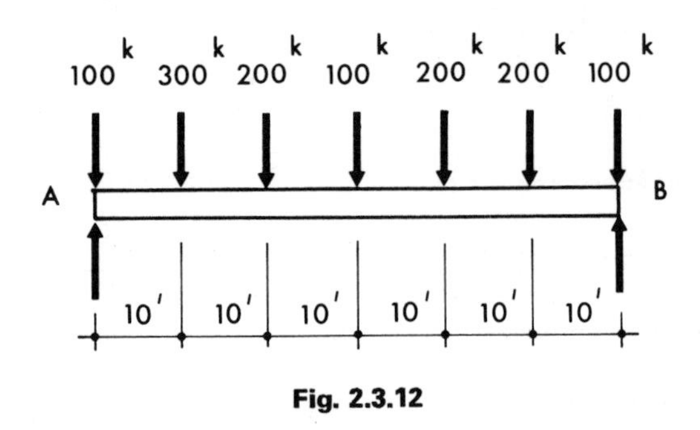

Fig. 2.3.12

2.3.6 A construction worker slowly lifts a bucket weighing 50 lb by pulling horizontally on the spokes of the capstan shown in Fig. 2.3.13. Determine the pull F and show in a diagram the horizontal and vertical forces exerted on the axle of the capstan.

2.3.7 A plumber threads a pipe by exerting equal and opposite forces of 10 lb at the opposite ends of a threader with arms 1 ft long. Determine the force system exerted by the threader on the pipe.

2.3.8 An elevator weighs 500 lb. In order to overcome the frictional forces in the rails, the force exerted by the motor on the elevator cable is 510 lb (Fig. 2.3.14). Determine the resultant of the forces applied to the pulley, under the assumption that the elevator moves with constant speed. (Why is this assumption made?)

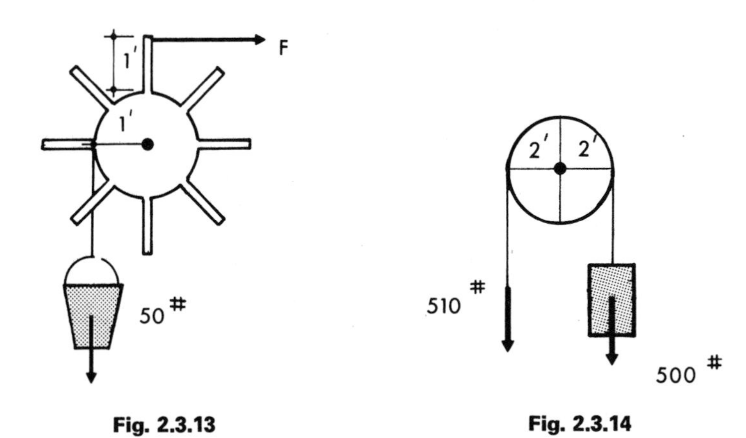

Fig. 2.3.13

Fig. 2.3.14

2.3.9 Figure 2.3.15 shows the force exerted by the wind on each floor of a five-story building. Evaluate and locate the resultant of the wind forces and the overturning wind moment.

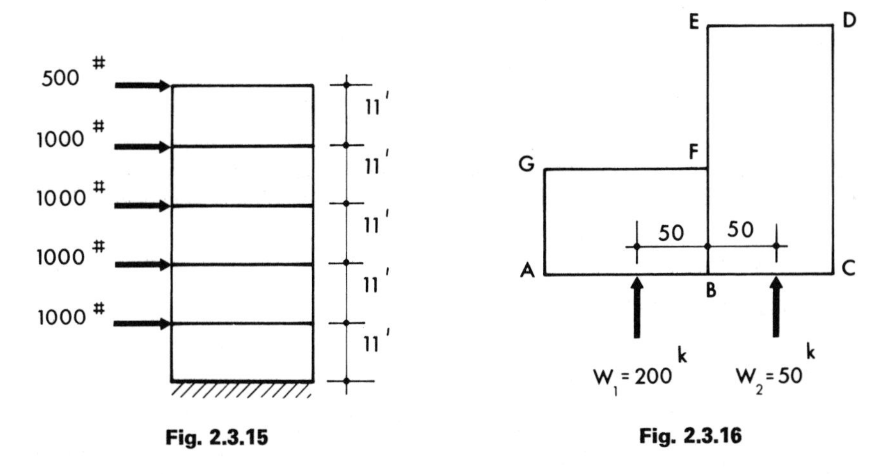

Fig. 2.3.15

Fig. 2.3.16

2.3.10 Figure 2.3.16 shows the plan of a building and the wind forces W_1 and W_2 exerted on the high-rise part *ABFG* and on the low-rise part *BCDE* of the building. Show the resultant wind force through the point *F*, and indicate what kind of motion the building foundation must prevent.

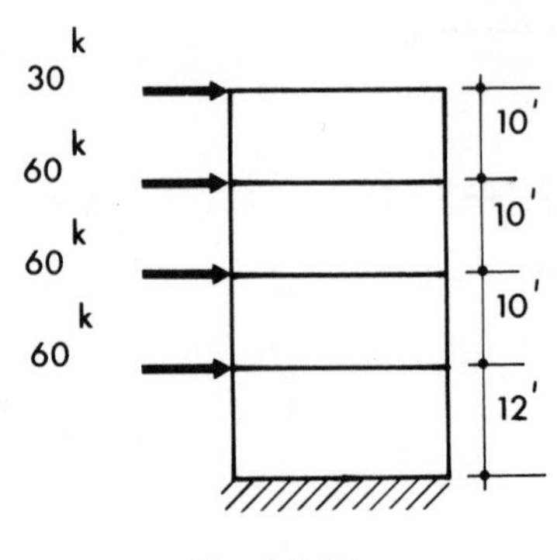

Fig. 2.3.17

2.3.11 Figure 2.3.17 shows the horizontal forces exerted by an earthquake on a four-story building. Evaluate and locate the resultant of the earthquake forces and the overturning moment of these forces.

2.3.12 Bolts are tightened by power wrenches capable of exerting a given torque, i.e., a given moment. A wrench is 1 ft long and rated for a maximum torque of 600 lb in. What is the maximum force one can exert on the wrench with one hand before the wrench starts slipping?

2.3.13 What are the values of the resultant force and resultant moment of a system of plane parallel forces capable of maintaining a body in equilibrium?

2.4 Distributed Line Loads

The forces considered in the previous sections were mostly assumed to act *at a point*. The forces exerted by the columns on a foundation mat (Fig. 2.4.1a) or the loads exerted by floor joists on beams (Fig. 2.4.1b) may be considered to act approximately at a point. Such forces are called *concentrated* and are measured in pounds, kips, tons, etc.

Other loads, however, are distributed along the length or on the surface or through the volume of an element. For example, the weight of a beam acts on each unit length of the beam and is measured in lb/ft or k/ft; the live load on a floor acts on each unit surface of floor and is usually measured in lb/sq ft (psf); the dead load of a concrete buttress acts on each unit volume of the buttress and is usually measured in lb/cu ft.

By use of the calculus one can evaluate the resultant of line, surface or vol-

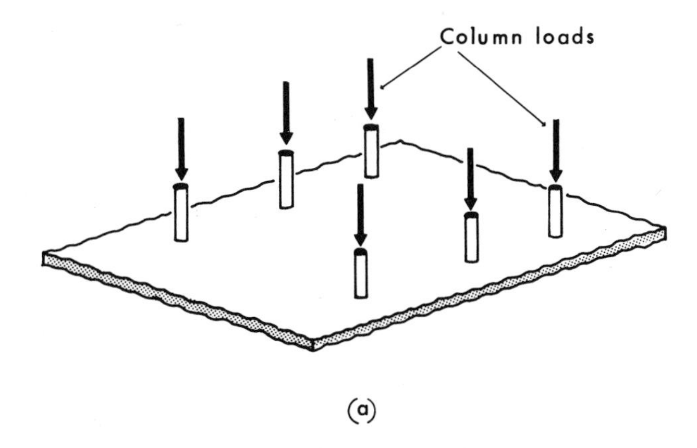

(a)

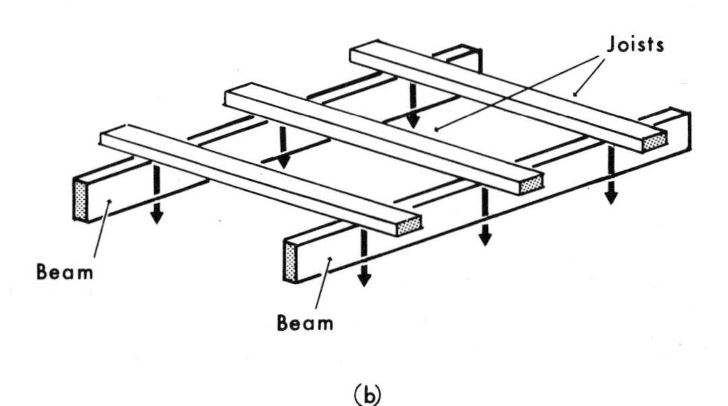

(b)

Fig. 2.4.1

ume loads distributed in the most general manner, but we are already in a position to compute the resultant of the distributed line loads most commonly encountered in practice. Once the resultant of a distributed load is known, the reactions equilibrating the load may be found by the methods used in Chapter 1 for concentrated loads. For example, the uniform dead load of the beam of Fig. 2.4.2 is w lb/ft. The total or resultant load on the beam is $W = wl$ lb and, by symmetry, acts at midspan. The resultant W of the distributed load is statically equivalent to the distributed load w acting on the entire beam. Again by symmetry, the beam reactions are $R = wl/2$.

A beam of nonuniform weight is shown in Fig. 2.4.3. The distributed dead load of the left half of the beam is equivalent to a force $W_1 = w_1(l/2)$ at a dis-

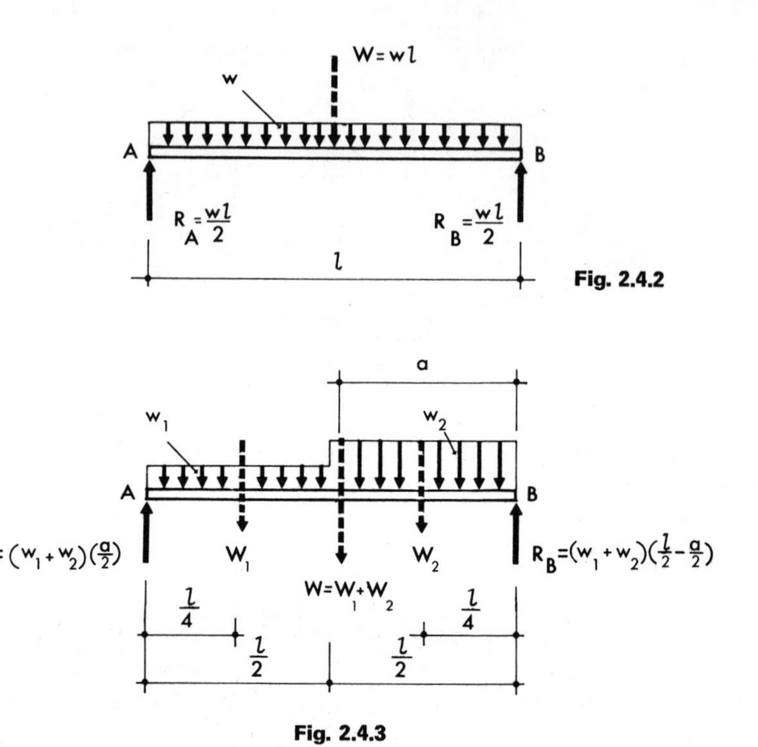

Fig. 2.4.2

Fig. 2.4.3

tance $l/4$ from A; the distributed dead load of the right half is equivalent to a force $W_2 = w_2(l/2)$ at a distance $l/4$ from B. Hence, the resultant of the entire load is a force $W = W_1 + W_2$ at a distance a from B measured by:

$$W_2\left(\frac{l}{4}\right) + W_1\left(\frac{3l}{4}\right) = (W_1 + W_2)a$$

$$\therefore \quad a = \frac{3W_1 + W_2}{W_1 + W_2}\left(\frac{l}{4}\right) = \frac{3w_1 + w_2}{w_1 + w_2}\left(\frac{l^2}{8}\right).$$

The 2 reactions, evaluated by taking moments about A and B, are:

$$R_A = (W_1 + W_2)\left(\frac{a}{l}\right) = (w_1 + w_2)\left(\frac{a}{2}\right),$$

$$R_B = (W_1 + W_2)\left(1 - \frac{a}{l}\right) = (w_1 + w_2)\left(\frac{l}{2} - \frac{a}{2}\right).$$

Figure 2.4.4 shows a beam loaded by w lb/ft downward on its left half and by w lb/ft upward on its right half. The resultant of this load is zero. The load

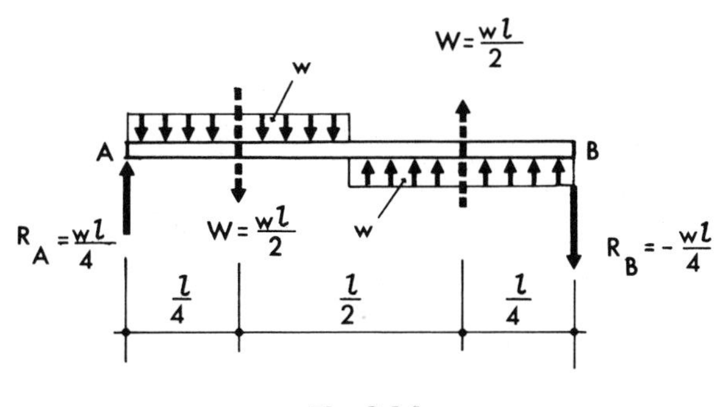

Fig. 2.4.4

is equivalent to a couple of moment $M = (wl/2)(l/2) = wl^2/4$. Assuming R_A and R_B to be positive (i.e., to act upward), and taking moments about B and A, we obtain:

$$-R_A l + \frac{wl}{2}\left(\frac{3l}{4}\right) - \frac{wl}{2}\left(\frac{l}{4}\right) = 0 \quad \therefore \quad R_A = \frac{wl}{4},$$

$$+R_B l + \frac{wl}{2}\left(\frac{3l}{4}\right) - \frac{wl}{2}\left(\frac{l}{4}\right) = 0 \quad \therefore \quad R_B = -\frac{wl}{4}.$$

The reactions constitute a couple of moment $-wl/4 \times l = -wl^2/4$, which equilibrates the moment $+wl^2/4$ of the load.

Figure 2.4.5 shows a beam carrying a *linearly distributed* grain load which

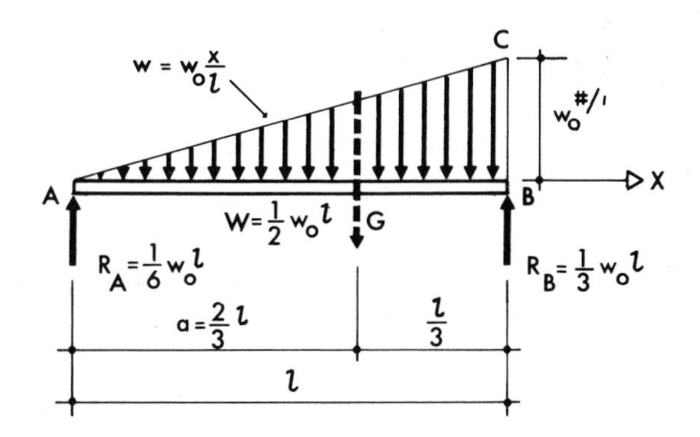

Fig. 2.4.5

grows from zero at A to w_0 lb/ft at B. The total or resultant load W is the area of the triangle ABC, $W = \frac{1}{2} w_0 l$ lb, or half the resultant of a uniform load of w_0 lb/ft. It is easy to verify that this resultant goes through the point G, a distance $a = 2l/3$ from A (see Appendix).* The reactions of the beam are therefore:

$$R_A = \tfrac{1}{3}W = \tfrac{1}{6}w_0 l, \qquad R_B = \tfrac{2}{3}W = \tfrac{1}{3}w_0 l.$$

Figure 2.4.6 shows a beam loaded by a triangularly distributed load, growing from A to C and decreasing from C to B, in which:

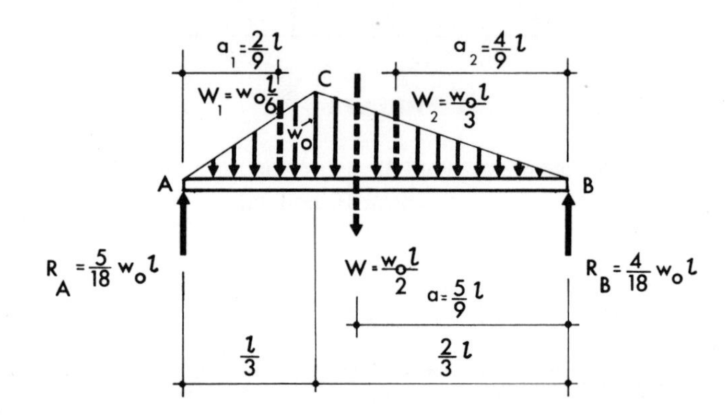

Fig. 2.4.6

$$W_1 = \frac{1}{2} w_0 \left(\frac{l}{3}\right) = w_0 \frac{l}{6}, \qquad W_2 = \frac{1}{2} w_0 \left(\frac{2l}{3}\right) = 2w_0 \frac{l}{6},$$

$$a_1 = \frac{2}{3}\left(\frac{l}{3}\right) = \frac{2}{9} l, \qquad a_2 = \frac{2}{3}\left(\frac{2l}{3}\right) = \frac{4}{9} l.$$

Hence, the resultant:

$$W = (1 + 2)w_0 \frac{l}{6} = w_0 \frac{l}{2}$$

is located at a distance a from B, obtained by equating the sum of the moments about B of W_1 and W_2 to the moment of W:

$$\left(2\frac{w_0 l}{6}\right)\left(\frac{4l}{9}\right) + \frac{w_0 l}{6}\left(l - \frac{2}{9} l\right) = \frac{w_0 l}{2} a$$

*By using the calculus, we can obtain this result very simply:

$$\int_0^l \left(w_0 \frac{x}{l}\right) x\,dx = a \int_0^l w_0 \frac{x}{l}\,dx \quad \therefore \quad \left(\frac{w_0}{l}\right)\frac{l^3}{3} = a\left(\frac{w_0}{l}\right)\frac{l^2}{2}$$

or:

$$a = \frac{2}{3} l.$$

or:

$$\frac{w_0 l^2}{6}\left(\frac{8}{9}+\frac{7}{9}\right)=\frac{w_0 l}{2}a \quad \therefore \quad a=\frac{5}{9}l$$

The reactions are:

$$R_A=\frac{5}{9}\left(\frac{w_0 l}{2}\right)=\frac{5}{18}w_0 l, \qquad R_B=\frac{4}{9}\left(\frac{w_0 l}{2}\right)=\frac{4}{18}w_0 l.$$

PROBLEMS

2.4.1 Find the reactions of the beam of Fig. 2.4.7.

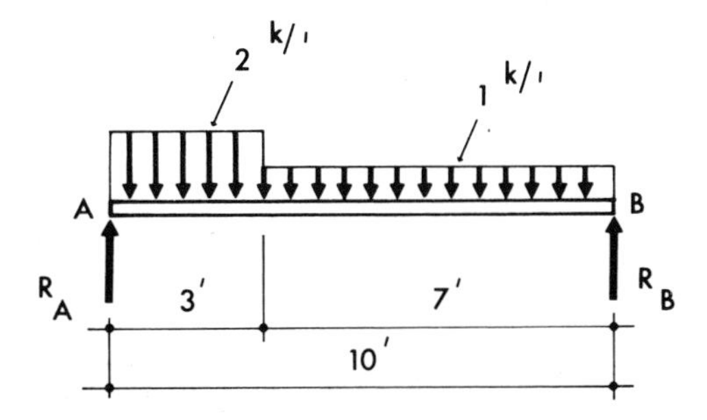

Fig. 2.4.7

2.4.2 Find the reactions of the beam of Fig. 2.4.8.

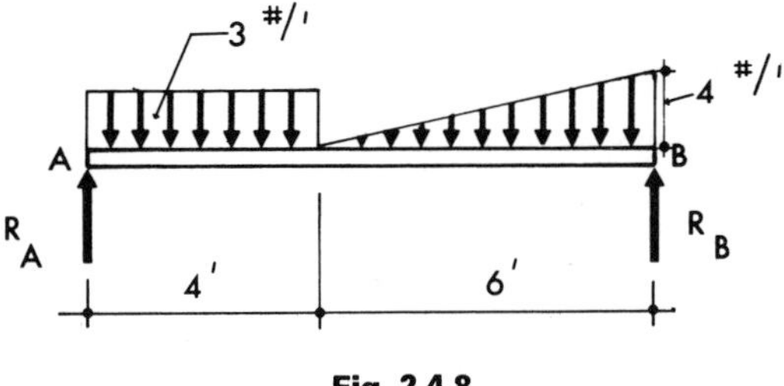

Fig. 2.4.8

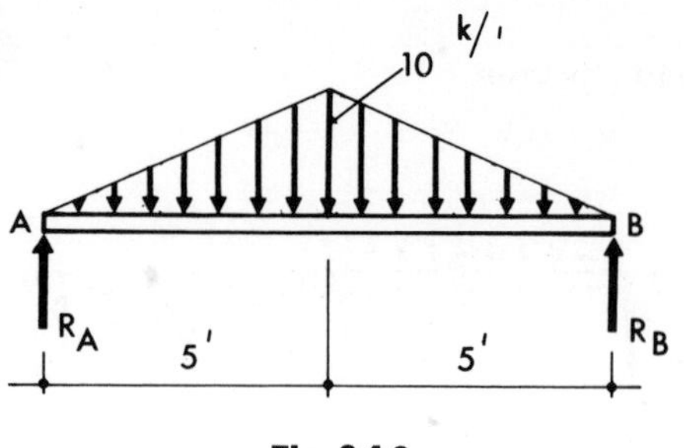

Fig. 2.4.9

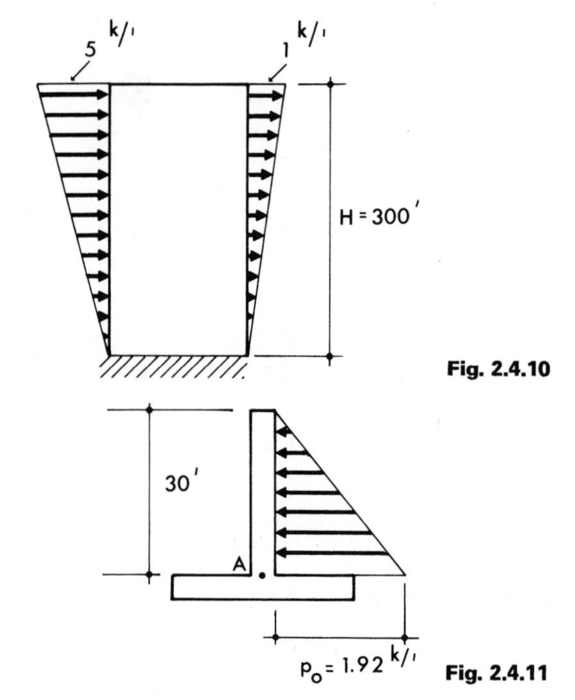

Fig. 2.4.10

Fig. 2.4.11

2.4.3 Find the reactions of the beam of Fig. 2.4.9.

2.4.4 Figure 2.4.10 shows the wind pressure on the left side and the wind suction on the right side of a building 300 ft high. Determine the wind resultant and the overturning moment.

2.4.5 Figure 2.4.11 shows the pressure exerted by the water on each foot width of a dam 30 ft high. Find the total pressure and the overturning moment exerted by the water on 1 ft width of dam.

2.4.6 Find the reactions due to the triangularly distributed load on the beam of Fig. 2.4.12.

2.4.7 The horizontal earth pressure p_0 at the bottom of the retaining wall of Fig. 2.4.13 is 200 lb/ft per foot width of wall. Determine the pressure resultant on the wall and the overturning moment.

2.4.8 Determine the reactions on the beam AB in Fig. 2.4.14, due to the load on the contributory floor area shaded in plan, if the load on the floor is 200 psf.

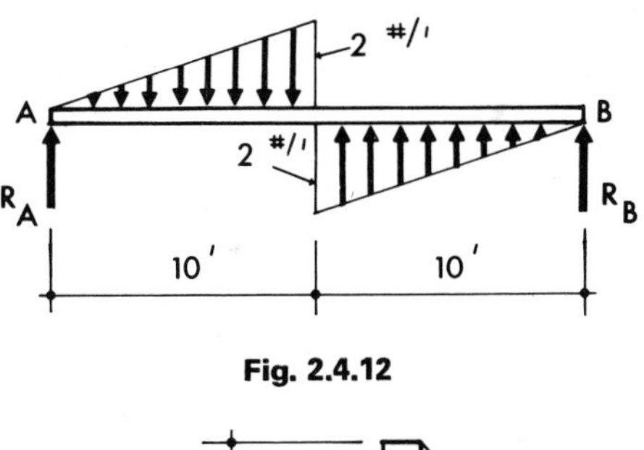

Fig. 2.4.12

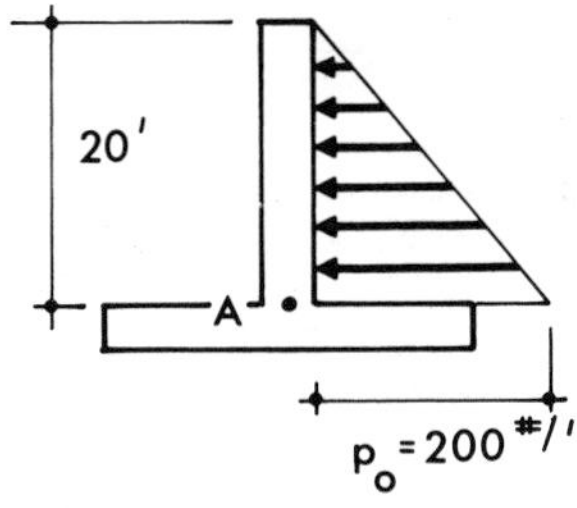

Fig. 2.4.13

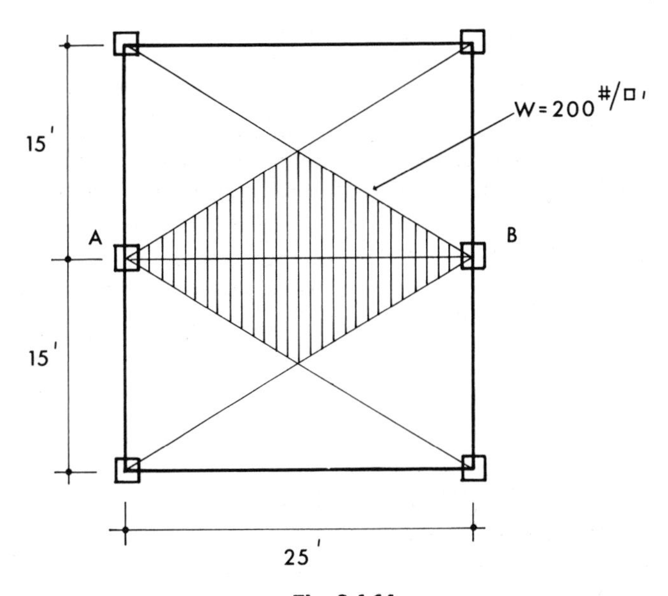

Fig. 2.4.14

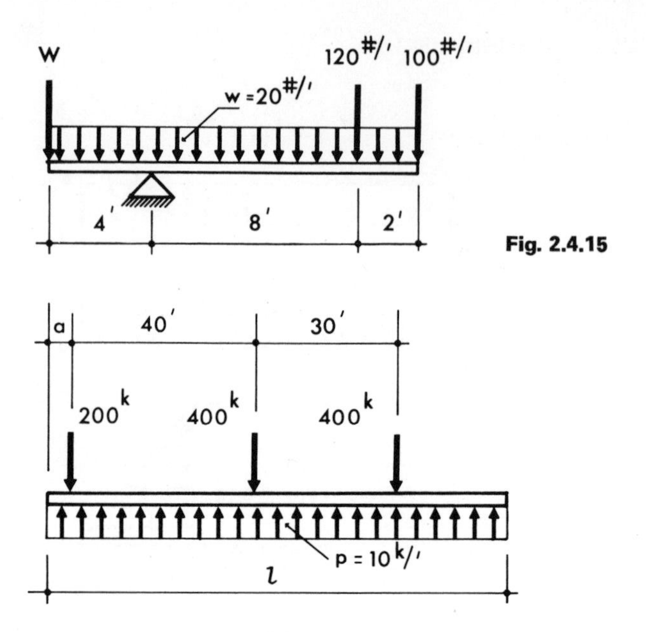

Fig. 2.4.15

Fig. 2.4.16

2.4.9 What is the heaviest weight W two men can lift by pushing down on the beam of Fig. 2.4.15 with forces of 100 lb and 120 lb as shown, if the beam weighs 20 lb/ft?

2.4.10 A foundation beam carries the 3 column loads shown in Fig. 2.4.16. If the soil reaction p on the beam is uniform and cannot be higher than 10 k/ft, determine the length l of the foundation beam and the distance a (between its left end and the 200 k load) so that the beam is in equilibrium.

2.4.11 The beam AB of Fig. 2.4.17 is supported on the two cantilevers CA and BD and carries a load of 9 k as shown. Determine the reactions at A and B and the reactions and moments at C and D.

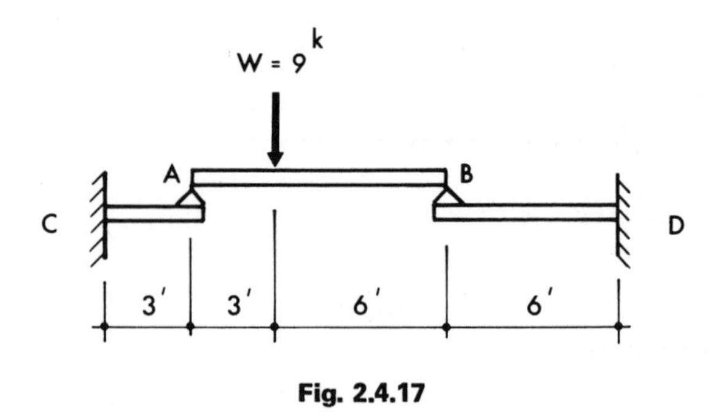

Fig. 2.4.17

2.4.12 The painter's scaffold of Fig. 2.4.18 carries a man weighing 150 lb and is lifted by two men pulling with forces P_A and P_B on the two ropes. The weight of the bridge is balanced by counterweights. Determine the values of

P_A and P_B as the man walks from A to B in terms of his distance a from A. What are the maximum and minimum values of P_A and P_B?

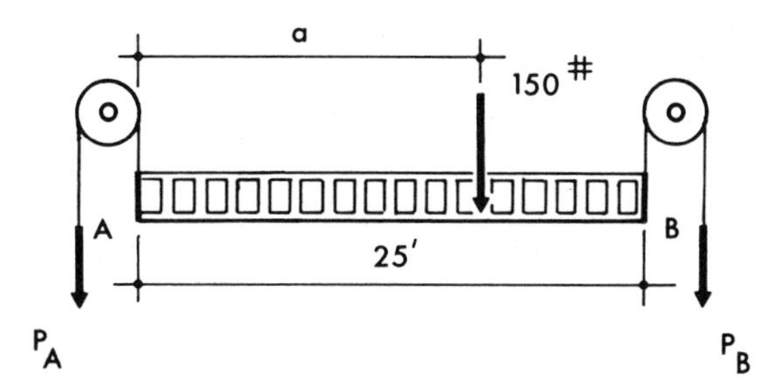

Fig. 2.4.18

2.4.13 A plank weighing 20 lb/ft is supported at points A and B, 10 ft apart, and it cantilevers 4 ft (Fig. 2.4.19). How far can a man weighing 130 lb walk left of A before the plank tips over?

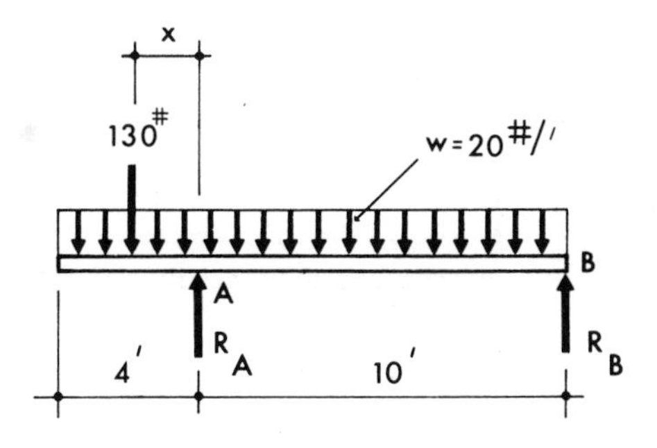

Fig. 2.4.19

2.4.14 You lift a row of books from a shelf by pressing on them. The books weigh 10 lb, and the coefficient of friction between the books and your hands is 0.25. (This means that the frictional force between the books and your hands is 1/4 of the pressure you exert.) What pressure P must you exert on the books in order to lift them from the shelf? Assume the coefficient of friction between the books to be at least 0.25.

2.5 Superposition

Structures must be designed for a variety of loads acting simultaneously on them (e.g., dead loads, wind loads, live loads, etc.), but it is often convenient and simpler to consider each load as acting separately and to obtain the total resultants, reactions and moments by adding or *superimposing* the resultants, reactions and moments due to each load. Superposition of stresses due to each load is often required by building codes, which permit a different allowable stress for different kinds of loads. For example, if the allowable stress for dead and live loads is f, the allowable stress for dead load, live load *and* wind is in many codes 1.33 f. Hence, the reactions due to each type of load must be obtained separately in order to check the stress of different load combinations.

The *method of superposition* may be illustrated by the reaction evaluation of the cantilever beam shown in Fig. 2.5.1, which is loaded by a uniform load

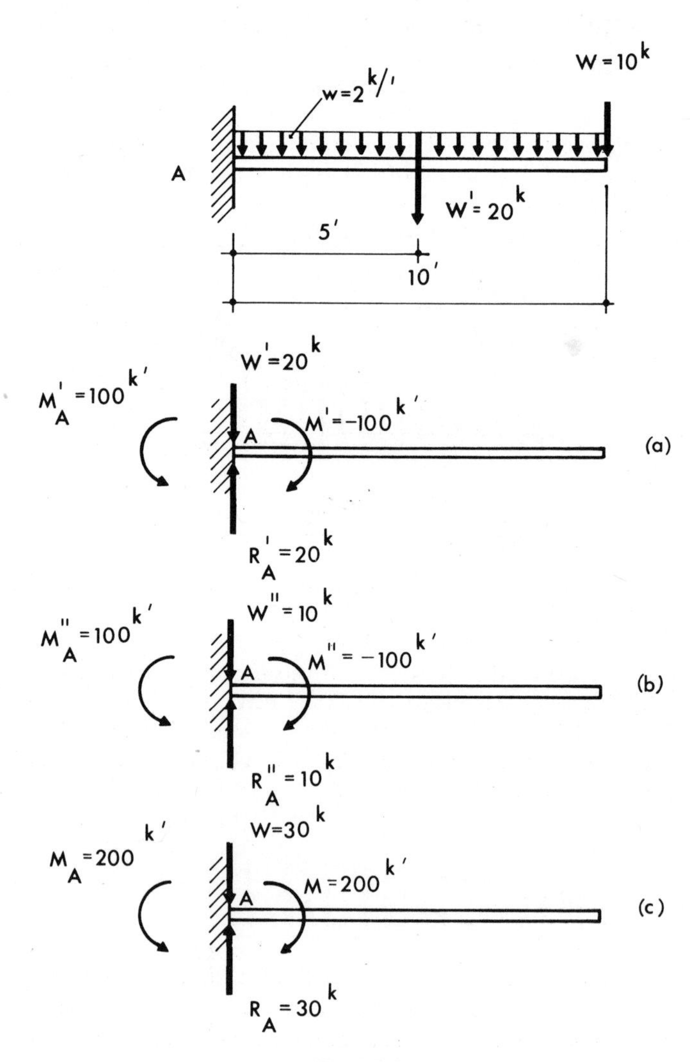

Fig. 2.5.1

$w = 2$ k/ft and a tip load $W = 10$ k. The resultant W' of w is a 20 k load, 5 ft from A; this is equivalent to a downward force of 20 k at A plus a clockwise moment $M' = -20 \times 5 = -100$ k ft (Fig. 2.5.1a). To equilibrate this force system, the support must exert on the beam an upward reaction $R'_A = 20$ k and a counterclockwise moment $M'_A = +100$ k ft. Similarly, the tip force is equivalent to a load of 10 k at A plus a moment $M'' = -10 \times 10 = -100$ k ft; the corresponding reactions are $R''_A = 10$ k upward and $M''_A = +100$ k ft. The total reactions are thus $R_A = 20 + 10 = 30$ k and $M_A = 100 + 100 = 200$ k ft. These results can be checked directly:

$$2 \times 10 + 10 - R_A = 0 \quad \therefore \quad R_A = 30 \text{ k},$$
$$2 \times 10 \times 5 + 10 \times 10 - M_A = 0 \quad \therefore \quad M_A = 200 \text{ k ft}.$$

PROBLEMS

2.5.1 Determine the reactions of the beam in Fig. 2.5.2 by superposition.

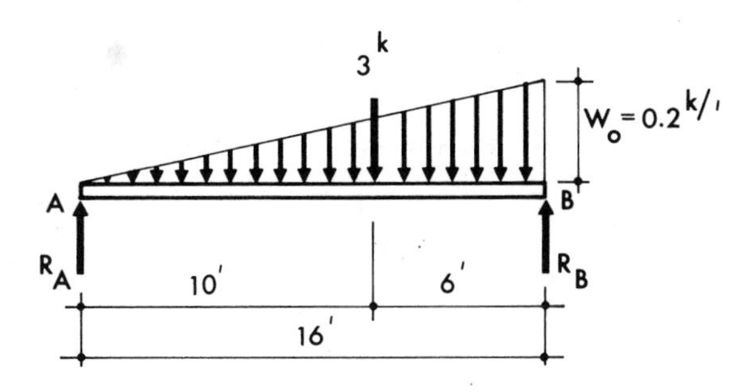

Fig. 2.5.2

2.5.2 Determine the reactions of the beam in Fig. 2.5.3 by splitting the distributed load into a uniform load w_A and a triangular load with $w_0 = w_B - w_A$.

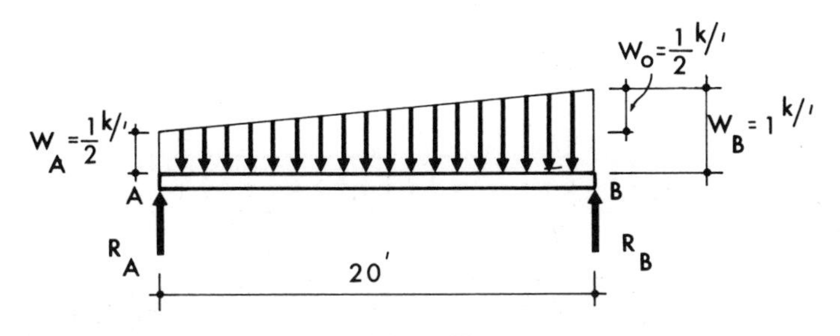

Fig. 2.5.3

2.5.3 The beam of Fig. 2.5.4 carries a uniform load between its supports and a concentrated cantilevered load. Evaluate its reactions by superposition. (Can you explain the value of R_A on physical grounds?)

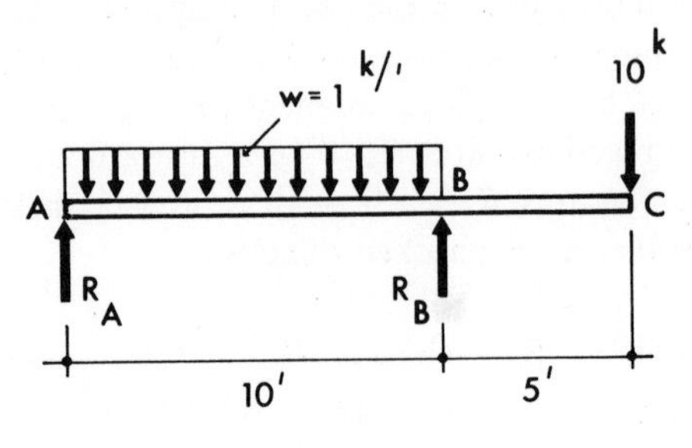

Fig. 2.5.4

2.5.4 The dike of Fig. 2.5.5 resists a triangular water pressure with an intensity at its base of 1.28 k/ft per foot of width and a concentrated load of 1 k per foot of width at its top due to ice expansion. The dike weighs 12 k per foot of width and is supported on two lines of piles 8 ft apart. Determine by superposition the pile reactions per foot of dike.

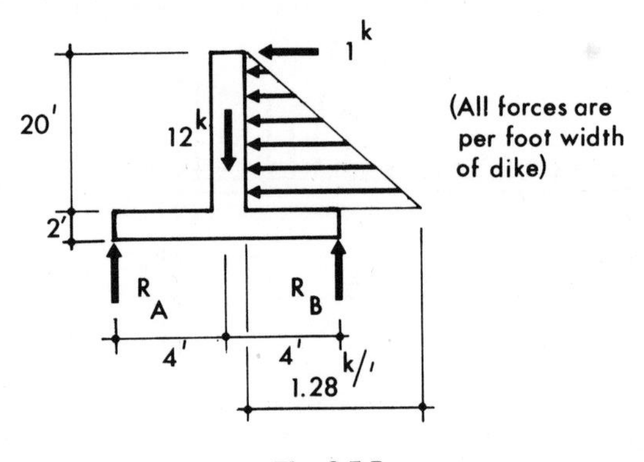

Fig. 2.5.5

2.5.5 Determine the reactions of the beam of Fig. 2.5.6 by superposition.

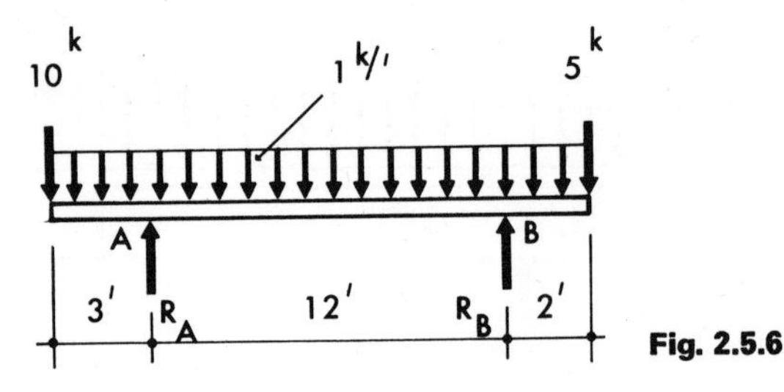

Fig. 2.5.6

2.5.6 The beam *CABD* of Fig. 2.5.7 carries a load $w = 0.25$ ksf on the contributory shaded area of floor between its supports *AB* and on the cantilevered portions *AC, BD*. Determine its reactions by considering separately the load on *AB* and those on *AC, BD*.

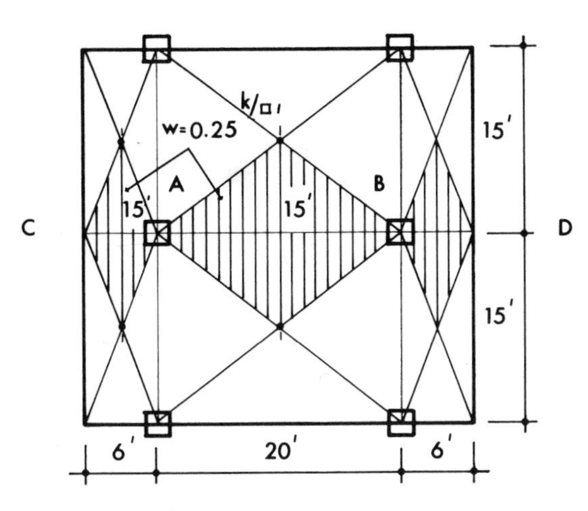

Fig. 2.5.7

2.6 The Parallelogram Law

Let a weight $W = 15$ lb hang from a wire as shown in Fig. 2.6.1a. In order to equilibrate the weight, the wire develops tensile forces T_1 and T_2 in the two cable portions meeting at C. (The equilibrium shape of the wire is called a *funicular* or *string polygon.*) This means that the system of 2 inclined forces T_1 and T_2 is statically equivalent to a vertical force upwards of magnitude $-W$ passing through C and that, conversely, an upward force $-W$ is statically equivalent to the 2 inclined forces T_1, T_2. T_1 and T_2 are called the *components* of $-W$ in the directions CA and CB, and $-W$ is called the *resultant* of T_1, T_2.

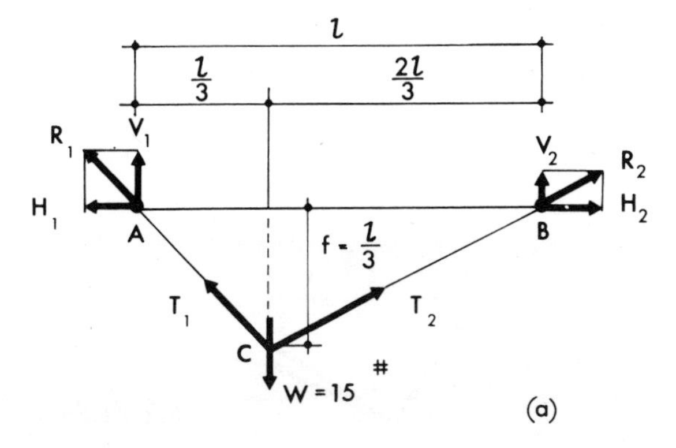

Fig. 2.6.1a

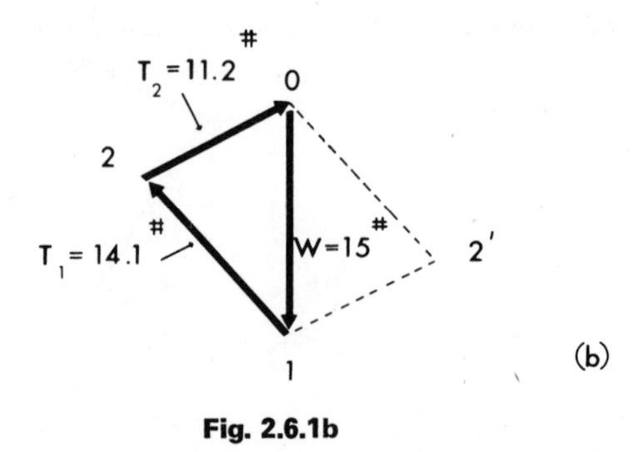

Fig. 2.6.1b

This equivalence allows the evaluation of T_1 and T_2 by means of the *force diagram* of Fig. 2.6.1b, in which 0–1 represents (in a certain scale) $W = 15$ lb, 1–2 is drawn parallel to *AC* and 2–0 is drawn parallel to *CB*. The closed diagram 0–1–2–0 shows that the 15 lb weight is equilibrated by $T_1 = 14.1$ lb and $T_2 = 11.2$ lb.

The force diagram of Fig. 2.6.1b shows a fundamental feature of force equivalence. Since the 2 forces T_1 and T_2, acting simultaneously at C, are statically equivalent to a force $-W$ acting upward at C, the resultant, $-W$, of T_1, T_2 is seen to be the side 1–0 of the triangle 1–2–0; i.e., it is the force obtained by drawing *consecutively* the arrows representing the 2 forces. Since we could have drawn an equivalent force diagram by drawing 1–2′ parallel to *CB* and 0–2′ parallel to *AC*, the resultant of T_1, T_2 is also the diagonal 1–0 of the parallelogram 1–2–0–2′ of sides T_1 and T_2.

This property of *concurrent forces* (i.e., forces passing through the same point) is known as *the parallelogram law*. It allows the substitution of a single force, the resultant, for 2 or *more* concurrent forces by first obtaining the resultant R_1 of 2 forces, then the resultant R_2 of R_1 and a third force and so on.

In Fig. 2.6.2 the resultant of the 3 forces 0–1, 1–2 and 2–3 is the force 0–3, i.e., the resultant R_2 of 0–2 and 2–3, where 0–2 is the resultant R_1 of 0–1 and 1–2.

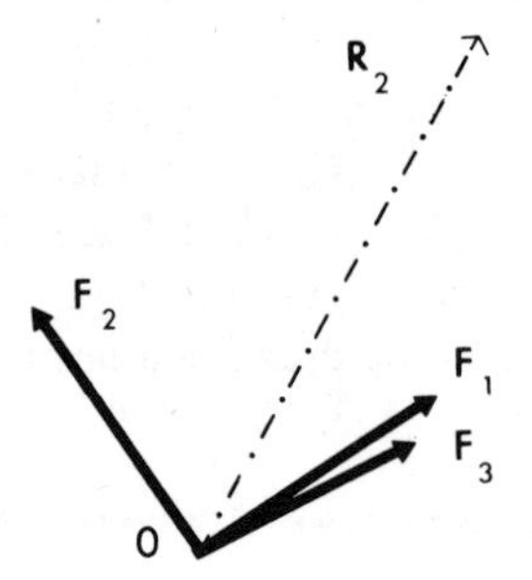

Fig. 2.6.2 a

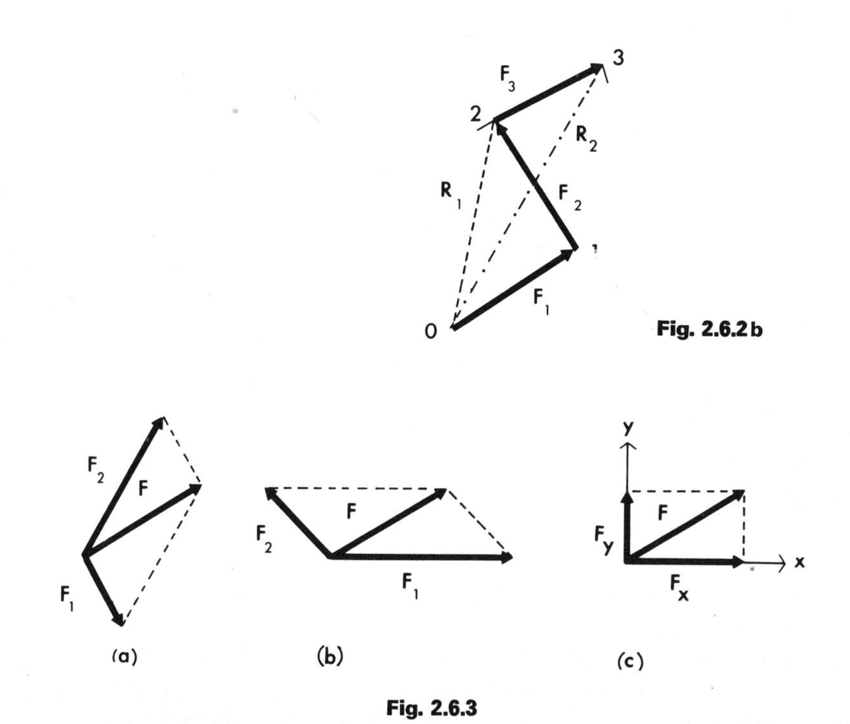

Fig. 2.6.2b

Fig. 2.6.3

As noticed above, since 2 forces F_1, F_2 are equivalent to their diagonal resultant F (Fig. 2.6.3a), the diagonal resultant F is equivalent to F_1 plus F_2.* Hence, the parallelogram law also shows that a force may be *split* into 2 *components* along *any* two given directions. The components F_1, F_2 of F are found by drawing parallels to the given directions from the ends of the arrow representing the force F. Figure 2.6.3 shows the same force F split into components along 3 different sets of 2 directions. In particular, Fig. 2.6.3c shows how F may be split into horizontal and vertical or *cartesian components* F_x and F_y.

To complete the solution of the wire problem of Fig. 2.6.1a we must determine the reactions on the wire at A and B. This is simply done by noticing that the reaction R_1 at A must equilibrate the tension T_1 and hence is a 14.1 lb force at 45° directed upwards. Its horizontal and vertical components are obtained in Fig. 2.6.4a by the parallelogram law and are $H_1 = -10$ lb and $V_1 = +10$ lb. Similarly, Fig. 2.6.4b shows that the horizontal and vertical components of the reaction $R_2 = 11.2$ lb at B are $H_2 = +10$ lb and $V_2 = +5$ lb. As shown in Fig. 2.6.4c, the diagrams in Figs. 2.6.4a, b could have been obtained directly from Fig. 2.6.1b by drawing a horizontal through 2 to meet the vertical 0–1 at point 3: $V_1 = 1\text{–}3$, $V_2 = 3\text{–}0$ and $H_1 = H_2 = 2\text{–}3$.

*F is also called the *vectorial sum* of the vectors F_1 and F_2.

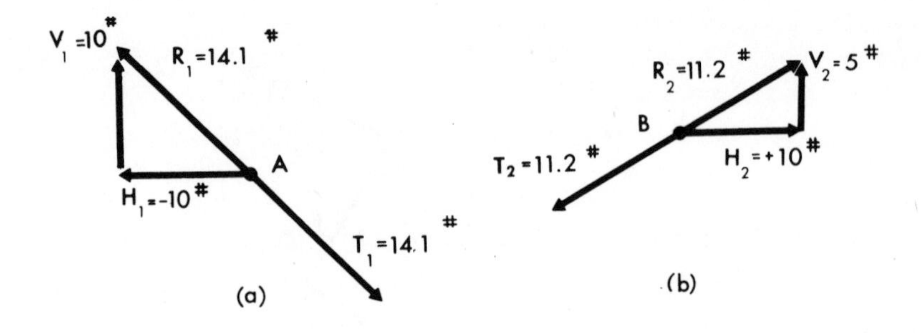

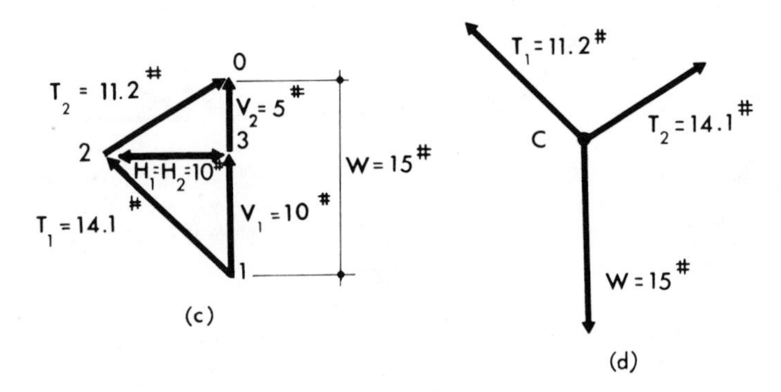

Fig. 2.6.4

Figure 2.6.4c contains the 3 *closed* force diagrams expressing the equilibrium of the forces applied at the 3 points C, A and B. The *equilibrium polygon* of point C, acted upon by W, T_1 and T_2, is 0–1–2–0. The segment representing W is directed from 0 to 1, indicating that W acts downward (Fig. 2.6.4d); the segment representing T_1 is directed from 1 to 2 (i.e., away from C), indicating a pull on C or that T_1 is tensile; T_2 is also tensile because the segment 2–0 is directed away from C. The equilibrium polygons for A and B are, respectively, 2–1–3–2 and 0–2–3–0, where 2–1 represents the tension T_1 on A (away from A) and 0–2 represents the tension T_2 on B (away from B). You will notice that the horizontal component of the reaction R_1 is $H_1 = 3\text{–}2$, a tensile force acting to the left on A, while the horizontal component of the reaction R_2 is $H_2 = 2\text{–}3$, a tensile force acting to the right on B. $H_1 = H_2$ is called the *thrust* of the wire on the supports.

The graphical solution to the wire problem may be easily checked by analysis. Taking moments about B and A (Fig. 2.6.1a), we obtain:

$$-V_1 \times l + 15 \times \tfrac{2}{3}l = 0 \quad \therefore \quad V_1 = 10 \text{ lb},$$
$$V_2 \times l - 15 \times \tfrac{1}{3}l = 0 \quad \therefore \quad V_2 = 5 \text{ lb}.$$

Since the angle between T_1 and the horizontal is 45°, the vertical and horizontal components of T_1 are equal; thus, $H_1 = V_1 = 10$ lb is a tensile force to the left. For horizontal equilibrium:

$$H_1 + H_2 = 0 \quad \therefore \quad H_2 = -H_1,$$

and $H_2 = 10$ lb is a force acting to the right at B. Computing T_1 and T_2 as the diagonals of the rectangles of sides V_1, H_1 and V_2, H_2, we find that:

$$T_1 = \sqrt{V_1^2 + H_1^2} = \sqrt{10^2 + 10^2} = 14.1 \text{ lb},$$
$$T_2 = \sqrt{V_2^2 + H_2^2} = \sqrt{5^2 + 10^2} = 11.2 \text{ lb}.$$

PROBLEMS

2.6.1 Evaluate the components of the force $F = 20$ lb in Fig. 2.6.5: (a) in the vertical and horizontal directions, (b) in the x- and the $\alpha = 135°$-directions, (c) in the y- and the $\beta = -45°$-directions.

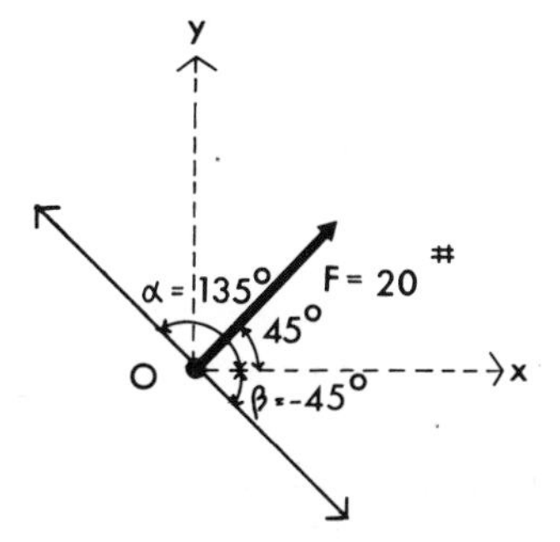

Fig. 2.6.5

2.6.2 A weight of 100 lb hangs from the midpoint of a steel wire spanning 20 ft. Evaluate analytically the tension in the wire and its thrust: (a) when the sag is 10 ft, and (b) when it is 5 ft.

2.6.3 A cable spans 100 ft and carries a weight of 2 k at a distance of 20 ft from its left support, with a sag of 30 ft. Determine graphically and check analytically the tension in the cable to the left and to the right of the load, the thrust and the vertical reactions at the supports.

2.6.4 A tower is guyed by four identical cables spaced by 90° in plan and attached to the tower at a height of 200 ft. The cables are anchored at a horizontal distance of 50 ft from the tower and prestressed with a tension of 5 k each. What horizontal and vertical forces does each cable exert on its anchorage? What compressive force do the cables exert on the tower?

2.6.5 A cable of span l carries a single load W. For what locations of the load on the cable will its thrust be, respectively, minimum and maximum if the sag f is kept constant? What is the value of the maximum thrust?

2.6.6 The two cables ADB and ADC of Fig. 2.6.6 carry the same load and are supported, respectively, at A and B, and at A and C. Are the tensions T_1, T_2, right and left of the load, the same in the two cables? Why?

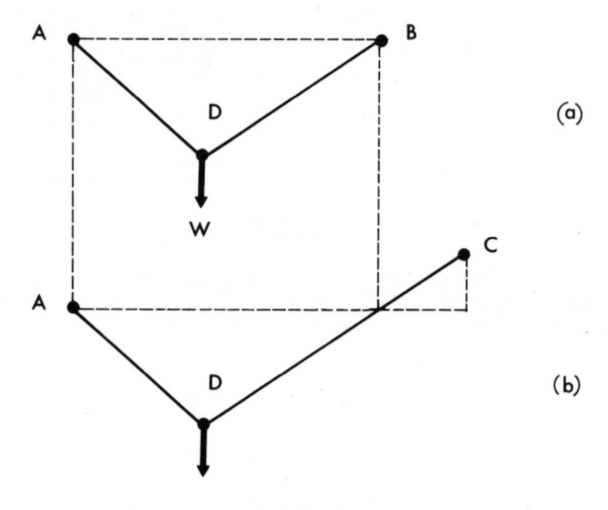

Fig. 2.6.6

2.6.7 A tower 100 ft high weighs 1 k/ft and is acted upon by a horizontal wind force of 0.15 k/ft. Find the resultant force acting on the tower, its angle θ with the vertical and the overturning moment.

2.6.8 Entering a crowded subway train, you are pushed by the man on your right with a force of 50 lb and by the man behind you with a force of 100 lb. In what direction do you tend to go with respect to the normal to the train?

2.6.9 A sign 3 ft wide and 4 ft high weighs 200 lb and hangs vertically from two hinges set at its upper edge. What angle to the vertical will it assume under a steady wind pressure of 10 psf? What are the horizontal and vertical components of the hinge reactions?

2.6.10 A bucket of sand weighing 50 lb is lifted to the 10th floor of a building by means of a cable going over a pulley set at the 12th floor and 3 feet away from the face of the building. What horizontal force H must be exerted by a worker to bring the bucket into the 10th floor, if the floors are 10 ft high?

2.6.11 A worker lifts a 50 lb bucket by pulling on a 45° rope going over a pulley. Find the pull T on the rope and the resultant R of the forces acting on the pulley.

2.6.12 A triangular bracket supports a weight of 100 lb at its tip B. One of its bars is horizontal; the other makes an angle of 60° with the horizontal. Determine the forces in the bracket bars when: (a) the upper bar is horizontal; (b) the lower bar is horizontal (Fig. 2.6.7).

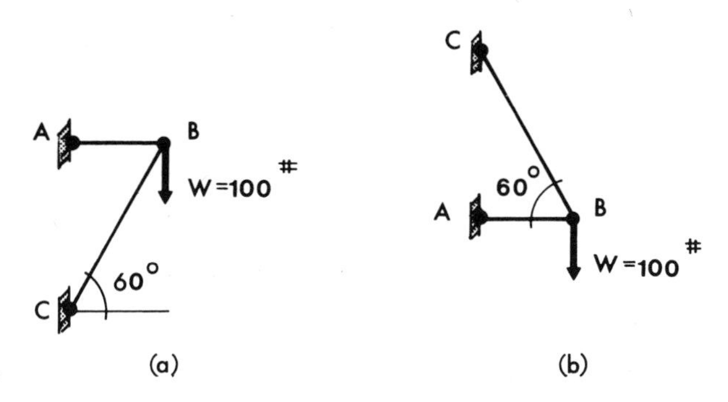

Fig. 2.6.7

2.6.13 The pulley of Problem 2.6.11 is attached to the tip B of the bracket in Fig. 2.6.7b. Find the forces in the bars of the bracket.

Chapter Three

3.1 Trusses

The first two chapters of this book have presented the basic principles required to analyze *all* statically determinate structures. These principles will now be applied to the analysis and design of *plane trusses*.

A plane truss is a structure composed of straight *bars* (usually of constant cross section) meeting at *joints*, where the bars are assumed to be *pinned*, i.e., free to rotate (Fig. 3.1.1). Hence, under loads applied only at the joints, the bars elongate in tension or shorten in compression, the truss deforms and the angles between the bars change. In reality, the bars are rigidly connected to gusset plates by welding, riveting or bolting (Fig. 3.1.2), so that the angles between the bars cannot change and, moreover, not all loads are applied at the joints. Hence, the bars of a real truss, besides elongating or shortening, also bend. But the stresses due to bending are often small as compared to those due to tension or compression. Because the *bending stresses* in a well designed truss (see Section 5.8) are less than 20% of the tensile or compressive stresses, they are called *secondary* and are usually ignored in preliminary design.

Plane Trusses

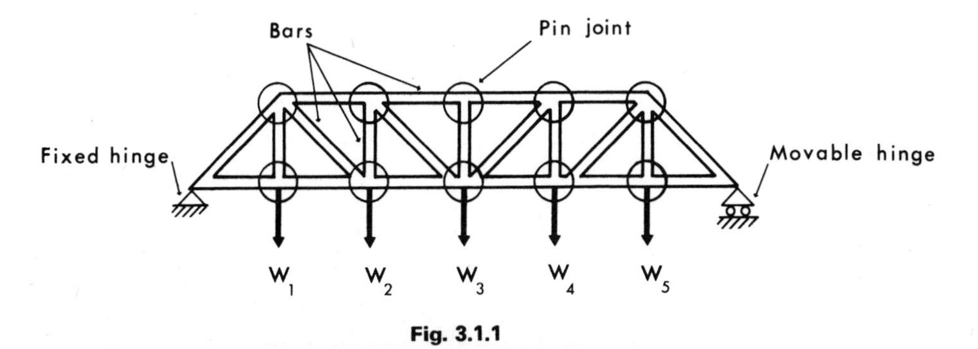

Fig. 3.1.1

Light trusses are used in buildings as standard structural elements to span distances of between 20 and 100 ft and are called *open-web joists* (Fig. 3.1.3). Heavy, built-up trusses are used in roof and bridge design to span distances of hundreds of feet. The upper and lower bars of a truss constitute its *upper* and

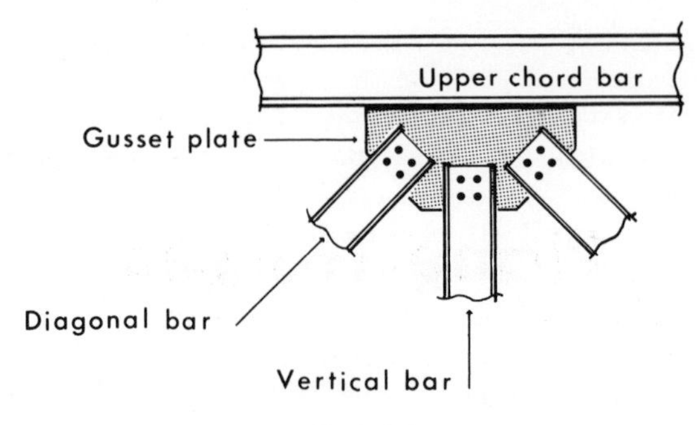

Fig. 3.1.2

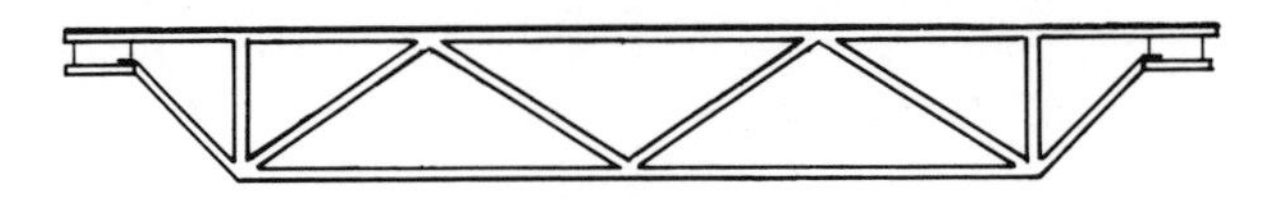

Fig. 3.1.3

lower chords; the vertical and inclined bars connecting the chords are called its *verticals* and *diagonals*, respectively (Fig. 3.1.2).

Since a joint may be connected to other joints by a variety of bar combinations, it becomes important to know whether a plane truss configuration is *statically determinate internally*, i.e., whether the forces in its bars can be determined by statics alone. To this purpose let us build a truss by the following procedure. We start by connecting 2 joints, A and B, by means of one bar (Fig. 3.1.4). Notice that to connect rigidly a joint C to the rigid system A-B, we need a minimum of 2 bars, thus creating the bracket A–B–C. To connect the next joint D to the bracket, we again need at least 2 bars. Hence, if we wish to build a truss with n_j joints, we need at least 1 bar to connect the first two and 2 bars to connect the remaining $n_j - 2$ joints, or all together a number n_b of bars given by:

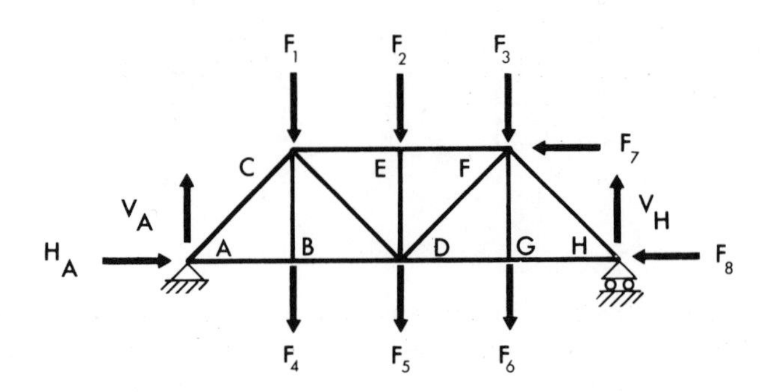

Fig. 3.1.4

$$n_b = 1 + 2(n_j - 2) = 2n_j - 3. \tag{3.1.1}$$

But since the bars of a plane truss are under axial tension or compression and, by assumption, the loads act in the plane of the truss and are applied to its joints, the bar forces also go through the joints. Therefore, the moment equation of plane equilibrium, $\sum M_y = 0$, is identically satisfied at each joint, and only 2 equations, say $\sum F_x = 0$, $\sum F_z = 0$, are available at each joint to determine unknown bar forces. Since these 2 equations are sufficient to determine the forces in the 2 bars needed to connect the joint to the preceding joints, a plane truss carrying known external loads at the joints, with a number of bars given by (3.1.1) and with joints connected in the manner previously described, is statically determinate *internally*.

You will notice that at joints such as A and H in the truss of Fig. 3.1.4, some of the "externally applied loads" are the reactions V_A, H_A and V_H needed

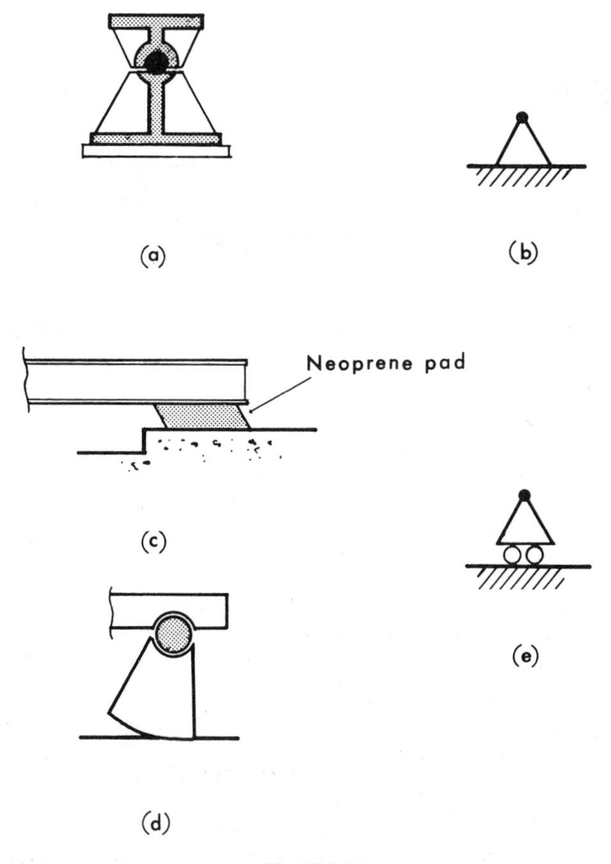

Fig. 3.1.5

to equilibrate the truss as a whole. These reactions must be known *beforehand* if the forces in the bars are to be determined by statics alone. To realize that this can often be done by statics, notice, for example, that many trusses are supported by one *fixed hinge* (Fig. 3.1.4, point A) capable of reacting both vertically and horizontally, and one *movable hinge* (Fig. 3.1.4, point H) capable of reacting only vertically (see also Section 5.1). Since the unknown reactions V_A, H_A and V_H can be evaluated by plane statics, say by taking moments about A and H and by the equation $\sum F_x = 0$, these trusses are said to be statically determinate *externally*. A fixed hinge is usually built as an actual pin-connection (Fig. 3.1.5a) and is symbolized as in Fig. 3.1.5b. A movable hinge is obtained by means of either a neoprene pad, which allows horizontal displacements, or a pendulum support (Fig. 3.1.5c, d) and is symbolized as in Fig. 3.1.5e.

PROBLEMS

3.1.1 Determine whether the truss of Fig. 3.1.6 is statically determinate or indeterminate internally.

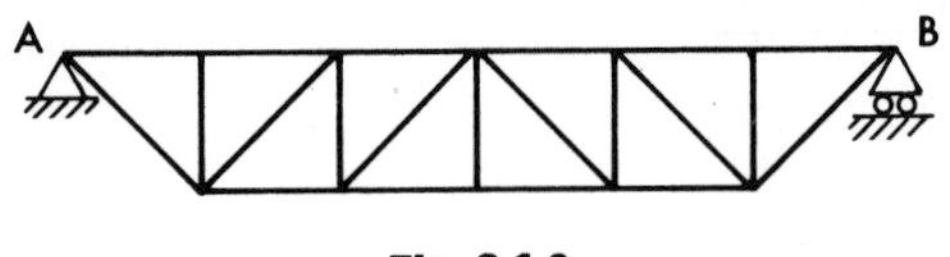

Fig. 3.1.6

3.1.2 Determine whether the truss of Fig. 3.1.7 is statically determinate or indeterminate internally.

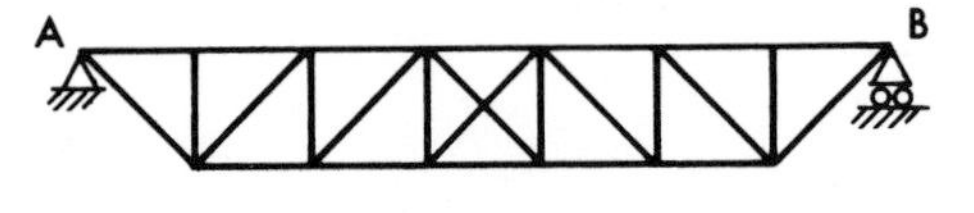

Fig. 3.1.7

3.1.3 The truss of Fig. 3.1.8 has $n_j = 12$ joints and $n_b = 21$ bars. By equation (3.1.1) it is statically determinate. Can you explain in physical terms why it is uncapable of supporting vertical loads and is hence *unstable* or *underdeterminate*?

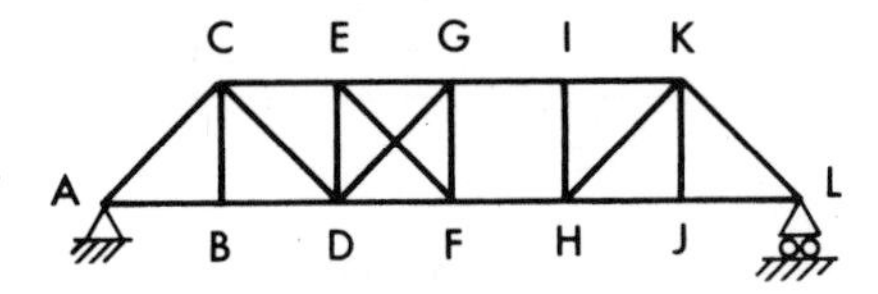

Fig. 3.1.8

3.1.4 Why is the truss of Fig. 3.1.9 statically determinate internally but indeterminate externally?

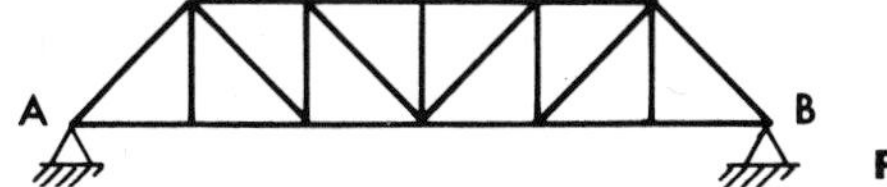

Fig. 3.1.9

3.1.5 The cantilevered truss of Fig. 3.1.10 is supported on two fixed hinges, yet it is statically determinate externally. Why?

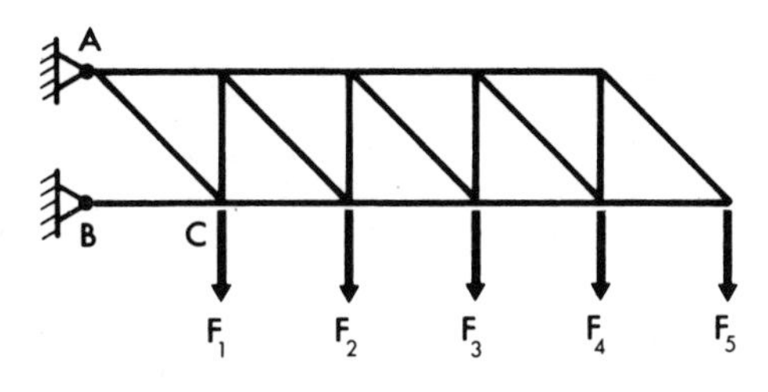

Fig. 3.1.10

3.1.6 The vertical truss of Fig. 3.1.11 is used as one of two stiffening trusses to absorb wind forces on a tall steel building. As shown in the figure, the wind loads may be considered to be pressure- and suction-loads of different magnitude. The truss is statically indeterminate internally. Can you think

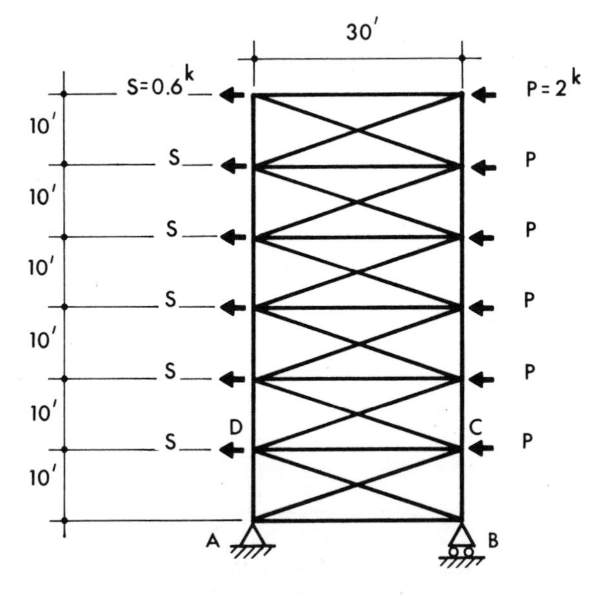

Fig. 3.1.11

of the truss as consisting of the superposition of two trusses, one loaded with the pressure loads, the other with the suction loads, which are each statically determinate internally? Sketch the two separate trusses.

3.1.7 The truss of Fig. 3.1.12 is unstable (statically underdeterminate). It becomes statically determinate by eliminating one load. Which one? Why?

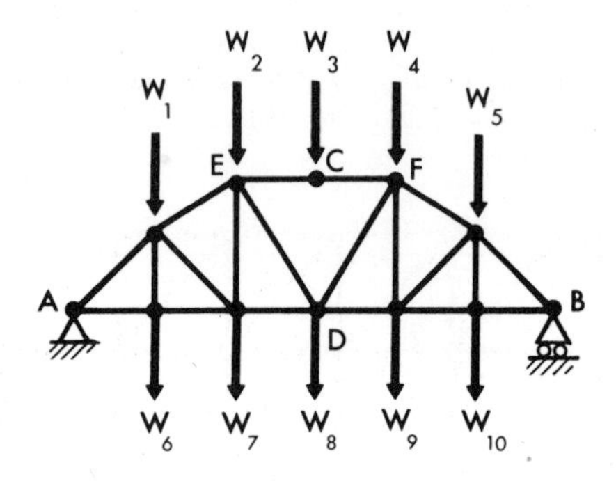

Fig. 3.1.12

3.1.8 Is the bar-joist of Fig. 3.1.13 statically determinate internally?

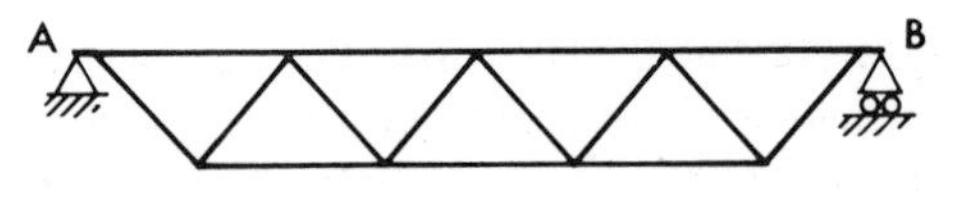

Fig. 3.1.13

3.2 The Section Method

When the forces in only a few critical bars are to be evaluated, trusses are analyzed by the so-called *section method.* This method consists in cutting the truss into *two free bodies* by means of a *section* through not more than 3 bars and writing the 3 equations that guarantee the equilibrium of either free body.

For example, to evaluate the force F_{GH} in the bar GH of the truss of Fig. 3.2.1a, separate the truss into 2 free bodies by means of a vertical cut or section immediately to the left of HE, and apply to the end of the cut bars in the left free body the forces F_{GH}, F_{DE} and F_{GE} exerted on them by the right free body (Fig. 3.2.1b). In the figure all 3 forces have been assumed to be tensile.

Since the reactions V_A, V_B are equal by symmetry (and equal to 50 k), and $H_A = 0$ because the loads are vertical, the left free body is in equilibrium under the action of the reaction $V_A = 50$ k, the two 20 k loads and the 3 unknown bar forces. To obtain F_{GH}, we take moments about E, the meeting

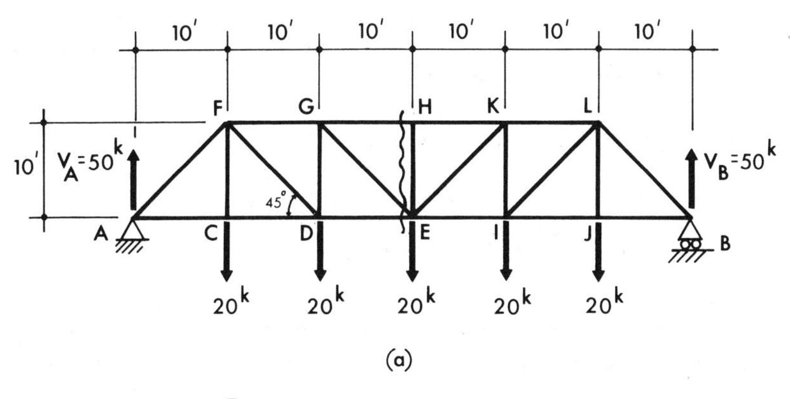
10′
10′
10′
10′
10′
10′
F
G
H
K
L
10′
$V_A = 50^k$
$V_B = 50^k$
45°
A
C
D
E
I
J
B
20^k
20^k
20^k
20^k
20^k

(a)

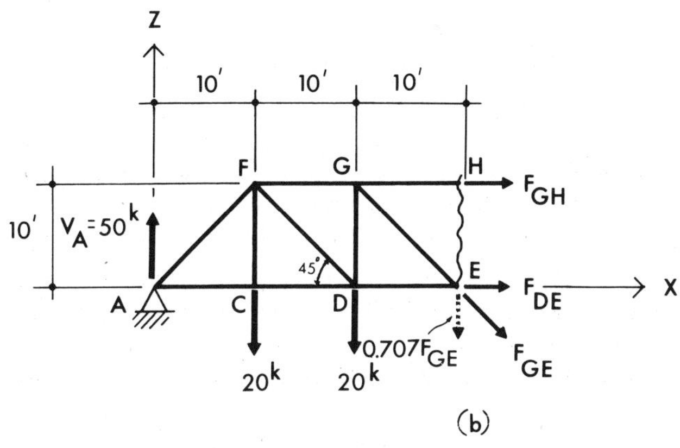
Z
10′
10′
10′
F
G
H
F_{GH}
10′
$V_A = 50^k$
45°
E
F_{DE}
X
A
C
D
$0.707F_{GE}$
F_{GE}
20^k
20^k

(b)

(c)

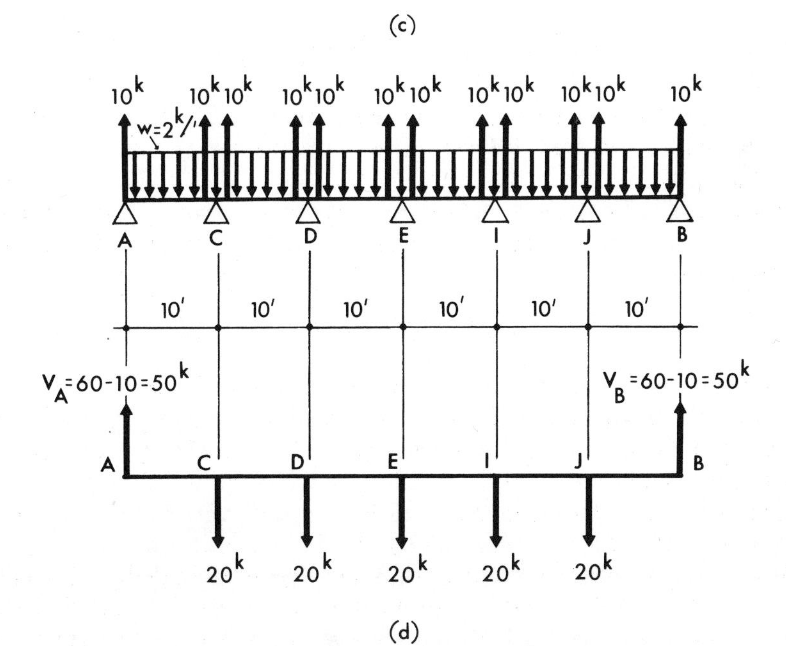
10^k
10^k 10^k
10^k 10^k
10^k 10^k
10^k 10^k
10^k 10^k
10^k
$w = 2^k/'$
A
C
D
E
I
J
B
10′
10′
10′
10′
10′
10′
$V_A = 60 - 10 = 50^k$
$V_B = 60 - 10 = 50^k$
A
C
D
E
I
J
B
20^k
20^k
20^k
20^k
20^k

(d)

Fig. 3.2.1

point of F_{GE} and F_{DE}, so as to eliminate the other two unknown forces:

$$-50 \times 30 + 20 \times 20 + 20 \times 10 - F_{GH} \times 10 = 0$$

$$\therefore \quad F_{GH} = -\frac{900}{10} = -90 \text{ k}.$$

The minus sign of F_{GH} shows that this bar force is compressive, contrary to the assumption made in Fig. 3.2.1b. To obtain F_{DE}, we take moments about G so as to eliminate F_{GH} and F_{GE}:

$$-50 \times 20 + 20 \times 10 + F_{DE} \times 10 = 0$$

$$\therefore \quad F_{DE} = 80 \text{ k}.$$

The plus sign of F_{DE} shows that this force is tensile, as originally assumed. (You will notice that, if the truss had been 15 ft deep rather than 10 ft deep, F_{GH} would have been $-900/15 = -60$ k, and F_{DE} would have been $800/15 = 533$ k. Thus, *the deeper the truss, the smaller the forces in the chord bars.*)

To obtain F_{GE}, we write the vertical equilibrium equation for the left free body, thus eliminating F_{GH} and F_{DE}. Notice that F_{GE} has a vertical component equal to $F_{GE} \cos 45° = 0.707\ F_{GE}$; the vertical equilibrium equation becomes:

$$+50 - 20 - 20 - 0.707\ F_{GE} = 0$$

$$\therefore \quad F_{GE} = \frac{10}{0.707} = 14.1 \text{ k}.$$

F_{GE} is positive (i.e., tensile) as originally assumed. (You will notice that if the diagonal GE had been inclined to the horizontal by 60° rather than by 45°, F_{GE} would have been $10/\cos 60° = 10/0.866 = 11.5$ k. *The steeper the diagonal the smaller its force*, which can never be less than 10 k in our case.) As a check of these results, the horizontal equlibrium equation for the left free body gives:

$$+F_{GH} + F_{DE} + 0.707F_{GE} = -90 + 80 + 10 = 0.$$

When a truss carries distributed loads or concentrated loads not acting at the joints, the bar forces (for preliminary design) are obtained by considering each loaded bar as a simply supported beam, by determining the beam reactions and by applying forces equal and opposite to the reactions at the corresponding joints. This procedure is referred to as *concentrating the loads at the joints*. For example, if the truss of Fig. 3.2.1 carried a uniform vertical load $w = 2$ k/ft on its lower chord, each lower-chord beam reaction would be 10 k (Fig. 3.2.1c), and the concentrated loads at the joints of the lower chord and the reactions V_A, V_B would be as shown in Fig. 3.2.1d. The bending effects of distributed loads and of concentrated loads not acting at the joints are evaluated by methods of Chapter 5, i.e., by considering the bars as beams.

PROBLEMS

3.2.1 Determine the forces in the bars *AC*, *AD* and *BD* of the truss of Fig. 3.2.2.

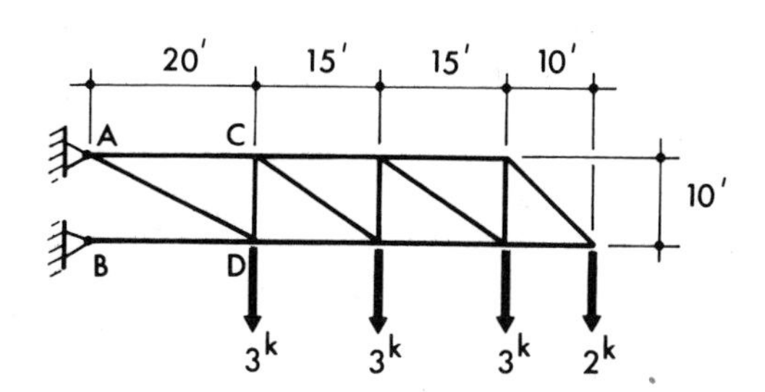

Fig. 3.2.2

3.2.2 Determine the forces in the bars *CE*, *DE* and *EF* of the truss of Fig. 3.2.3. (Use section indicated by wavy line to evaluate the force in *EF*.)

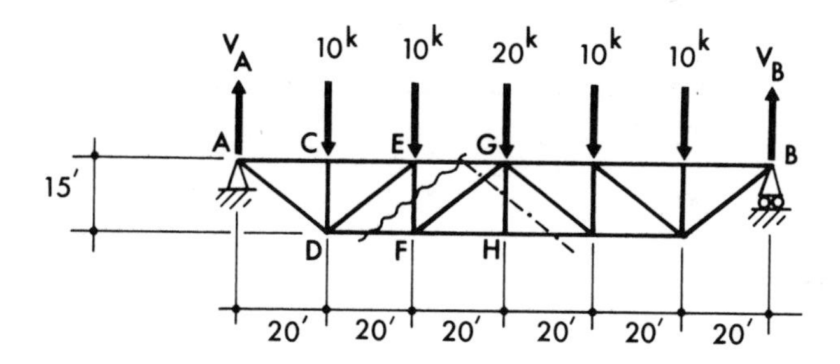

Fig. 3.2.3

3.2.3 Determine the force in the bar *FG* of the truss of Fig. 3.2.4.

3.2.4 Determine the force in the bar *FG* of the truss of Fig. 3.2.4 when the only load on the truss is a horizontal wind load of 10 k acting to the left and applied at *E*. (Determine the reactions at *A* and *B* first.)

3.2.5 Horizontal wind loads acting to the left, of 1 k each, are applied to the joints of the lower chord of the truss in Fig. 3.2.3. Determine the forces in the bars *EG*, *GF* and *FH*. Evaluate the force in the bar *GH* by the indicated dotted section and vertical equilibrium. Can you explain the result physically?

3.2.6 The vertical truss of Fig. 3.1.11 is built without the diagonals parallel to *AC*. Determine the forces in the bars *AD*, *DB* and *BC* due to the pressure loads on the right side of the truss only.

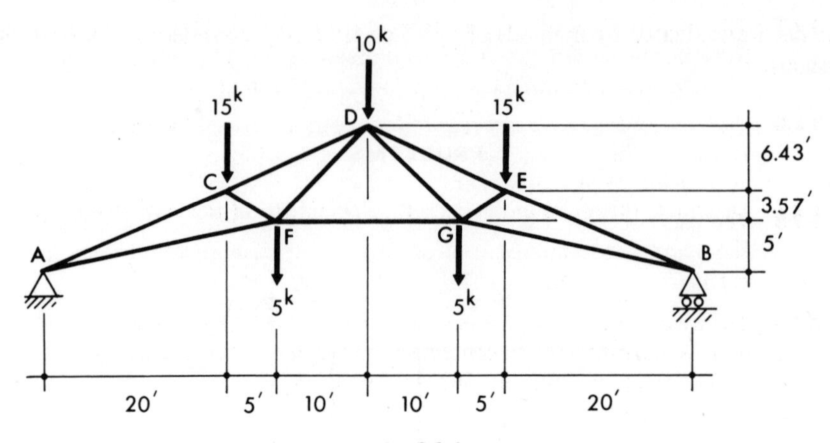

Fig. 3.2.4

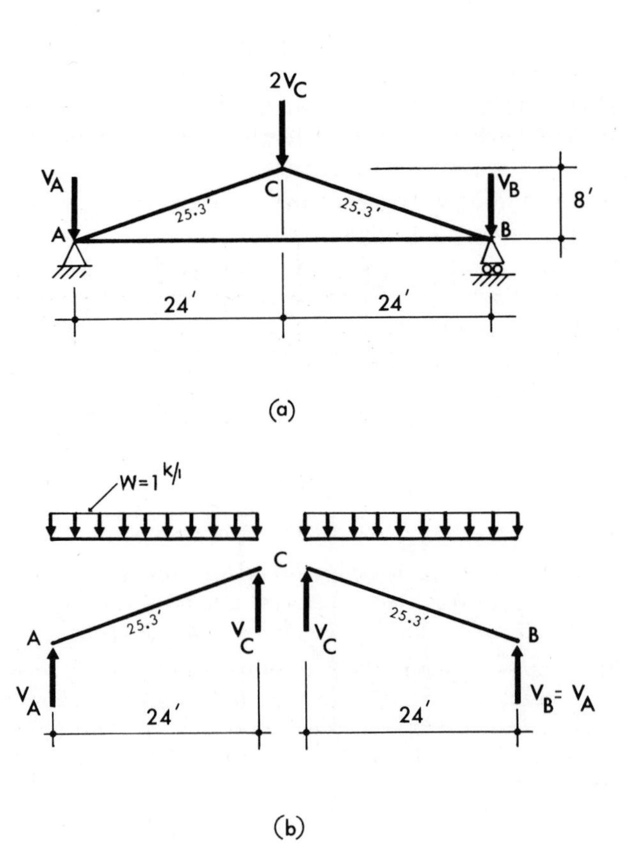

Fig. 3.2.5

3.2.7 The truss of Fig. 3.2.5 carries a snow load of 1 k/ft. Determine the tensile force in the tie-rod *AB* and the compressive forces in *AC* and *BC* by concentrating the uniform load at the joints, as shown in Fig. 3.2.5b.

3.2.8 The truss of Fig. 3.2.2 carries a uniform load $w = 2$ k/ft on the lower chord. Determine the forces in the bars *AC*, *AD* and *BD* by concentrating the load at the joints of the lower chord.

3.2.9 The truss of Fig. 3.2.3 carries a uniform load of 1 k/ft on its upper chord and a concentrated load of 10 k at *H*. Determine the force in the bar *EG*.

3.2.10 The truss of Fig. 3.2.4 carries a snow load of 1.5 k/ft uniformly distributed over its upper bars and a concentrated load of 5 k midway between *F* and *G*. Determine the force in the tie-rod *FG*.

3.3 The Joint Method

When the forces in all the bars of a truss must be evaluated, the so-called *joint method* is preferable to the section method.

The joint method considers each joint as a *free body* and states that each joint, isolated from the truss by a "section" drawn around it, is in equibrium under the action of the loads applied to it and of the forces in the bars connected to it. Since joint equilibrium in a plane requires the satisfaction of 2 equations, say $\sum F_x = 0$ and $\sum F_z = 0$, this method *allows the evaluation of the unknown forces in two bars.* The method may be applied analytically or graphically; the graphical solution presents decided advantages of simplicity and rapidity, as will be seen later.

To evaluate analytically the forces in the bars of the truss of Fig. 3.3.1

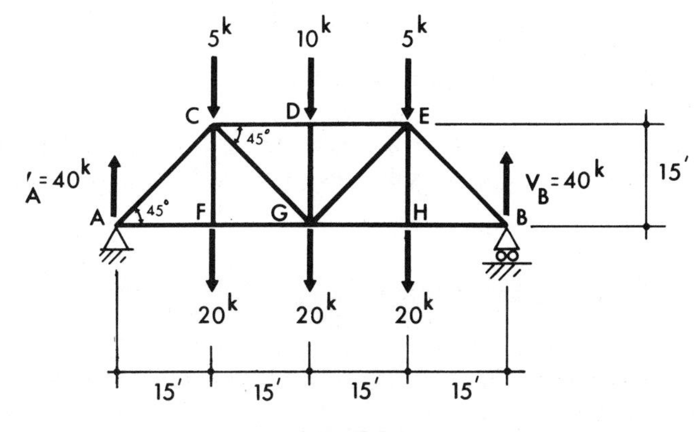

Fig. 3.3.1

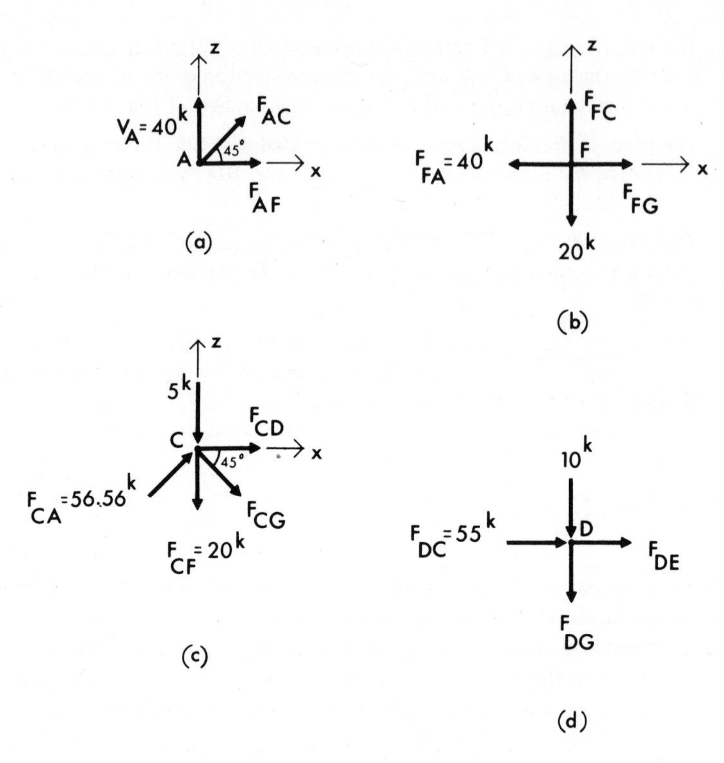

Fig. 3.3.1 (a–d)

under the given loads, evaluate the reactions first, isolate joint A (Fig. 3.3.1a) and write equilibrium equations in the horizontal and vertical directions, with reference to the x- and z-axes shown, assuming all bar forces to be tensile:

$$F_{AF} + 0.707F_{AC} = 0, \qquad 40 + 0.707F_{AC} = 0$$

$$\therefore \quad F_{AC} = -56.56 \text{ k}, \qquad F_{AF} = 40 \text{ k}.$$

F_{AF} is positive (i.e., is tensile), as assumed, and F_{AC} is negative (i.e., is compressive), contrary to our assumption. Moving to point F, we obtain similarly (Fig. 3.3.1b):

$$F_{FG} - F_{AF} = 0, \qquad F_{FC} - 20 = 0, \qquad F_{FG} = F_{AF} = 40 \text{ k},$$

$$F_{FC} = 20 \text{ k}.$$

We can now move to joint C, where 2 bar forces are known and 2 are unknown (Fig. 3.3.1c):

$$0.707 \times 56.56 + 0.707F_{CG} + F_{CD} = 0,$$
$$-5 - 20 + 0.707 \times 56.56 - 0.707F_{CG} = 0,$$
$$\therefore \quad F_{CG} = \frac{40 - 25}{0.707} = +21.20 \text{ k},$$
$$F_{CD} = -0.707 \times 56.56 - 0.707 \times 21.20 = -55 \text{ k}.$$

Finally, from the equilibrium of joint D (Fig. 3.3.1d):

$$55 + F_{DE} = 0, \qquad -10 - F_{GD} = 0$$
$$\therefore \quad F_{DE} = -55 \text{ k}, \qquad F_{GD} = -10 \text{ k}.$$

By symmetry, the forces in the bars of the right half of the truss are equal to those in the corresponding bars of the left half and need not be computed.

The same results can be obtained graphically by separate force diagrams for each joint, as was done in Chapter 2 (see Section 2.6). For example, Fig. 3.3.1a_1 and Fig. 3.3.1c_1 show the force diagrams for joints A and C. But it is more practical to combine the force diagrams for *all* the joints in a single diagram by the following systematic procedure (Fig. 3.3.2a, b).

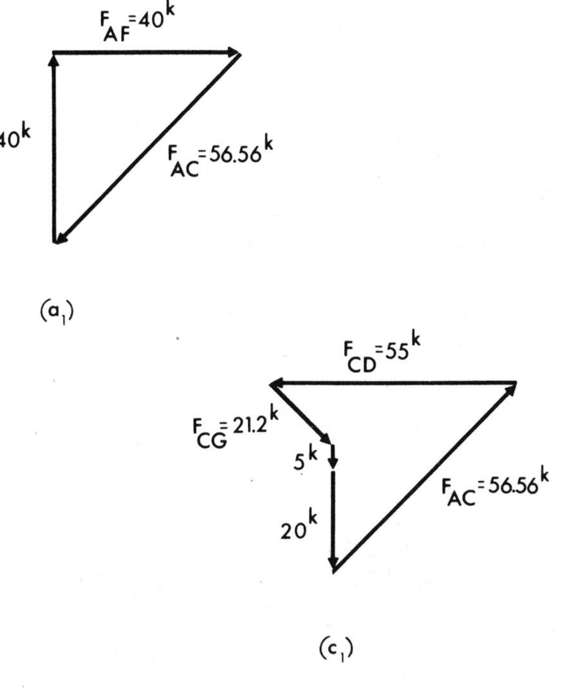

Fig. 3.3.1 (a_1, c_1)

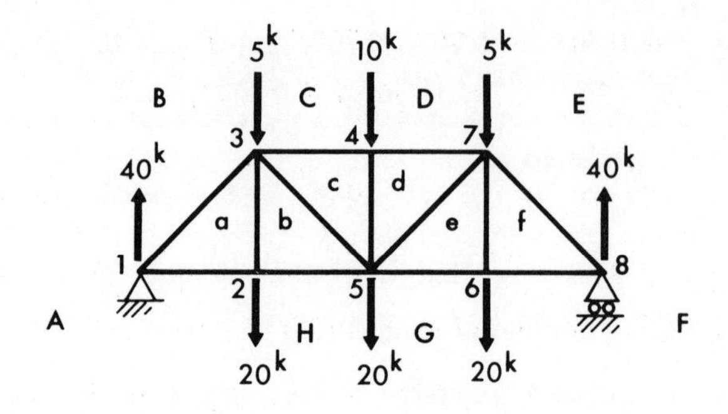
5k
10k
5k
B
C
D
E
3
4
7
40k
40k
c
d
a
b
e
f
1
8
2
5
6
A
H
G
F
20k
20k
20k

(a)

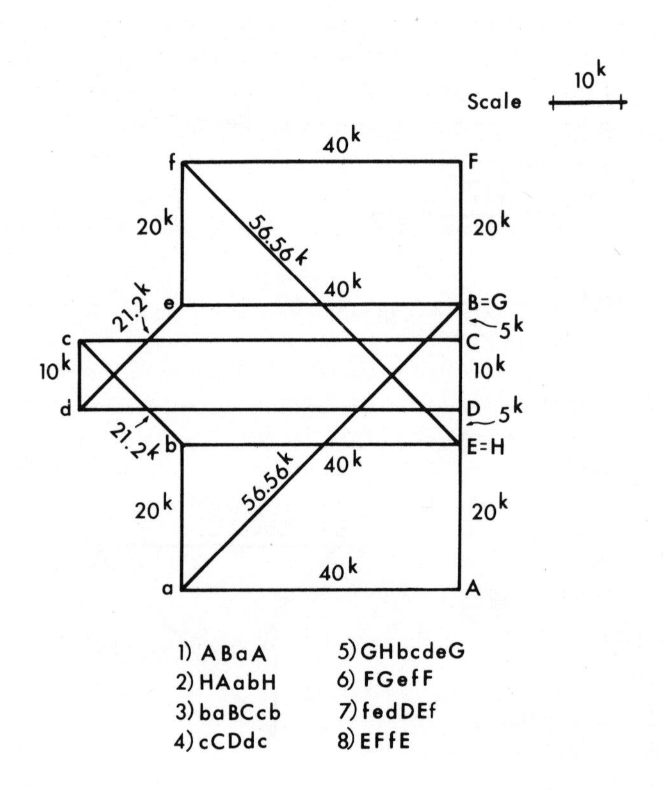
Scale
10k
40k
f
F
20k
56.56k
20k
40k
21.2k
e
B=G
c
5k
C
10k
10k
d
D
5k
21.2k
b
E=H
56.56k
40k
20k
20k
40k
a
A
1) ABaA
2) HAabH
3) baBCcb
4) cCDdc
5) GHbcdeG
6) FGefF
7) fedDEf
8) EFfE

(b)

Fig. 3.3.2

1. Label each joint with a number.
2. Label each interior mesh area with a lower case letter.
3. Label each exterior area between 2 successive loads or reactions with an upper case letter.
4. Define each bar by the two letters used to label the adjoining interior mesh areas, or the adjoining interior mesh area and the adjoining exterior area (this is known as *Bow's notation* for the bars).
5. Define each load by the two letters used to label the adjoining exterior areas.
6. Draw (in a chosen scale) the closed diagram of the external loads and the reactions after computing the reactions analytically, if preferable.
7. Draw the closed force diagrams of the forces acting at each joint, moving *clockwise* around the joint.
8. Notice that the forces in the bars are in the same scale as the loads, and that the joints must be taken in such a sequence that not more than 2 bar forces be unknown at each joint.

Figure 3.3.2b illustrates the application of the method to the truss of Fig. 3.3.2a and consists of the combined force diagrams for all of its joints, taken in the numbered order. With $AB = +40$ k, $BC = -5$ k, $CD = -10$k, $DE = -5$ k, $EF = +40$ k, $FG = -20$ k, $GH = -20$ k, $HA = -20$ k, the closed diagram of the external loads and the reactions is *ABCDEFGHA*, where *G* happens to coincide with *B* and *H* with *E*.

Joint 1: Draw the reaction *AB*, and, going consecutively clockwise around the joint, draw the parallels *Ba* from *B* and *aA* from *A* to the bars *Ba* and *aA*. The closed force diagram is *ABaA*.

Joint 2: The load *HA* and the bar force *Aa* are known; draw consecutively, going clockwise around the joint, the parallels *ab* from *a* and *bH* from *H* to the bars *ab* and *bH*. The closed force diagram is *HAabH*.

Joint 3: The forces *ba*, *aB* and *BC* are known; draw consecutively the parallels *Cc* from *C* and *cb* from *b* to the bars *Cc* and *cb*. The closed force diagram is *baBCcb*.

Similarly, the closed force diagrams for the remaining joints are:

Joint 4: *cCDdc*.
Joint 5: *GHbcdeG*.
Joint 6: *FGefF*.
Joint 7: *fedDEf*.
Joint 8: *EFfE*.

(Because of symmetry, the upper half of the force diagram need not have been drawn for joints 5 to 8.) The force diagram of Fig. 3.3.2b helps visualize a number of properties of the corresponding truss which were noticed before analytically. For example, given the external forces, and hence the reactions, the side *AF* of the diagram is fixed. The diagram then shows that if *Ba* had been inclined at less than 45° to the horizontal, *Ba* and *aA* would have been larger, and the same would hold for *bc* and *Cc* if *bc* had been less inclined, while *ab* is always equal to the 20 k load at 2. On the other hand, if the diagonals had been more inclined, because of a greater truss depth, *Cc* and *Hb* would have been smaller.

Figure 3.3.3a, b gives the graphical solution for a truss similar to that

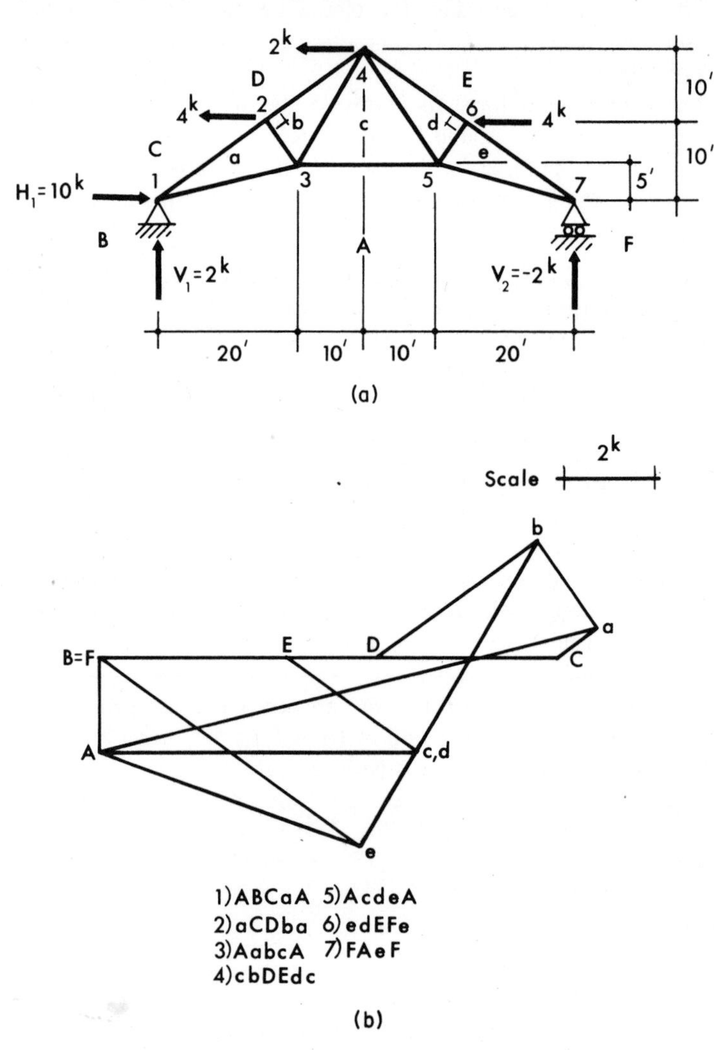

Fig. 3.3.3

in Fig. 3.2.4, but acted on by wind loads. The vertical reactions are obtained by taking moments about joint 7 and by vertical equilibrium:

$$-V_1 \times 60 + 4 \times 10 + 2 \times 20 + 4 \times 10 = 0$$

$$\therefore \quad V_1 = 2\text{ k}, \qquad V_7 = -2\text{ k}.$$

The horizontal reaction H_1 at the fixed hinge is obtained by horizontal equilibrium:

$$H_1 - 4 - 2 - 4 = 0 \quad \therefore \quad H_1 = 10\text{ k}.$$

The closed diagram of the external loads, *ABCDEFA*, appears in Fig. 3.3.3b, which contains the force diagrams for all the joints.

PROBLEMS

3.3.1 Evaluate graphically the forces in the bars of the truss of Fig. 3.3.4, and check analytically the forces in bars *Ba* and *cb*.

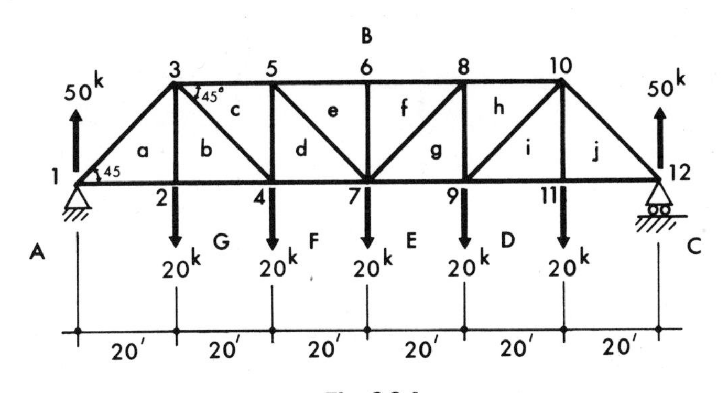

Fig. 3.3.4

3.3.2 Label joints, interior meshes and exterior areas for the truss of Fig. 3.2.4, and evaluate the forces in its bars graphically. Check the force in the horizontal tie-rod *FG* analytically. *Note:* Label joint *A* as 1, the reaction at *A* as *AB*.

3.3.3 Evaluate graphically the forces due to wind in the bars of the truss of Fig. 3.3.5, and check the force *ij* analytically.

3.3.4 Evaluate graphically the forces in the bars of the truss of Fig. 3.3.6. Check the force in bar *cd* analytically.

3.3.5 Evaluate graphically the forces in the bars of the truss of Fig. 3.3.7. Check the force in bar *ed* analytically.

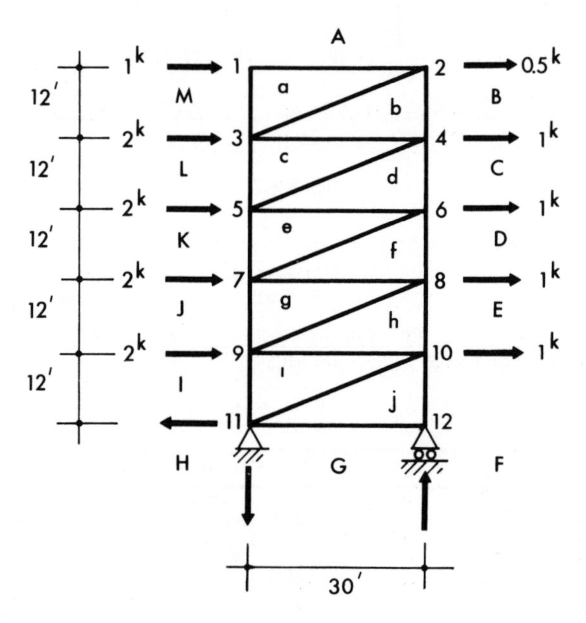

Fig. 3.3.5

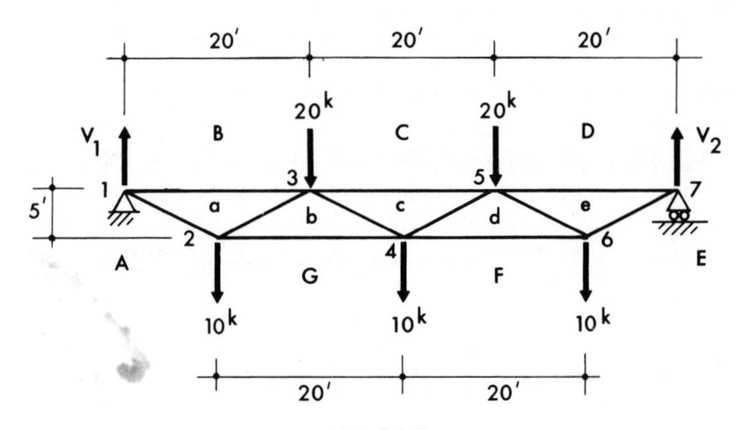

Fig. 3.3.6

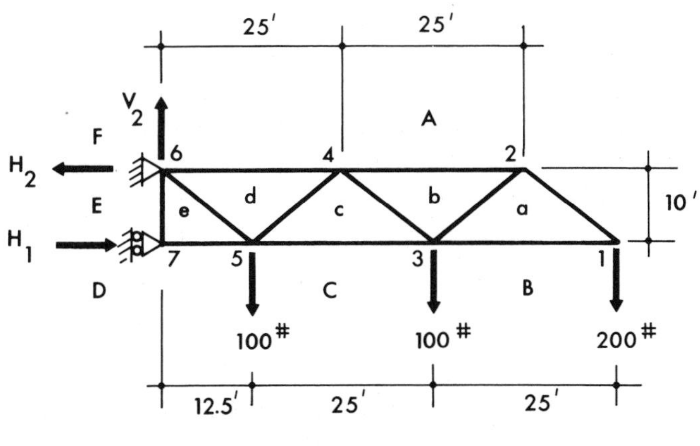

Fig. 3.3.7

3.3.6 The bar joist of Fig. 3.3.8 carries a uniform load of 0.5 k/ft on its upper chord. Concentrate the distributed load at its joints, and evaluate graphically the forces in its bars. Check analytically the force in bar *Ed*.

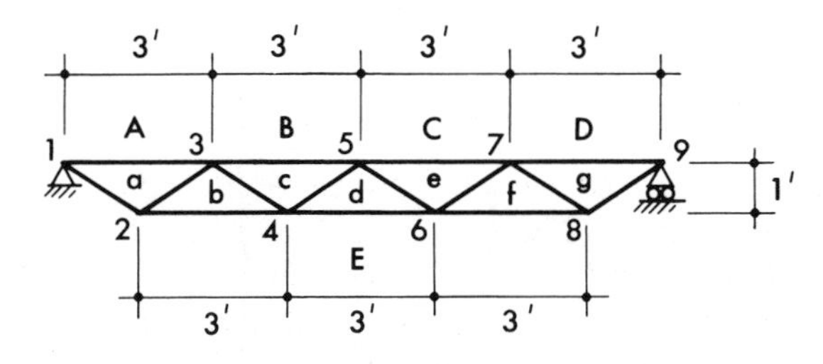

Fig. 3.3.8

3.4 Tension and Compression Members

The bars of a truss are acted upon by *axial forces*, which are either tensile or compressive. Consider the bar *AB* of Fig. 3.4.1, which is in equilibrium under the action of two equal and opposite forces. If we cut a free body *AC*, by

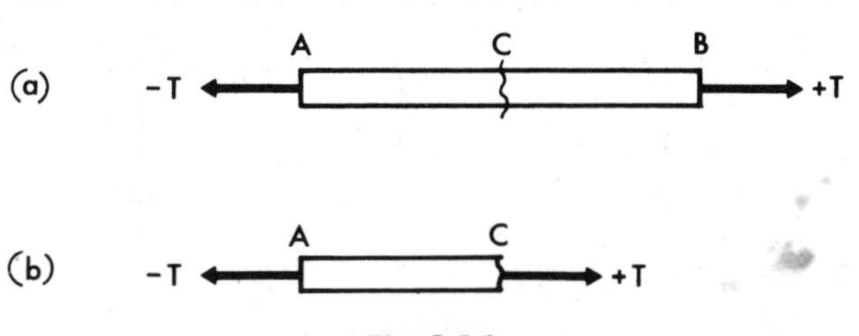

Fig. 3.4.1

means of a section at C perpendicular to the bar axis, the force acting on the section at C must also be equal to T for equilibrium in the direction of the bar axis. This means that the free body CB exerts on the free body AC an *internal force* T. Experiments show that, except for sections near the ends of the bar, *the internal force* T *is evenly distributed over the bar cross section*: each square inch of cross section carries the same amount of force, which is called the *tensile stress* f_t on the section. Hence, if the area of the cross section is A sq in., $T = f_t \times A$, and the tensile stress becomes:

$$f_t = \frac{T}{A}. \tag{3.4.1}$$

Stresses are usually measured in pounds per square inch (psi) or kips per square inch (ksi).

Compressive axial forces C are also evenly distributed over the area of the cross section of a bar and, calling f_c the *compressive stress*, we see that:

$$f_c = \frac{C}{A}. \tag{3.4.2}$$

The *design* of structural elements acted upon by axial forces consists in choosing their area A, so that for a given force T or C the tensile or compressive stress is maintained within allowable limits. The *analysis* of these elements when their area is known consists in verifying that the stresses f_t or f_c due to given forces T or C are within allowable limits.

The allowable limit of the stress f, or, for short, the *allowable stress* F is determined experimentally and depends on the material of the bar and on the bar shape, on whether the bar force is tensile or compressive, on whether it may change sign under changing loads, as well as on the cause of the force (dead load, live load, wind load, earthquakes, temperature differences, etc.) and on its type (applied slowly or suddenly, permanently or only occasionally, etc.). Table 3.4.1 gives average allowable tensile stresses F_t for the structural materials most commonly used in tensile elements.

Table 3.4.1

Material	Allowable tensile stress F_t in psi
Structural steel A-36	24,000
Steel reinforcing bars	20,000
Aluminum	20,000
Wood	1,500
Fiber reinforced plastics	6,000

The allowable stress F_t is chosen to be either a fraction of the stress under which the material breaks in tension, the so-called *ultimate tensile stress* or *ultimate strength* F_u, or as a percentage (usually 60%) of the stress at which the material starts elongating rapidly or *flowing* under a constant load, a stress called the *yield point* F_y of the material.* Some materials, such as concrete, have very low resistance to tension and are not used to build tensile elements. Others, called *brittle materials*, have a tendency to break *suddenly* under tension, and their behavior is considered structurally dangerous. The most commonly used and least expensive tensile material is steel.

A large variety of materials, such as masonry, concrete, wood and, of course, all metals, have *compressive resistance*. Their *allowable compressive stress* F_c is established on the basis of tests and is given in Table 3.4.2.

Table 3.4.2

Material	Allowable compressive stress F_c in psi
Masonry	300**
Concrete	1,800
Marble	4,500
Wood	1,200
Steel	24,000
Aluminum	20,000

**Depends on mortar strength.

The allowable compressive stresses given in Table 3.4.2 are valid under the assumption that the compressed bar is not slender, since slender bars tend to bend or *buckle* under axial compressive loads (Fig. 3.4.2). The slenderness

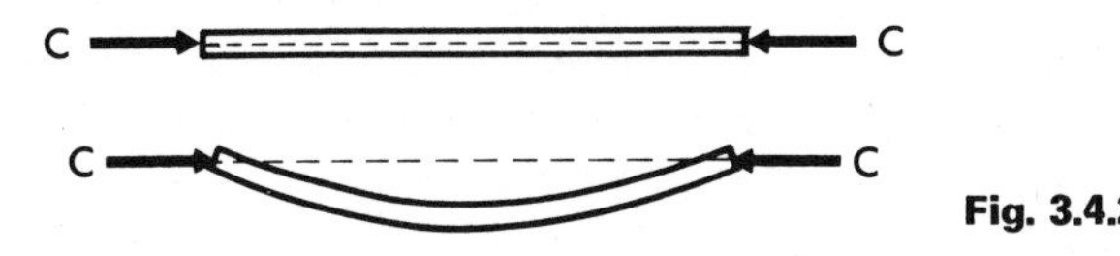

Fig. 3.4.2

of a hinged bar is measured by the ratio of its *reduced length* l (i.e., the length free to buckle) to a length r called the *radius of gyration of its cross section*, which is related to its cross-sectional shape and dimensions (see Section A.2). For example, given a rectangular section $b \times h$ (where $b < h$), $r = h/\sqrt{12}$ for buckling (i.e., bending out) in the h-direction; for a circular hollow section of diameter D and small thickness h, the radius of gyration is $r = D/\sqrt{8}$. (The value or r for the most common cross sections is given by (A.2.6) in

*Some materials, like concrete, do not have a clearly defined yield point.

Table A.1.) For standard steel sections, the steel handbooks (e.g., the *Manual of Steel Construction* of the American Institute of Steel Construction) list the two values of r for buckling in the directions of the two axes of symmetry of the section. The allowable compressive stress for steel bars depends on the *slenderness ratio* l/r and decreases with increasing values of l/r as shown in Fig. 3.4.3 for the case of steel. Slenderness ratios larger than 200 are not allowed by building codes.

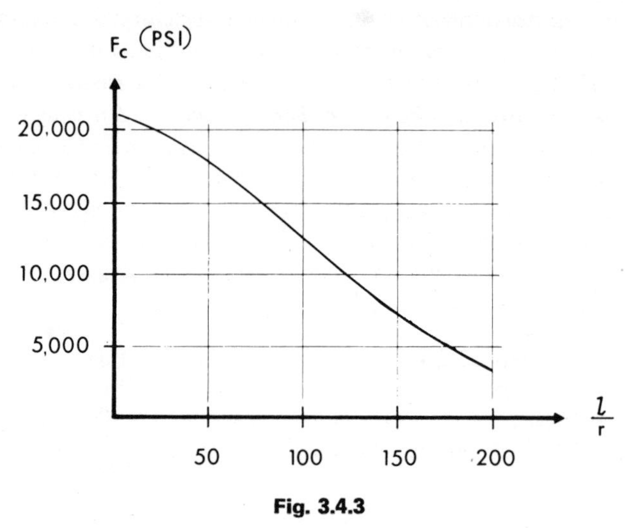

Fig. 3.4.3

3.5 Preliminary Design of Trusses

Once the forces in the bars of a truss have been determined, the cross sections of the bars are chosen or checked on the basis of the allowable stresses in tension and compression discussed in Section 3.4. Although the design of the connections between bars and gusset plates cannot be the subject of an elementary book, some consideration must be given to the connections, even in preliminary design, as shown by the following examples.

The bar GH of the upper chord of the truss in Fig. 3.2.1, which is 10 ft long, was found to be subjected to a compressive force of 90 k. The required cross section for an allowable stress $F_c = 20$ ksi is $A = F_{GH}/F_c = 90/20 = 4.5$ in.^{2}. Choosing to build up the bar by means of two angles connected by bolts (as shown in Fig. 3.5.1), we find from the table on coupled angles of the *Manual of Steel Construction* of the American Institute of Steel Construction that two $2\frac{1}{2} \times 2\frac{1}{2}$ in. angles with a thickness of $\frac{1}{2}$ in. have exactly this area. To check that this bar is not too slender, we find from the same table that the radius of gyration of the two angles is $r = 0.74$ in., from which we

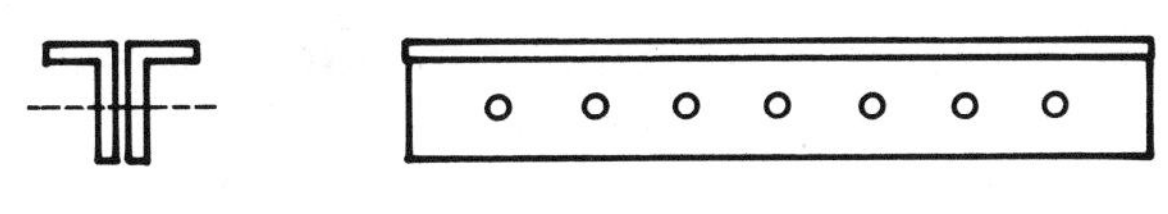

Fig. 3.5.1

compute the ratio $l/r = (10 \times 12)/0.74 = 162$.* The graph of Fig. 3.4.3 shows that, for $l/r = 162$, $F_c = 6$ ksi rather than 20 ksi as assumed. Hence, we must choose a heavier section, say two 4×4 in. angles $\frac{1}{2}$ in. thick, with an area $A = 7.5$ in.^{2} and a radius of gyration $r = 1.22$ in., giving a slenderness ratio $l/r = 120/1.22 = 98.5$ and an $F_c = 13.0$ ksi. The stress in the bar for this section is $f_c = 90/7.5 = 12$ ksi, so that the two 4×4 in. angles are satisfactory.

The bar DE in the truss of Fig. 3.2.1 is subjected to a tensile force of 80 k. When a bar is in tension, the area of the bolt or rivet holes must be deducted from its gross area. The *net area* of the bar (i.e., its area less the area of the bolt or rivet holes) may be assumed to be 85% of the gross area A. Hence, with an $F_t = 22$ ksi, the gross area A is given by:

$$0.85A \times 22 = 80 \quad \therefore \quad A = 4.28 \text{ in.}^2.$$

The nearest area obtainable by using two angles is $A = 4.50$ in.^{2} for two $2\frac{1}{2} \times 2\frac{1}{2}$ in. angles $\frac{1}{2}$ in. thick, so that the actual stress is:

$$f_t = \frac{80}{0.85 \times 4.5} = 21 \text{ ksi.}$$

The diagonal GE in the truss of Fig. 3.2.1 is subjected to a tension of 14.1 k. Its area is given by:

$$0.85A \times 22 = 14.1 \quad \therefore \quad A = 0.75 \text{ in.}^2.$$

A single angle $2 \times 1\frac{1}{4}$ in., $\frac{7}{16}$ in. thick, has exactly this area.

The heaviest compressed bars in the truss of Fig. 3.3.1, the 15 ft bars CD and DE, are under a compression of 55 k. For a low allowable stress $F_c = 8$ ksi, the required area is 6.9 in.^{2}. Choosing a structural T ST5WF/22.5, weighing 22.5 lb/ft, with $A = 6.62$ in.^{2} and $r = 1.25$ in., we obtain $f_c = 55/6.62 = 8.3$ ksi and $l/r = (15 \times 12)/1.25 = 144$, from which the graph of Fig. 3.4.3 gives $F_c = 7$ ksi (less than the actual stress $f_c = 8.3$ ksi.) If we try a structural T ST5WF weighing 30 lb/ft, with $A = 8.83$ in.^{2} and $r = 1.21$ in., we obtain $f_c = 55/8.83 = 6.2$ ksi and $l/r = (15 \times 12)/1.21 = 148$, from which the graph of Fig. 3.4.3 gives $F_c = 6.5$ ksi (> 6.2 ksi). Hence, the ST5WF/30 is satisfactory.

*The reduced length of truss bars is usually assumed to be their total length, since the bars are hinged and unsupported.

The tensile diagonal CG in the truss of Fig. 3.3.1 is subjected to a tensile force $T = 21.2$ k. Its required area for $F_t = 22$ ksi is:

$$A = \frac{21.2}{22 \times 0.85} = 1.13 \text{ in.}^2.$$

An angle with unequal legs $2\frac{1}{2} \times 1\frac{1}{2}$ in., $\frac{1}{2}$ in. thick, with an area of 1.15 in.^{2} and a stress:

$$f_t = \frac{21.2}{0.85 \times 1.15} = 21.65 \text{ ksi}$$

is satisfactory.

When I beams are used as truss bars, the connection of the bar to the gusset plate may take place through the web alone (Fig. 3.5.2). In this case, the effective area of the bar is the area of the web only.

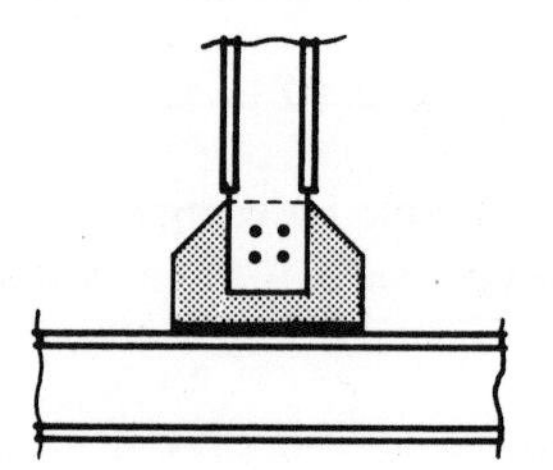

Fig. 3.5.2

PROBLEMS

3.5.1 Check whether a $1\frac{1}{2} \times 1\frac{1}{2}$ in., $\frac{1}{4}$ in. thick angle can be used as a diagonal to resist a tensile force of 14 k.

3.5.2 Choose a two equal-angle cross section for a bar 10 ft long to resist a compressive force of 100 k.

3.5.3 A bar in the upper chord of a truss must resist a compressive force of 100 k and is 10 ft long. Choose a WF section for this bar.

3.5.4 The upper chord of a truss carrying a load of 2 k/ft is built-up by means of two unequal angles $4 \times 3\frac{1}{2}$ in., $\frac{1}{2}$ in. thick. The length of the chord bars is 10 ft. Determine the maximum span of the truss if its depth is 10 ft and the limit span is governed by the compressed bars of its upper chord.

3.5.5 Two diagonals, one sloping upward to the right and the other to the left, have forces of 10 k, respectively, tensile and compressive. The l/r of the diagonals is 80. Which one requires a larger area if $F_t = 20$ ksi?

3.5.6 A truss bar 7 ft long is designed to resist a tensile force of 10 k with an $F_t = 22$ ksi. The bar is built by means of an equal legs angle. Determine its dimensions and the maximum compressive load it can resist.

3.5.7 Two combinations of two unequal legs angles, one 4 × 3 in., 5/16 in. thick and the other $3\frac{1}{2} \times 2\frac{1}{2}$ in., 3/8 in. thick, have about the same area: $A = 4.18$ in.^{2} for the first, and $A = 4.22$ in.^{2} for the second. Which can resist a higher compressive force for the same bar length?

3.5.8 Two $3\frac{1}{2} \times 2\frac{1}{2}$ in. angles, $\frac{1}{4}$ in. thick and two $3 \times 2\frac{1}{2}$ in. angles, 5/16 in. thick have the same l/r. Which can carry the larger tensile force?

3.5.9 A 14WF10/68 and a 21WF$8\frac{1}{4}$/68 having the same weight, 68 lb/ft, are used as 12 ft bars for a truss. (a) Which one resists the larger force in compression, if bending can only take place in the x-x direction? (b) If bending can only take place in the y-y direction? (c) Which one resists the larger tensile force?

3.5.10 Determine the two equal legs angle combination capable of resisting the same compressive force as the combination of two $3\frac{1}{2} \times 2\frac{1}{2}$ in. angles, $\frac{1}{2}$ in. thick, in a bar 8 ft long.

Chapter Four

4.1 Cable Supported Structures

Steel cables, first developed in connection with suspension bridges, are used to support large span roofs and other structures because of the high strength of their steel strands and of their relatively small dead load. Because the diameter of a cable is always very small in comparison with its length, cables are very flexible and can develop *only* tension. Therefore, when a load is applied to a cable, the cable acquires spontaneously a shape that will allow it to support the load by tensile forces only, the so-called *funicular* or *string polygon* shape. If the load changes location or new loads are added, the cable must change shape to acquire the shape of the funicular polygon corresponding to the new loading condition. Hence, a cable is *unstable*, i.e., it does not have a permanent shape like a truss, but changes shape with changing loads.

The large displacements due to the change in shape of a cable under varying loads must not be confused with the small displacements due to the stretching of the cable under the tensile forces it develops. We shall neglect these small displacements and consider the cable to be *inextensible*.

A cable hanging from two points and acted upon by known loads is a static-

Cables

ally determinate structure. In the following sections we shall determine its funicular shape, its reactions, the tensile forces it develops and its required cross section. Unless otherwise specified, we will assume that the two support points are at the same level, and that the horizontal *span* l between support points, as well as its *sag* f (i.e., the vertical distance between the horizontal through the supports and the lowest point in the cable) are known.

4.2 Symmetrical Funicular Polygons

Consider a cable of span l and sag f loaded *symmetrically* by vertical loads W_1, W_2, etc. at distances a_1, a_2, etc. from the left support A (Fig. 4.2.1a). Because of symmetry, the vertical reactions at A and B are equal, and the central portion of the cable between E and F is horizontal. The value of the horizontal component of the reactions, the *thrust* H, may be obtained directly

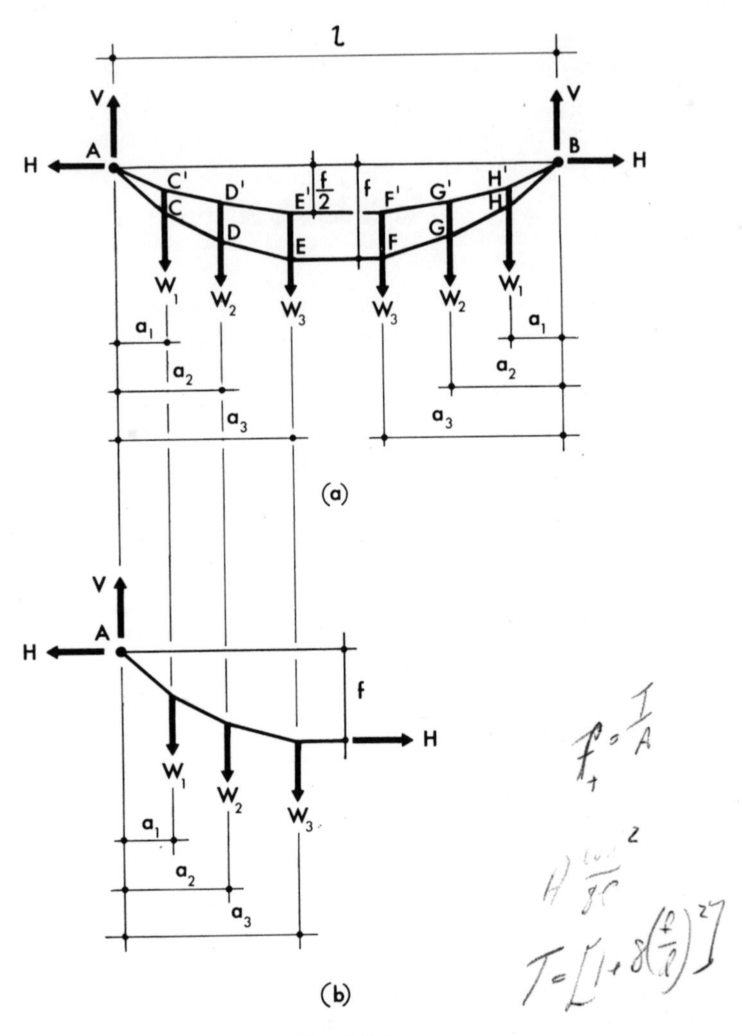

Fig. 4.2.1

by the equilibrium of a free body consisting of the left half of the cable (Fig. 4.2.1b). By horizontal equilibrium, the tension in E–F is H, and by rotational equilibrium about A:

$$-W_1a_1 - W_2a_2 - W_3a_3 + Hf = 0$$

$$\therefore \quad H = \frac{1}{f}(W_1a_1 + W_2a_2 + W_3a_3),$$

or, calling M_A the moment of the loads on the left half of the cable about A:

$$H = \frac{1}{f} M_A. \tag{4.2.1}$$

This equation shows that *the thrust in the cable due to vertical loads is inversely proportional to the sag*. If the load locations and l remain unchanged, but f is is cut in half, H doubles, while the cable shape becomes a funicular polygon $A, C', D', E', \ldots$ (Fig. 4.2.1a). Equation (4.2.1) allows the determination of the funicular shape of a symmetrically loaded cable, as shown by the following example.

The weight of the roadway of the suspension bridge of Fig. 4.2.2a is carried to each of its two cables by a 50 k tensile force in each of 6 vertical hangers set 20 ft apart. The cables span 120 ft with a 30 ft sag at midspan. We wish to determine their funicular shape. To this purpose we notice that, since, by symmetry, $V_a = V_B = 150$ k, *when H is known* a force diagram 0–1–2–0 (Fig. 4.2.2b), representing the equilibrium of the forces applied to the point A, gives the unknown force F_{AC} in AC and thus defines the direction of F_{AC}, i.e., the

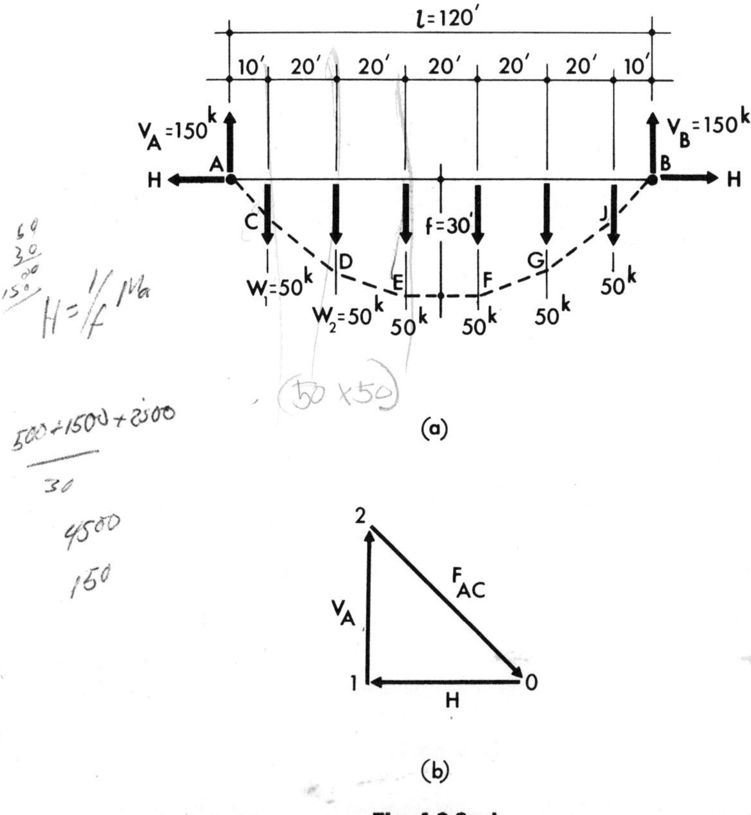

Fig. 4.2.2a-b

slope of the first side AC of the funicular polygon. Then a force diagram 0–2–3–0, in which F_{AC} and $W_1 = 50$ k are known, determines F_{CD} and, hence, the slope of CD. Proceeding in this way, we see that the shape of the funicular polygon as well as the tensile forces in each of its sides can be determined as soon as H is determined by means of (4.2.1).

In Fig. 4.2.2d, which gathers the force diagrams for all the loaded points of the cable, the 50 k loads are represented in a certain scale by the segments 0–1, 1–2, 2–3, 3–4, 4–5, 5–6; the vertical reactions $V_A = V_B = 150$ k are represented by 3–0 and 6–3; the thrust H, given by (4.2.1), is:

$$H \times 30 - 50 \times 50 - 50 \times 30 - 50 \times 10 = 0$$
$$\therefore \quad H = 150 \text{ k},$$

and is represented by 3–P. The equilibrium diagrams for the various cable points are:

(A) P–3–0–P; (C) P–0–1–P; (D) P–1–2–P;
(E) P–2–3–P; (F) P–3–4–P; (G) P–4–5–P;
(J) P–5–6–P; (B) P–6–3–P.

The funicular polygon is started at A by drawing AC parallel to 0–P and continued by drawing CD parallel to 1–P, DE parallel to 2–P, EF parallel to 3–P, etc.

The funicular polygon for two nonparallel, symmetrical forces is obtained by the same procedure.* The cable in Fig. 4.2.3 is *stabilized* (i.e., tightened) by pulling on it with two inclined cables at 30° to the vertical. The tension

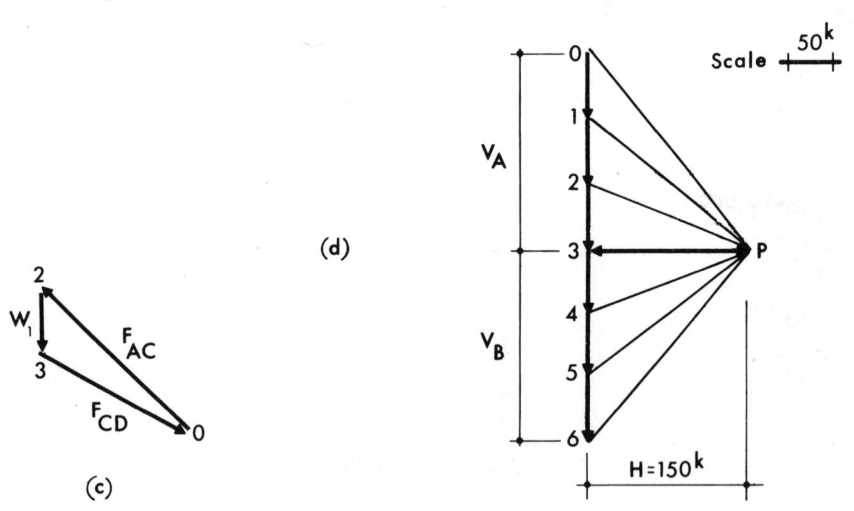

Fig. 4.2.2c–d

*If an additional set of symmetrical forces were put on the cable, the problem could not be solved by the method of this section (see Problem 4.2.4).

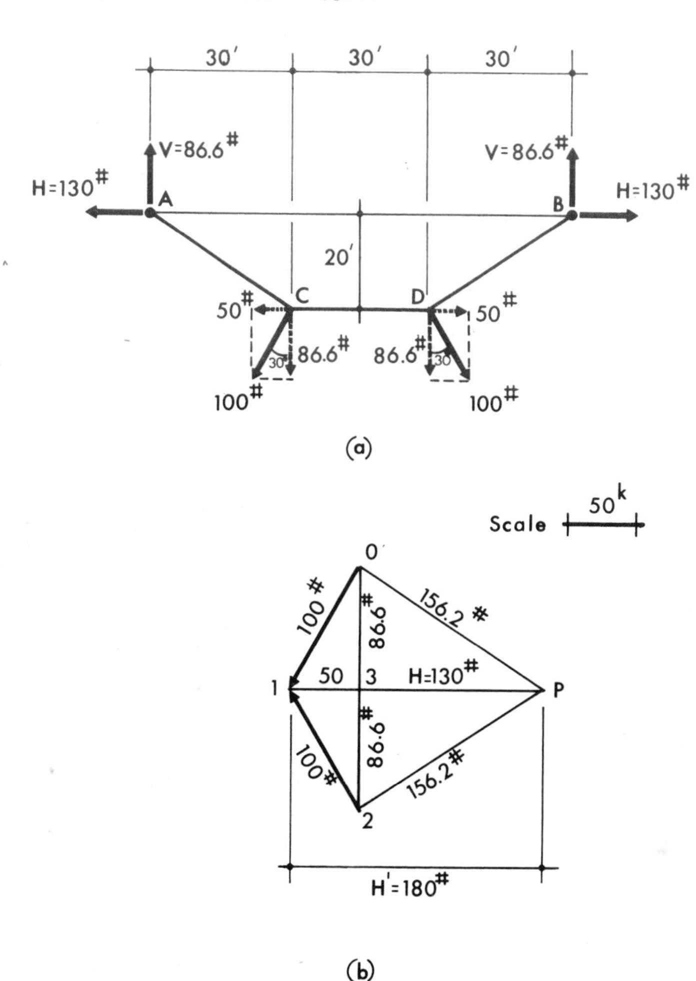

Fig. 4.2.3

in each cable is 100 lb. Because of symmetry, the vertical reactions V are equal and, by vertical equilibrium of the entire cable, equal to $100 \times \cos 30^\circ = 100 \times 0.866 = 86.6$ lb. The moment of the left 100 lb force about A is easily computed by splitting it into its vertical component 86.6 lb and its horizontal component $100 \times \sin 30^\circ = 100 \times 0.50 = 50$ lb:

$$M_A = 86.6 \times 30 + 50 \times 20 = 3598 \text{ lb ft},$$

whence by (4.2.1) the tensile force in CD is:

$$H' = \frac{3598}{20} \doteq 180 \text{ lb}.$$

By horizontal equilibrium of the left half of the cable, the external thrust H is given by:

$$-H - 50 + H' = 0 \quad \therefore \quad H = 180 - 50 = 130 \text{ lb.}$$

The diagram of the external forces (Fig. 4.2.3b) is P–3–0–1–2–3–P, in which the reactions V_A and V_B are represented by the segments 3–0 and 2–3, 1–P represents the tensile force H' in CD and 3–P the external thrust H. The equilibrium diagrams for the cable points are:

(A) P–3–0–P; (C) P–0–1–P;
(B) P–2–3–P; (D) P–1–2–P.

PROBLEMS

4.2.1 Draw the funicular polygon, and evaluate the tensions in the sides of the cable of Fig. 4.2.4.

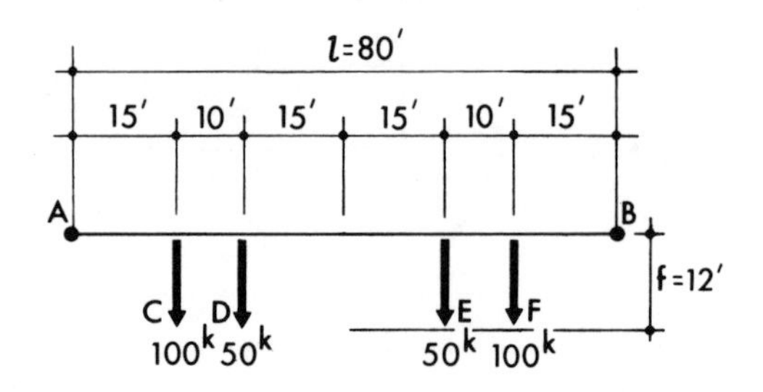

Fig. 4.2.4

4.2.2 Draw the funicular polygon, and evaluate the tensions in the sides of the cable of Fig. 4.2.5. *Note:* Only half of the center load must be considered supported by the left half of the cable in determining M_A in equation (4.2.1).

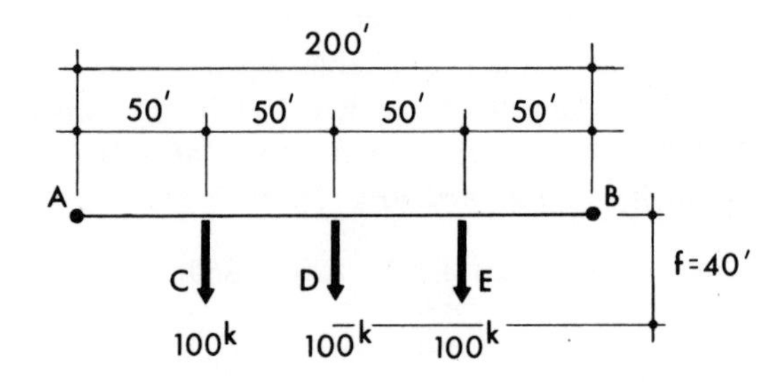

Fig. 4.2.5

4.2.3 The shallow cable roof of Fig. 4.2.6 is supported by radial cables connecting an outer compression ring and an inner tension ring, set 55 ft below the outer ring. The cables are spaced by 40 ft on the outer ring. The dead load and the live load on the roof add up to a load of 100 psf, which is carried to the cables by circumferential joists evenly spaced radially by 30 ft. The length of the joists l may be assumed to vary linearly between 10 ft at the inner ring and 40 ft at the outer ring. The concentrated loads on the cables are the loads on the trapezoidal contributory areas, which may be approximated by $30 \times l$ sq ft. Determine the shape of the funicular polygon of the cables and the tensile forces in the sides of the polygon.

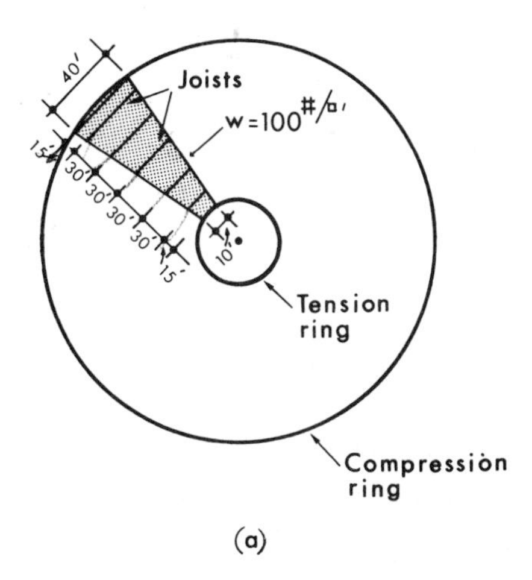

(a)

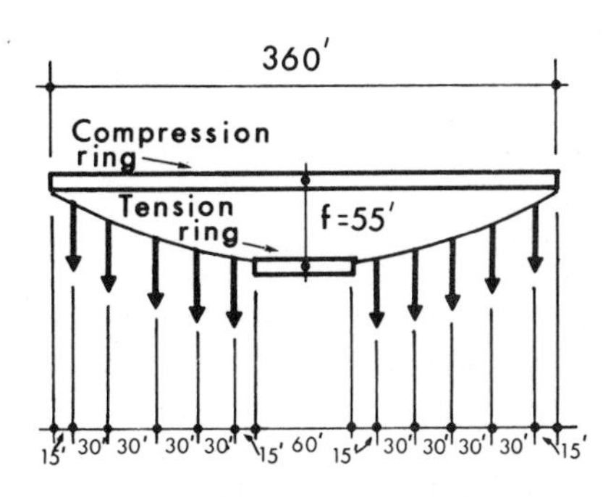

(b)

Fig. 4.2.6

4.2.4 The funicular shape and the tensile forces in the sides of the cable of Fig. 4.2.7 cannot be determined by the method of Section 4.2. Why?

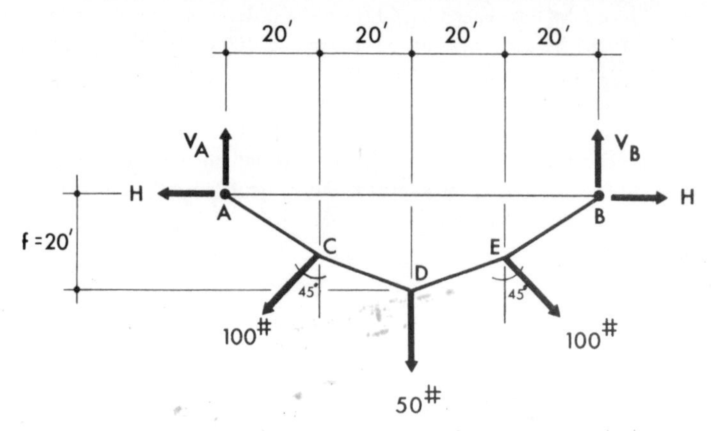

Fig. 4.2.7

4.2.5 A closed loop of wire 6 ft long is stretched by six equal radial forces of 10 lb each, 60° apart. Determine its funicular shape and the tensile forces in its sides.

4.2.6 A weight of 15 k hangs from two wires anchored 30 ft apart in the ceiling of a hall. One wire is 22 ft long, the other 28 ft long. Determine graphically the tensile forces in the wires.

4.2.7 A tightrope walker moves on a rope spanning 50 ft with a maximum sag of 15 ft. Obtain graphically the shape of his path as he moves from $x = l/3$ to $x = -l/3$. What mathematical curve defines the path? *Note:* $x = 0$ is the mid-span point.

4.2.8 A cable of given length L and span l carries a load W at mid-span with a sag $f \ll l$. What is its sag if it carries two loads $W/2$ at its third points? For what loading condition is the maximum tension greater?

4.3 Funicular Curves

As the number of loads applied to a cable grows and their spacing decreases, the funicular polygon approaches a *funicular curve*, which is the cable shape for a distributed load. For example, if the hangers in a suspension bridge are closely spaced, the load of the roadway is practically distributed uniformly in *horizontal projection* on the cable (Fig. 4.3.1a), and the cable shape may be assumed to be a curve. Let us determine the thrust H and the reactions $T_A = T_B$ at the cable supports by referring the right half of the cable OB to the x-, y-axes shown (Fig. 4.3.1b). By horizontal equilibrium, the tension in the cable at 0 equals H, and by moments about B:

$$-Hf + \frac{wl}{2}\left(\frac{l}{4}\right) = 0 \quad \therefore \quad H = \frac{wl^2}{8f}. \tag{4.3.1}$$

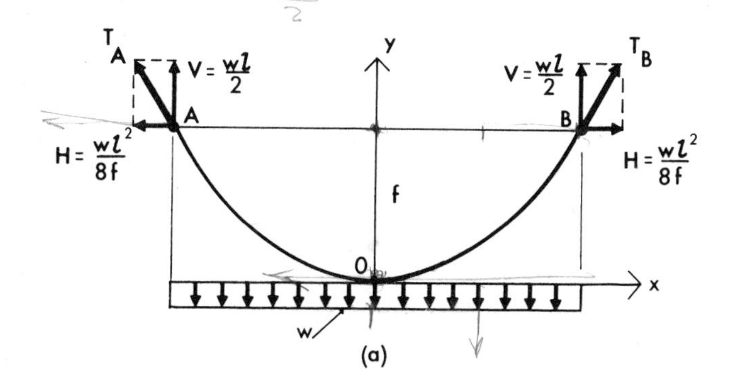

(a)

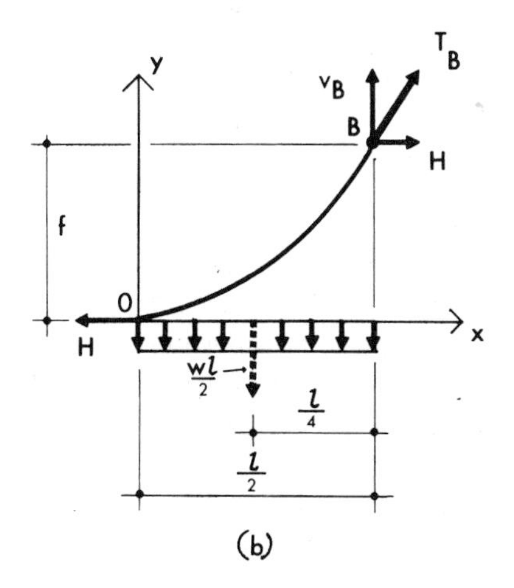

(b)

Fig. 4.3.1a–b

By symmetry, $V_A = V_B = V = wl/2$, and the tension in the cable at the supports is:

$$T_B = T_A = \sqrt{H^2 + V^2} = H\sqrt{1 + (V/H)^2}$$

$$= H\sqrt{1 + \left(\frac{wl/2}{wl^2/8f}\right)^2} = H\sqrt{1 + 16(f/l)^2}. \qquad (4.3.2)$$

Since in most cables f/l is less than $1/10$ and:

$$\text{for} \quad x = \frac{f}{l} \ll 1, \quad \sqrt{1 + 16x^2} \doteq 1 + \frac{16}{2}x^2 = 1 + 8\left(\frac{f}{l}\right)^2,$$

the value of the tension in the cable at the supports, which is the highest value of the tension in the cable, becomes:

$$T_A = T_B = H\left[1 + 8\left(\frac{f}{l}\right)^2\right] = \frac{wl^2}{8f}\left[1 + 8\left(\frac{f}{l}\right)^2\right]. \qquad (4.3.3)$$

(c)

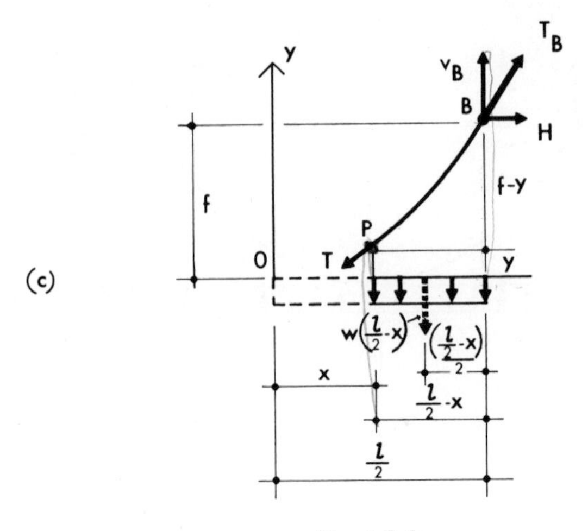

Fig. 4.3.1c

For a commonly used value of $f/l = 0.10$, $1 + 8(f/l)^2 = 1.08$ and the maximum cable tension is only 8% larger than its thrust.

To determine the shape of the funicular curve, we must consider the equilibrium of a free body consisting of a portion of the cable between a section at x and the support B (Fig. 4.3.1c). Calling y the ordinate of the point P of abscissa x and taking moments about P, we obtain:

$$V\left(\frac{l}{2} - x\right) - H(f - y) - w\left(\frac{l}{2} - x\right)\frac{l/2 - x}{2} = 0,$$

or, with $V = wl/2$ and $H = wl^2/8f$:

$$\frac{wl}{2}\left(\frac{l}{2} - x\right) - \frac{wl^2}{8f}(f - y) - \frac{w}{2}\left(\frac{l^2}{4} - lx + x^2\right)$$

$$= \frac{wl^2}{4} - \frac{wlx}{2} - \frac{wl^2}{8} + \frac{wl^2 y}{8f} - \frac{wl^2}{8} + \frac{wlx}{2} - \frac{wx^2}{2}$$

$$= \frac{wl^2 y}{8f} - \frac{wx^2}{2} = 0,$$

from which:

$$y = 4f\left(\frac{x}{l}\right)^2. \qquad (4.3.4)$$

The symmetrical curve $y = 4f(x/l)^2$ is called a *quadratic parabola* and has ordinates given by Table 4.3.1.

Table 4.3.1

x/l	0	0.1	0.2	0.3	0.4	0.5
y/f	0	0.04	0.16	0.36	0.64	1.00

The funicular curve of a cable under its own weight, which is *uniformly distributed along the cable curve*, is called a *catenary* and lies outside the parabola of equal span and sag (Fig. 4.3.2), but to all practical purposes may be taken to be a parabola for shallow cables with f/l equal to or less than 1/10.

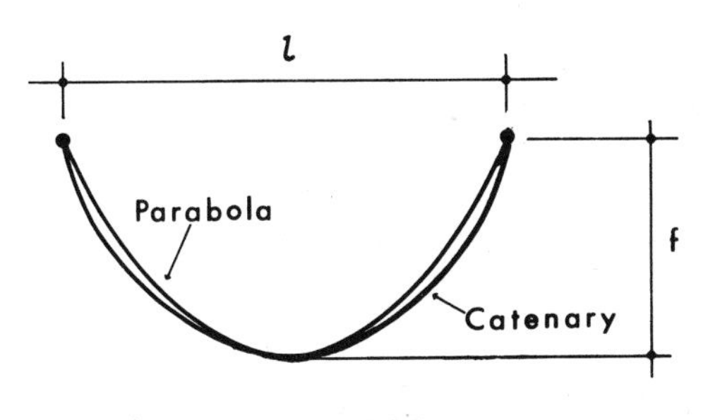

Fig. 4.3.2

PROBLEMS

4.3.1 A cable-suspended roof of the type shown in Fig. 4.2.6 has an inner ring with a radius r much smaller than the radius R of its outer ring. Hence, the load on the cables may be approximated by the triangular load of Fig. 4.3.3.

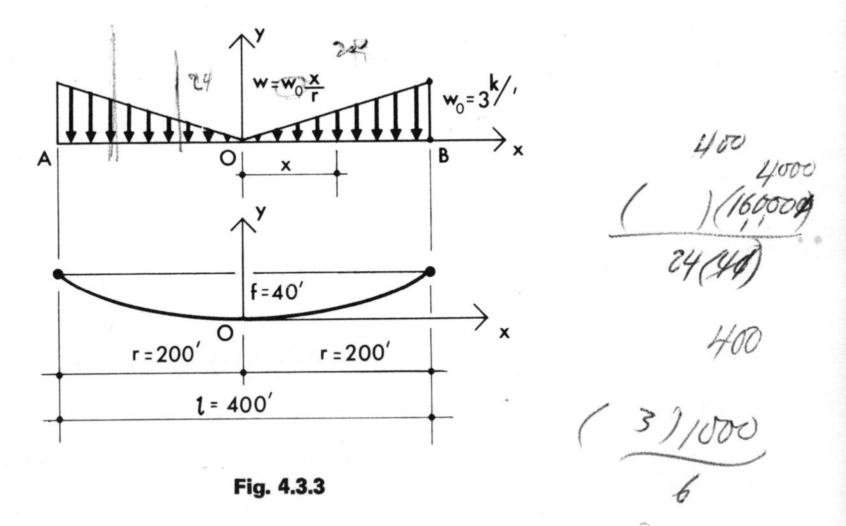

Fig. 4.3.3

Determine the thrust H and the maximum tension T in the cables for $l = 400$ ft and $f = 40$ ft.

4.3.2 Determine analytically the funicular shape of the cables of the roof in Problem 4.3.1 (Fig. 4.3.3).

4.3.3 The cables of Fig. 4.3.3 carry the triangular load shown in the figure plus the concentrated load $W = 100$ k of a structure (supporting the light and air conditioning systems) which hangs at the center of the circular roof. Determine the thrust and the maximum tension in the cables, assuming the sag to be unchanged.

4.3.4 The funicular polygon for a loop of wire acted upon by n equal, radial forces acting outward and evenly spaced by an angle $\theta = 2\pi/n$, is a regular polygon with n sides. What is the funicular curve for a wire loop acted upon by a constant radial pressure p acting outward? If the length of the loop is l, what is the tension in the loop? (Use a free body consisting of half the loop.)

4.3.5 The snow load on the cables of a circular, cable-suspended roof, which is dish-shaped, varies as shown in Fig. 4.3.4. Evaluate the thrust and the maximum tension in the cables for $l = 200$ ft and $f = 20$ ft.

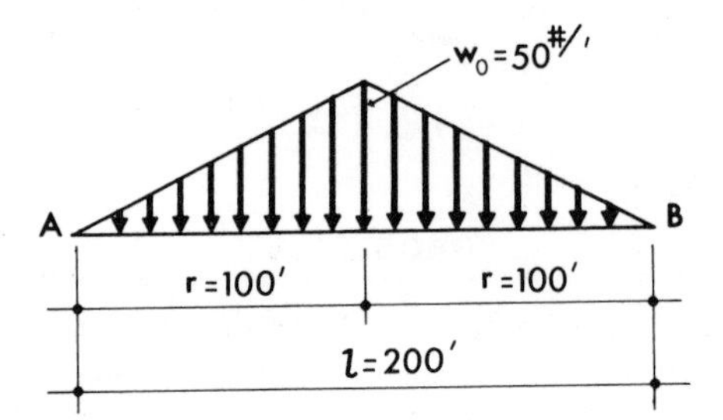

Fig. 4.3.4

4.3.6 The total distributed load on one of the cables supporting a circular roof of radius $R = 100$ ft is shown in Fig. 4.3.5. Determine the thrust and the maximum tension in the cable for $l = 200$ ft and $f = 25$ ft.

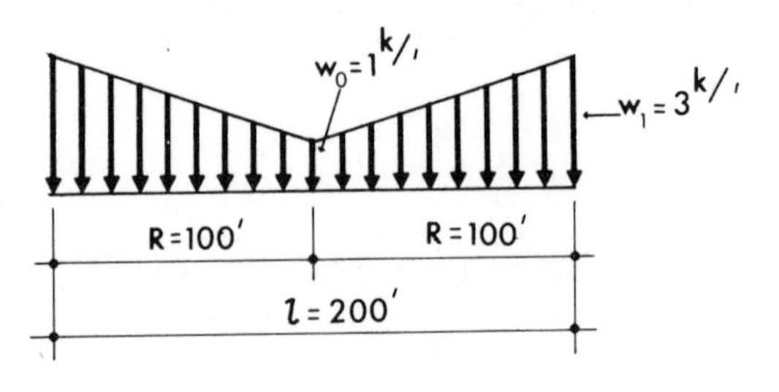

Fig. 4.3.5

4.4 Unsymmetrical Loads

When a cable is loaded unsymmetrically, the points of application of the loads move laterally and, moreover, the location of the lowest point in the cable, which defines its sag, may not be obvious. But, as shown by the following examples, if we assume the *action line* of the loads to be known, the methods of the previous sections may be applied to unsymmetrical loads as soon as the sag location is determined. The cable of Fig. 4.4.1a is stabilized by a pull $W_1 = 141$ lb at 45° to the vertical and a vertical pull $W_2 = 150$ lb. Splitting the 141 lb force into horizontal and vertical components at E (for convenience and since *the moment of a force does not change if the force is moved along its line of action*), we obtain by moments about B and A:

$$100 \times 30 + 150 \times 20 - V_A \times 45 = 0 \quad \therefore \quad V_A = 133 \text{ lb},$$

$$-100 \times 15 - 150 \times 25 + V_B \times 45 = 0 \quad \therefore \quad V_B = 117 \text{ lb}.$$

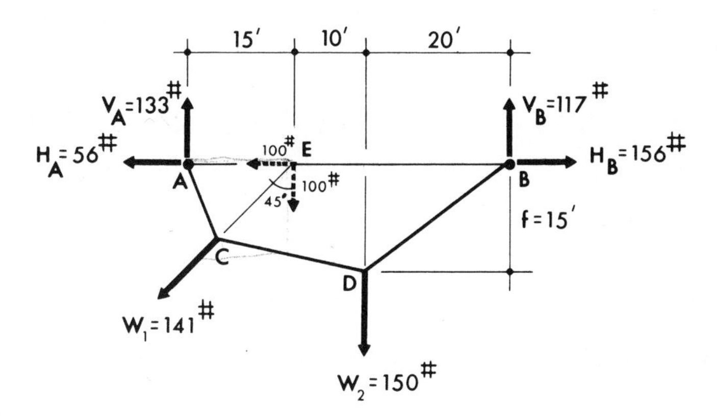

Fig. 4.4.1a

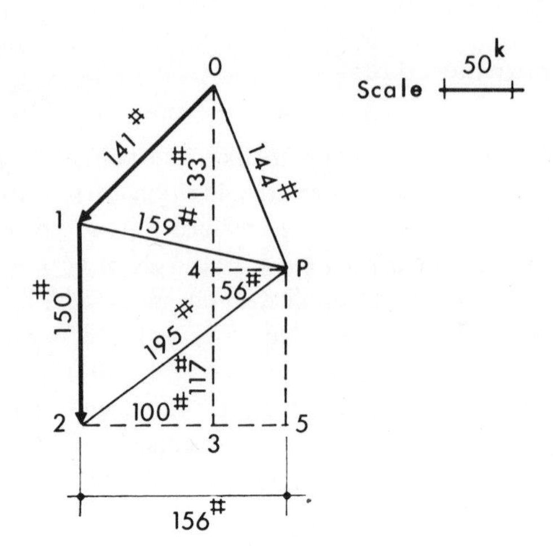

Fig. 4.4.1b

The force diagram in Fig. 4.4.1b has sides 0–1 and 1–2 representing W_1 and W_2. The load resultant 0–2 has a horizontal component 2–3 and a vertical component 3–0, which is split into $V_A = 4\text{–}0$ and $V_B = 3\text{–}4$. Since in this case the sag f certainly occurs under the load W_2 and, hence, the slope of the side *DB* is determined, *P* is the intersection of the horizontal through the point 4 with a parallel to *DB* through the point 2. The force diagrams for the loaded points are:

(A) *P*–4–0–*P*; (C) *P*–0–1–*P*; (D) *P*–1–2–*P*; (B) *P*–2–5–*P*.

It is seen that the thrust at *A* is 4–*P* = 56 lb, while the thrust at *B* is 2–5 = 156 lb; the difference in thrusts is due to the horizontal component of W_1 which equals 100 lb to the left.

The cable of Fig. 4.4.2a carries a triangular snow load. We wish to determine the abscissa a of its lowest point 0 in order to evaluate its thrust H and its maximum tension T_B. Taking moments about B and A, we obtain first the vertical reactions:

$$\tfrac{1}{2}w_0 l(l/3) - V_A l = 0 \quad \therefore \quad V_A = w_0 l/6,$$
$$\tfrac{1}{2}w_0 l(2l/3) - V_B l = 0 \quad \therefore \quad V_B = 2w_0 l/6. \tag{a}$$

To locate 0, we cut a free body consisting of the cable portion between A and 0 (Fig. 4.4.2b) and take moments about A *and* about 0:

$$Hf - \frac{1}{2}\,w_0\left(\frac{a}{l}\right)a\left(\frac{2a}{3}\right) = 0 \quad \therefore \quad Hf = \frac{w_0}{3}\left(\frac{a^3}{l}\right)$$
$$Hf - \left(\frac{w_0 l}{6}\right)a + \frac{1}{2}\,w_0\left(\frac{a}{l}\right)a\left(\frac{a}{3}\right) = 0 \quad \therefore \quad Hf = \frac{w_0}{6}\left(al - \frac{a^3}{l}\right). \tag{b}$$

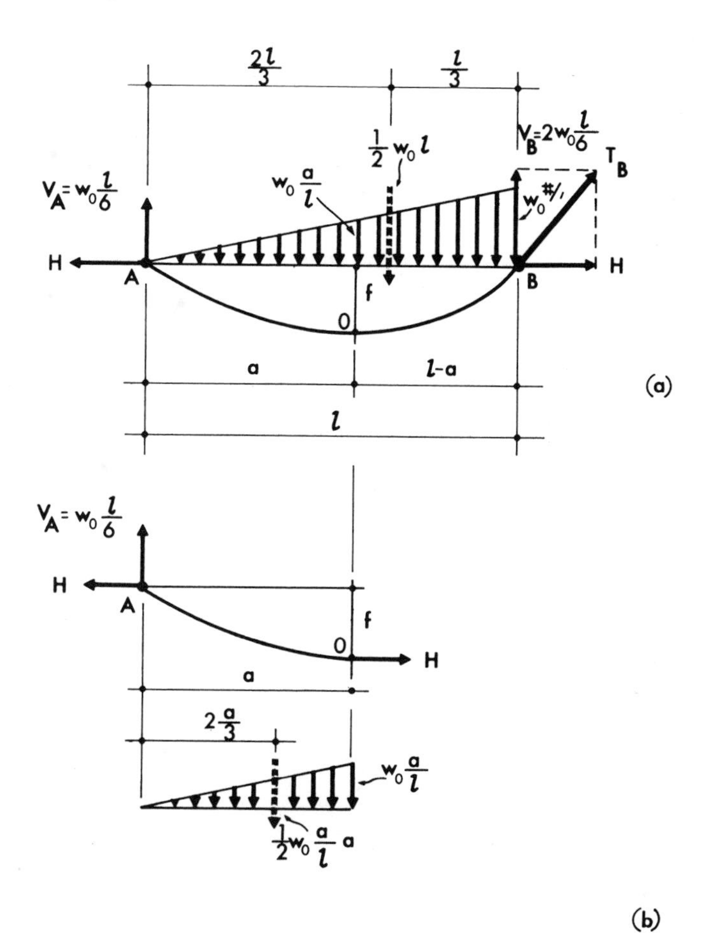

Fig. 4.4.2

Equating these two values of Hf, we obtain:

$$\frac{w_0}{3}\left(\frac{a^3}{l}\right) = \frac{w_0}{6}\left(al - \frac{a^3}{l}\right)$$

$$\therefore \quad \frac{1}{2}\frac{a^3}{l} = \frac{al}{6}, \qquad \frac{a^2}{l^2} = \frac{1}{3}, \qquad \frac{a}{l} = \frac{1}{\sqrt{3}} = 0.58$$

and from (b):

$$H = \frac{w_0}{3}\left(\frac{a^3}{fl}\right) = \frac{w_0}{3fl}\left(\frac{l}{\sqrt{3}}\right)^3 = \frac{1}{15.6}\frac{w_0 l^2}{f}$$

$$= 1.026\,\frac{(w_0/2)l^2}{8f}.$$

The maximum cable tension occurs at B, where:

$$T_B = \sqrt{H^2 + V_B^2} = H\sqrt{1 + (V_b/H)^2}$$
$$= H\sqrt{1 + 27(f/l)^2}.$$

PROBLEMS

4.4.1 Determine the funicular polygon and the tensions in the cable of Fig. 4.4.3.

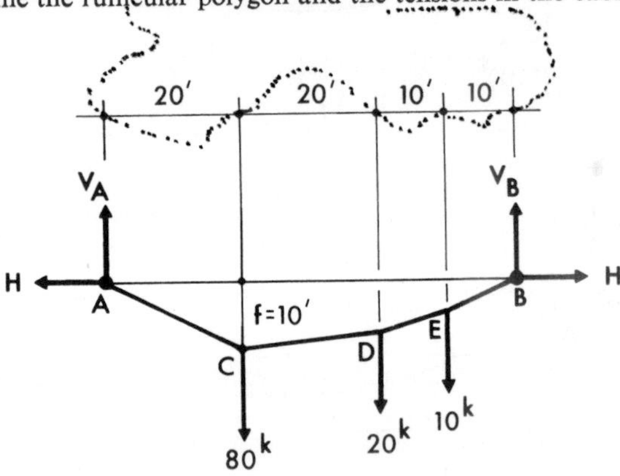

Fig. 4.4.3

4.4.2 The cable of Fig. 4.4.4 is stabilized by a vertical pull down of 100 lb and vertical pull up of 100 lb. Determine its funicular polygon and the tensions in its sides.

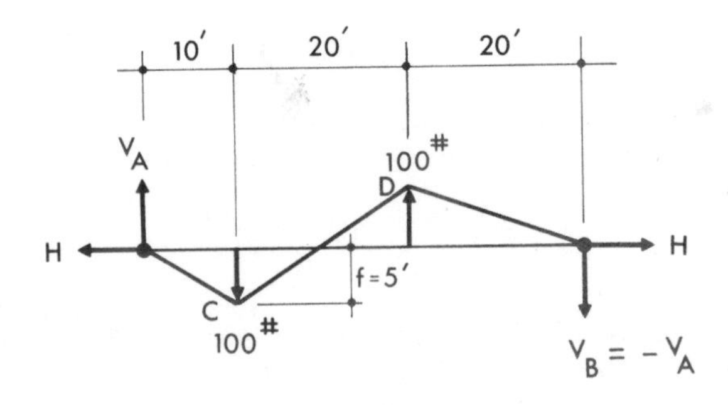

Fig. 4.4.4

4.4.3 Determine the funicular polygon for the cable of Fig. 4.4.5 and the thrusts H_A and H_B. Can you explain physically why $H_A = H_B$?

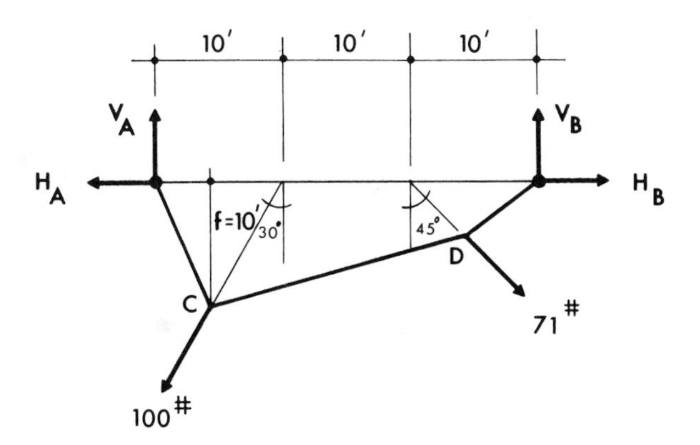

Fig. 4.4.5

4.4.4 A cable of span l and sag f carries a distributed load that varies linearly from w_0 k/ft to $2w_0$ k/ft between its left and right supports. Determine the abscissa a of its lowest point, its thrust and its maximum tension.

4.4.5 A cable of span l and sag f carries a uniform load w_0 k/ft and an additional uniform load w_0 on its left half. Determine its thrust and maximum tension.

4.4.6 A cable is designed to carry a uniform load w_0. Could it carry a load $W = w_0 l$ at its third point if the sag f is the same for both loading conditions?

4.5 Cable Design

The nominal (or theoretical) stress in a cable is obtained by the basic tension formula (see Section 3.4):

$$f_t = \frac{T}{A}, \tag{4.5.1}$$

where A is the *apparent* area of the cross section of the cable of diameter d:

$$A = \frac{\pi}{4} d^2 \doteq \frac{d^2}{1.27}. \tag{4.5.2}$$

But, because of the twisted-strand construction of the cable, the apparent area is larger than the *resistant* or *effective area* A_e. Hence, either A_e is used in place of A in (4.5.1) or a lower allowable stress must be adopted. For most cables one may assume that:

$$A_e = \tfrac{2}{3} A, \qquad F_t = 100{,}000 \text{ psi} = 100 \text{ ksi}. \tag{4.5.3}$$

On the other hand, when strands of various diameters are tested under tension, they break under the *ultimate loads* T_u given in Table 4.5.1. Depending on the type of structure and the kind of load, *safety factors* of between 2 and 11 are used in connection with the ultimate loads of Table 4.5.1; for example, a factor of 2 for small static structures and a factor of 11 required by code for elevator cables.

Table 4.5.1

d (in.)	$\frac{1}{2}$	$\frac{5}{8}$	$\frac{3}{4}$	$\frac{7}{8}$	1	$1\frac{1}{4}$	$1\frac{1}{2}$	$1\frac{3}{4}$	2	3	4
T_u (k)	30	48	68	92	122	192	276	376	490	1,076	1,850

For example, the cable of a suspension bridge carrying a uniform load $w = 100$ k/ft uniformly distributed horizontally over a span of 300 ft with a sag of 30 ft develops by (4.3.1) a thrust:

$$H = \frac{100(300)^2}{8 \times 30} = 37{,}500 \text{ k},$$

and by (4.3.3) a maximum tension:

$$T = 37{,}500 \left[1 + 8\left(\frac{30}{300}\right)^2\right] = 37{,}500 \times 1.08 = 40{,}500 \text{ k}.$$

For $F_t = 100$ ksi, the required effective area is by (4.5.1):

$$A_e = \frac{40{,}500}{100} = 405 \text{ in.}^2;$$

by (4.5.3) the apparent area is:

$$A = \frac{3}{2}\, 405 = 608 \text{ in.}^2,$$

and by (4.5.2) the required diameter is:

$$d = \sqrt{\frac{4}{\pi} A} = \sqrt{1.27 \times 608} = \sqrt{772} = 27.8 \text{ in.}$$

Using (more realistically) Table 4.5.1 with a factor of safety of 2, we find that a cable consisting of 4 in. strands, with an ultimate load:

$$T_u = 2 \times T = 2 \times 40{,}500 = 81{,}000 \text{ k}$$

must have:

$$n = \frac{81{,}000}{1{,}850} = 24 \text{ strands.}$$

PROBLEMS

4.5.1 Determine the diameter of two cables with sags of, respectively, 10 ft and 5 ft on a span of 100 ft, carrying a uniform load of 2 k/ft, for $F_t = 100$ ksi.

4.5.2 A cable 100 ft long spans 60 ft and is to be designed for two loading conditions: (1) a concentrated load of 100 k at mid-span; (2) two concentrated loads of 60 k at the third points. Check that the sag under the third points loading is 28.8 ft, and determine the cable diameter for the worst loading condition for $F_t = 100$ ksi.

4.5.3 Determine the maximum or *ultimate span* l_u of a cable 1 in. in diameter supporting a load $w = 1$ k/ft uniformly distributed horizontally, for *sag-span* ratios $f/l = 0.1$ and $f/l = 0.05$. Use Table 4.5.1 to determine T_u.

4.5.4 Determine the maximum safe load w(k/ft) uniformly distributed horizontally that can be carried by a 2 in. diameter cable spanning 1,000 ft with a sag of 80 ft. Use Table 4.5.1 and a coefficient of safety of 2.

4.5.5 Determine the diameter of the cable in Fig. 4.4.2 if $F_t = 50$ ksi, $l = 400$ ft, $f = 30$ ft and $w_0 = 30$ k/ft.

4.5.6 A steel wire with an ultimate stress $F_u = 200$ ksi and a diameter of $\frac{1}{2}$ in. carries a mid-span load of 1 k over a span of 10 ft. For what value of the sag will the wire break?

4.5.7 The safety factor for elevator cables is 11. Determine the diameter of a cable capable of lifting an elevator weighing 5,000 lb if the increase in load due to the acceleration is 10%. Use Table 4.5.1.

4.5.8 A circular pipe of reinforced concrete 4 ft in diameter carries water at a pressure of 2 atmospheres (30 psi). The tension in the pipe must be taken by hoops of reinforcing bars $\frac{1}{4}$ in. in diameter. Determine the required number n of hoops per foot of pipe if $F_t = 18{,}000$ psi for reinforcing bar steel. (See Problem 4.3.4.)

Chapter Five

5.1 Beam Supports and Reactions

Beams are the structural elements most commonly used to transfer loads horizontally to vertical supports and hence, to the ground, but they may also be inclined (e.g., those carrying stairs) or vertical (e.g., those supporting retaining walls). Beams are made out of materials capable of resisting both tension and compression, such as steel and wood, or of composite materials such as reinforced concrete, in which one material is strong in compression and the other in tension. Beams span from a few feet up to a few hundred feet (they are then called *girders*) and carry uniform loads like their own dead load, linearly varying loads like the contributory loads of floors (see Problem 2.4.8) or concentrated loads like those of picked-up joists and columns. Although some beams have cross sections which vary in depth, width or shape along their length, we shall only consider beams of *constant cross section.* This may have the shape of a rectangle, a hollow rectangle, an I or a T (the corresponding beams are called rectangular, box-, I- or T-beams) or any other shape (circular, triangular, etc.) (Fig. 5.1.1).

Fig. 5.1.1

Beams

Let us consider a horizontal beam supported at 2 points (often its ends) and acted on by loads in a vertical plane. Depending on the type of support, the supported sections of the beam may behave in one of the following ways:

a. The "supported" section is free to move vertically and horizontally *and* to rotate. We call this a *free section* because it is actually unsupported. The section at the tip of a cantilever is free (Fig. 5.1.2).

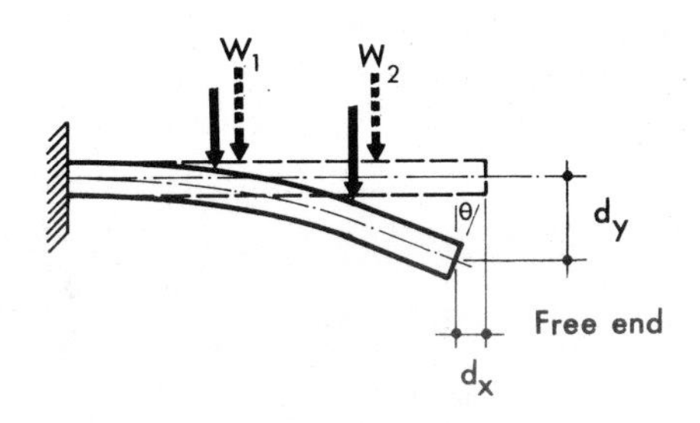

Fig. 5.1.2

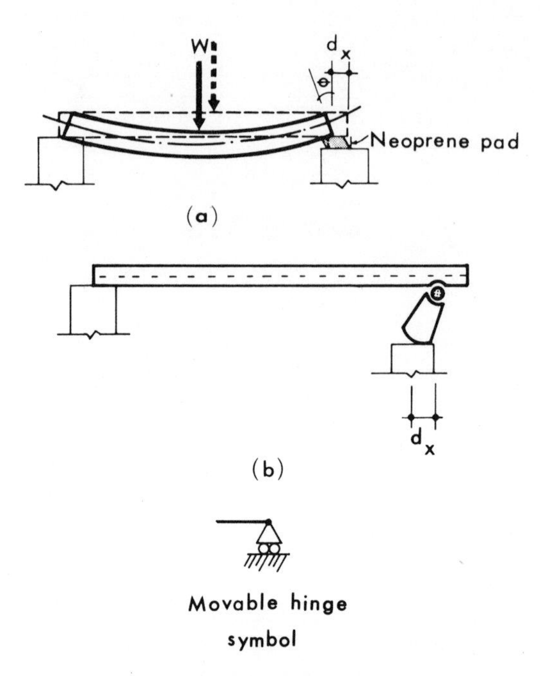

Fig. 5.1.3

b. The supported section is free to move horizontally and to rotate but is prevented from moving vertically. We call this type of support a *movable hinge* or *roller*. In practice such a hinge is obtained by resting a beam on a rigid vertical support (for example, a wall) but interposing a neoprene pad (Fig. 5.1.3a) or a pendulum (Fig. 5.1.3b) so as to permit both rotations and horizontal displacements (these may be due to the loads or to thermal conditions).

c. The support section is free to rotate but is prevented from moving both horizontally or vertically. We call this type of support a *fixed hinge*. Due to friction, a beam resting directly on a wall behaves practically as if it had a fixed hinge there (Fig. 5.1.4a). A steel beam riveted or bolted to a gusset plate is often considered hinged when the connection allows a certain amount of rotation (Fig. 5.1.4b). A fixed hinge in a concrete column is obtained by crossing the reinforced bars and introducing a "paper joint" at the section (Fig. 5.1.4c).

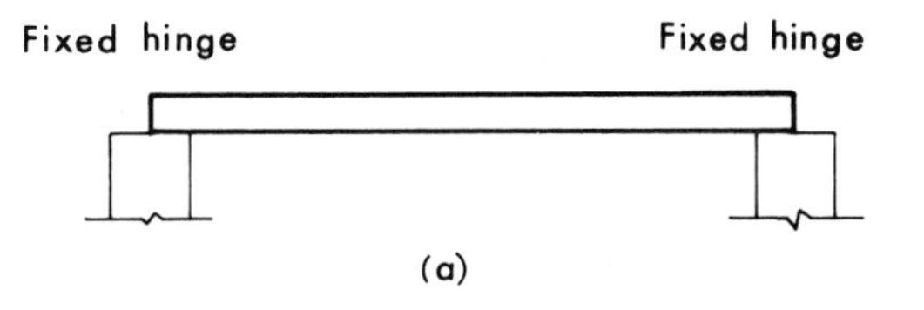

(a)

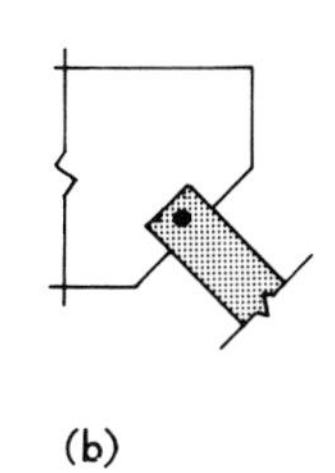

(b)

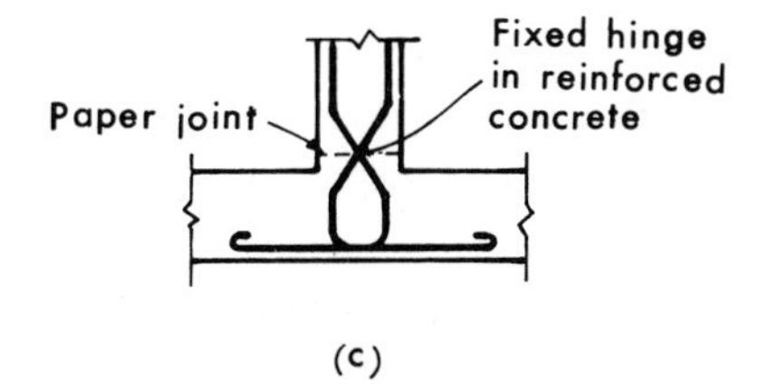

(c)

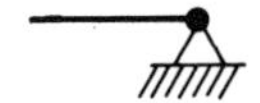

Fixed hinge symbol

Fig. 5.1.4

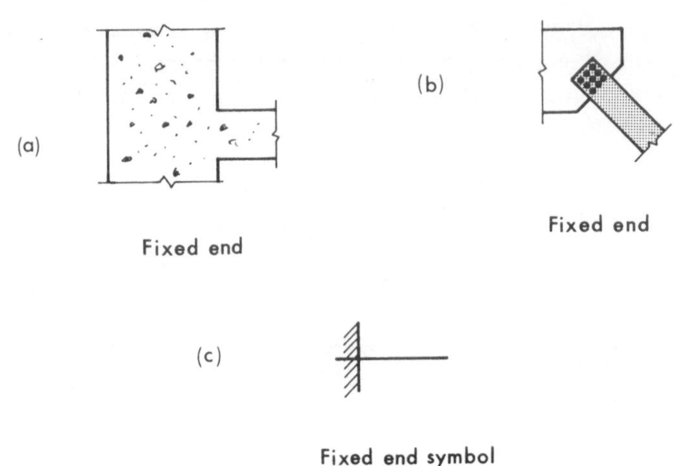

Fig. 5.1.5

d. The support section is prevented from moving vertically and horizontally *and* from rotating. We call this a *fixed* or *built-in section.* A concrete beam monolithically connected to a large column is fixed there (Fig. 5.1.5a). The end of a steel beam welded or bolted by high-strength bolts to a gusset plate is fixed (Fig. 5.1.5b).

In practice, no beam support is completely free to move or to rotate or totally prevented from moving or rotating. The definitions given above are approximations of the real behavior of the beam supports and must be used judiciously.

5.2 Support Reactions and Statical Determinacy

The reactions developed by a support to maintain a horizontal beam in equilibrium under the applied loads, depend on the type of support.

a. At a *free section* of a beam, there is no support and hence, there are *no reactions* to prevent motion or rotation (Fig. 5.2.1).

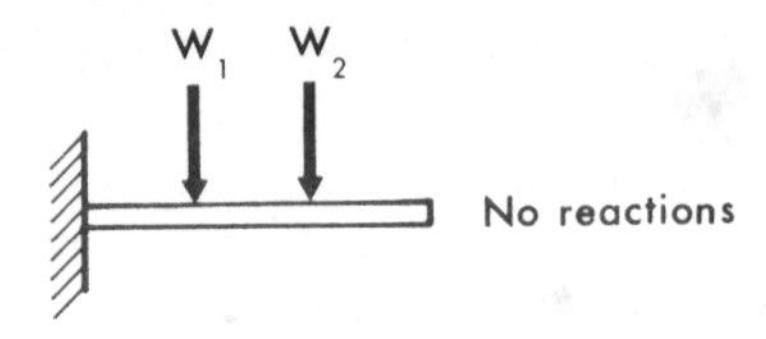

Fig. 5.2.1

b. At a *movable hinge* or *roller*, a *single* vertical reaction V is developed, capable of preventing displacement in the vertical direction, or, in general, in a direction perpendicular to the plane of rolling (Fig. 5.2.2).

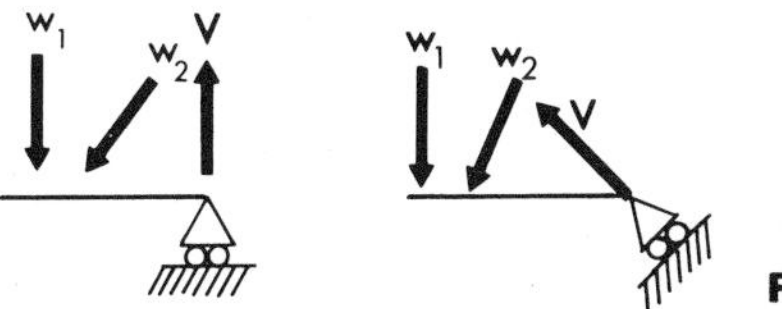

Fig. 5.2.2

c. At a *fixed hinge*, both a vertical reaction V and a horizontal reaction H are developed, capable of preventing both vertical and horizontal displacements (Fig. 5.2.3).

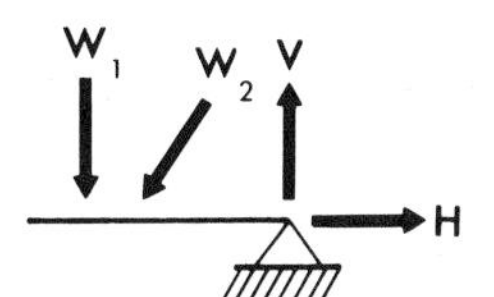

Fig. 5.2.3

d. At a *fixed* or *built-in section*, vertical and horizontal reactions V and H prevent vertical and horizontal displacements, but the end rotation must also be prevented. Since rotation is produced by moments (see Section 1.4), a fixed support also develops a reactive moment M capable of preventing rotation, i.e., of developing a rotation equal and opposite to that which would be induced by the loads if the section were free to rotate (Fig. 5.2.4).

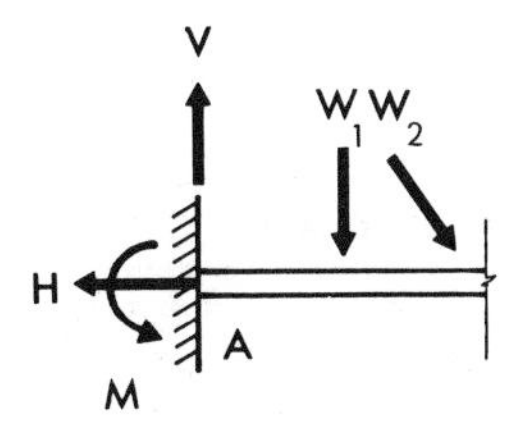

Fig. 5.2.4

The section A of the beam in Fig. 5.2.4 is fixed and develops reactions V and H and a reactive moment M. It is often impossible to determine exactly how the reactive moment M is physically developed. (Figure 5.2.5 shows four different sets of forces capable of developing a reactive moment inside the supporting wall of the beam in Fig. 5.2.4. Check that each set of forces has a vertical resultant and a resultant moment.) But whatever the internal force system, the moment must be capable of maintaining the rotational equilibrium of the entire beam and of preventing the rotation of its fixed section.

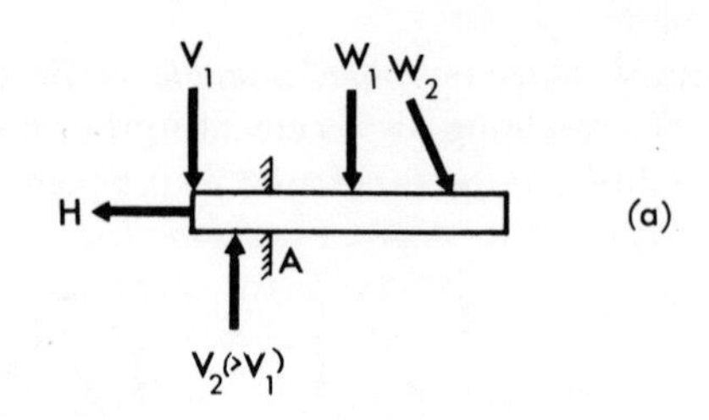

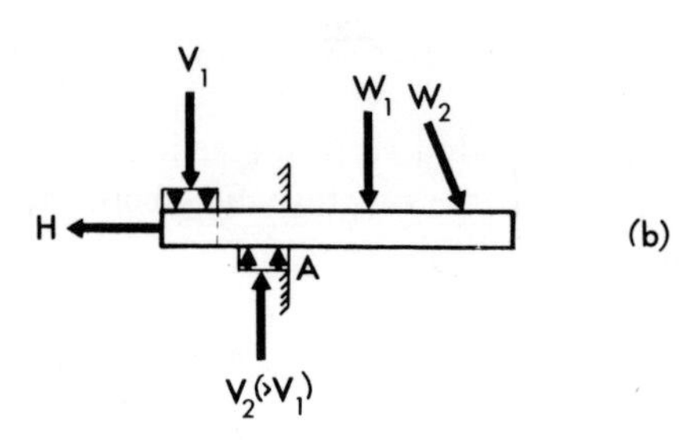

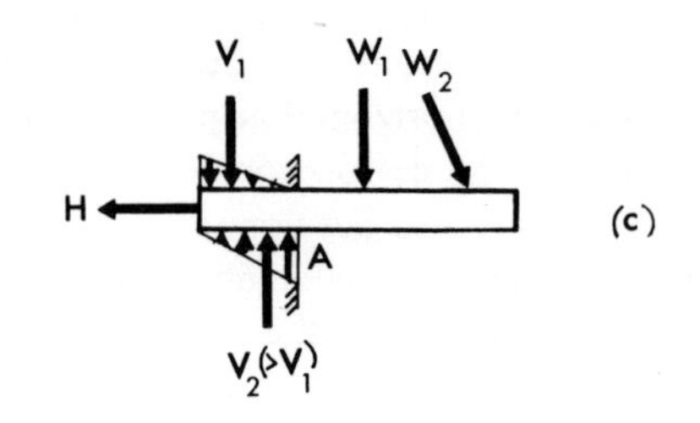

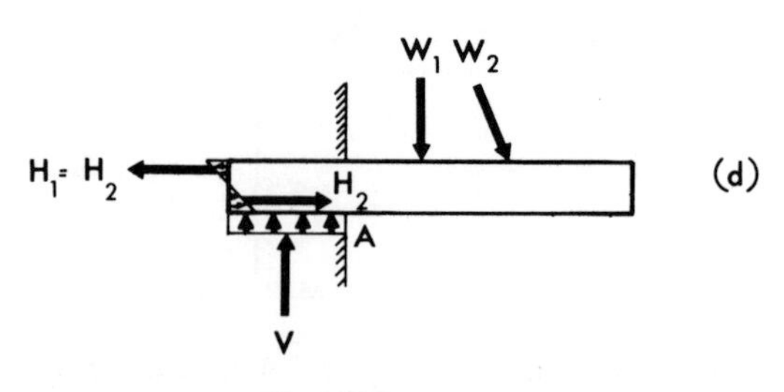

Fig. 5.2.5

We conclude from this discussion that when the beam reactions are unknown:

a. a free section entails no unknowns;
b. a movable hinge entails 1 unknown, V;
c. a fixed hinge entails 2 unknowns, V and H;
d. a fixed section entails 3 unknowns, V, H and M.

When all the loads acting on a beam lie in the plane of the beam, say the vertical plane, the reactions act also in this plane and only 3 equations of plane equilibrium, equations (1.4.2), can be written for the unknown reactions. Hence, *a beam under loads acting in a plane is statically determinate only if its supports do not develop more than 3 unknown reactions.** Thus, a cantilever beam is statically determinate, since it develops the 3 reactions V, H and M at its root. A beam supported on one fixed hinge and a roller (Fig. 5.2.6), a so-called

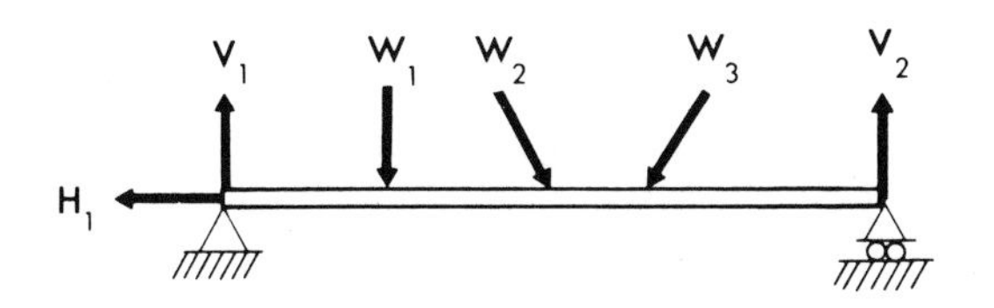

Fig. 5.2.6

simply supported beam, develops reactions V_1, H_1 and V_2 and, hence, is statically determinate. But a beam supported on two fixed hinges (Fig. 5.2.7) develops 4 reactions, V_1, H_1, V_2 and H_2 and is *statically indeterminate once*, since only 3 equations of statics may be written for the 4 unknowns and $4 - 3 = 1$. A beam with 2 fixed ends develops 6 reactions and is $6 - 3 = 3$ times statically indeterminate.

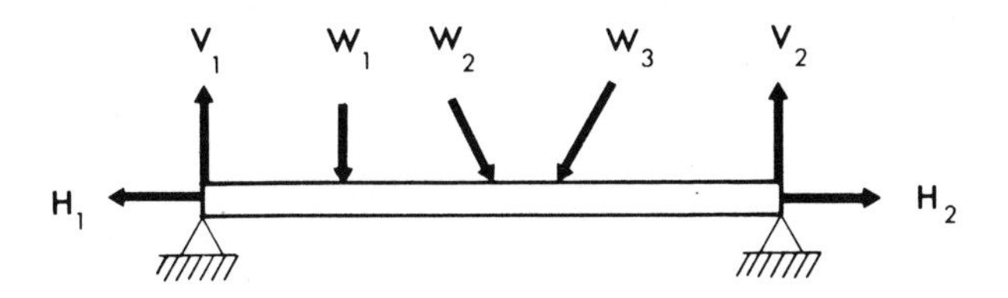

Fig. 5.2.7

A particular case of support occurs sometimes in practice which prevents the vertical (*or* horizontal) displacement and the rotation of a section, but not its horizontal (*or* vertical) displacement. This type of support, to be called a *movable built-in support* (but often referred to simply as a built-in support), is capable of developing a reaction V (or H) and a moment M, but not a reaction H (or V), and is symbolized by the "double pendulum" of Fig. 5.2.8a. For example, in a frame the top of a column, rigidly connected to a deep stiff beam, is supported on a movable built-in support since it may move horizontally

*At times the determinacy or indeterminacy of a beam may depend on the loads acting on it (see the problems at end of this section).

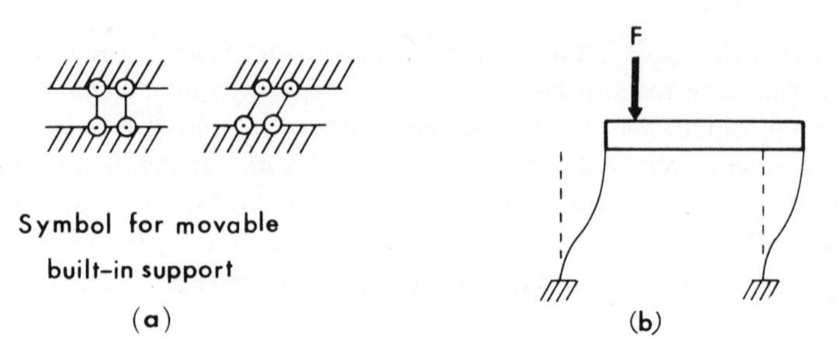

Fig. 5.2.8

under the action of unsymmetrical loads, but can neither rotate nor displace vertically (Fig. 5.2.8b).*

PROBLEMS

5.2.1 What are the support conditions at the ends of the beam in a post-and-lintel system?

5.2.2 What are the approximate support conditions at the ends of a beam in a simple frame: (a) when the beam is relatively stiff and the columns relatively flexible, and (b) when the beam is relatively flexible and the columns relatively stiff? (In a frame, the beam ends are rigidly connected to the top of the columns.)

5.2.3 What are the approximate support conditions at the sections of a uniformly loaded beam resting directly on two walls and with overhangs about one-half the length of the central beam span?

5.2.4 A concrete beam frames into the concrete core of a building at one end and into the heavy columns of the building's facade at the other. The outside columns are heated by the sun, while the core is maintained at room temperature by air conditioning. What are the support conditions at the inner end and at the outer end of the beam?

5.2.5 Under the action of wind forces, the floors of a steel building are displaced horizontally. What are the end conditions in the columns if the floor girders are very stiff in comparison with the columns?

5.2.6 The support end of a diving board is connected to a fixed horizontal pin and supported on a horizontal roller. Which of the support conditions 5.2 a to d approximate the support condition of the board at the supported end?

5.2.7 The foot of the columns in two concrete frames is reinforced by bars as shown in Fig. 5.2.9a and b, respectively. What are the support conditions in the columns of the two frames at the section *AB*?

*The value of the horizontal reaction *H* is not identically zero in this case but negligibly small if the columns are flexible.

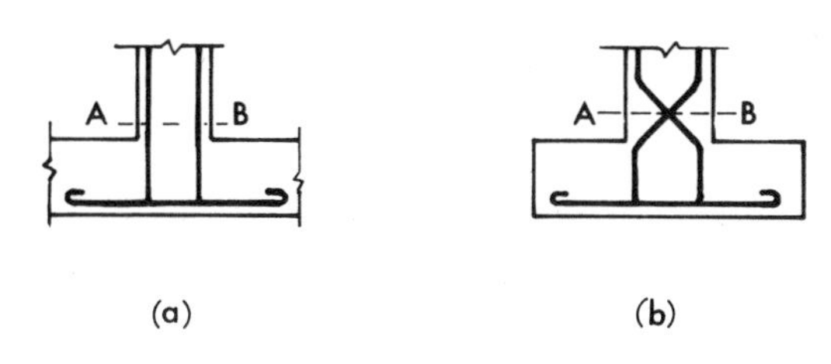

Fig. 5.2.9

5.2.8 The girder of a bridge is to be erected in winter when the outside temperature is 0°F. The temperature may rise to 120°F in summer. What support conditions would you choose for the two girder ends? Why?

5.2.9 A beam is built-in into a heavy wall at one end and is supported on a movable hinge at the other. Is it statically determinate or indeterminate?

5.2.10 A beam is supported on a movable hinge at its left end and on a fixed hinge at another section. It cantilevers out to the right of the fixed-hinge section. Is it statically determinate or indeterminate? For a certain cantilever length and under uniform load the fixed hinge section does not rotate, i.e., it behaves like a fixed section. Is the beam in this case statically determinate or indeterminate?

5.2.11 A beam is supported on two movable hinges at its ends and a fixed hinge at mid-span. Is it statically determinate or indeterminate?

5.2.12 A beam is simply supported and acted upon by two equal concentrated loads, one acting down at the left third point and one acting up at the right third point (Fig. 5.2.10). Draw qualitatively the deformed shape of the beam. If, moreover, its mid-span section were supported on a movable hinge, would the beam still be statically determinate? Would it be statically determinate if the two loads were both acting down and the mid-span movable hinge were maintained?

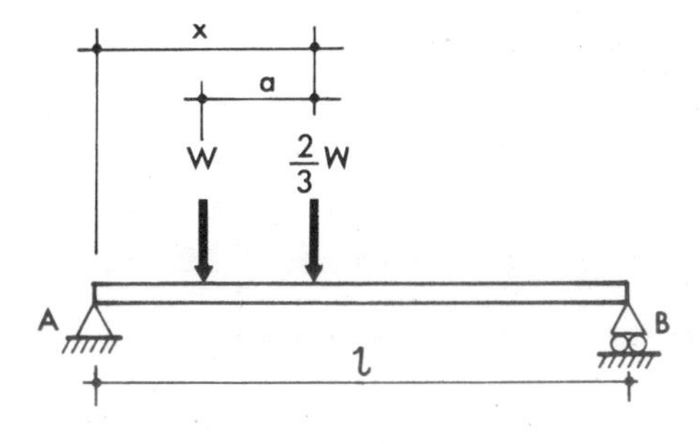

Fig. 5.2.10

5.3 Determination of Support Reactions

Whenever a beam is loaded in a plane, as is most often the case, the evaluation of its statically determinate reactions, both forces and moments, is obtained by the three basic equations of plane statics. Numerous examples of such evaluations were given in Section 1.4, and a few additional examples will be given here.

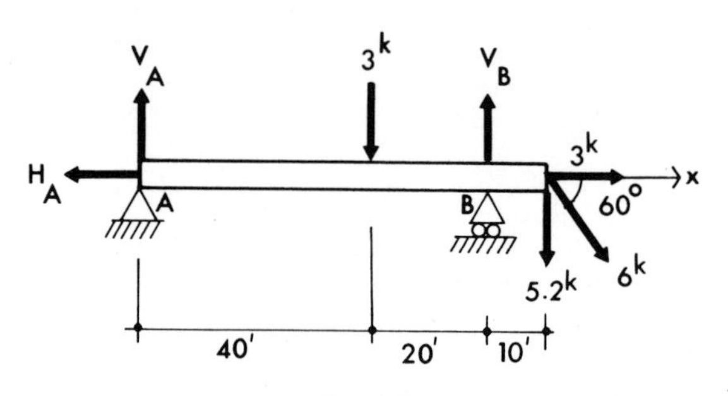

Fig. 5.3.1

The reactions of the simply supported beam of Fig. 5.3.1 are obtained by taking moments about A and B and by horizontal equilibrium (after splitting the 6 k force into a horizontal component of $6 \times \cos 60^\circ = 3$ k and a vertical component of $6 \times \sin 60^\circ = 5.2$ k):

$$\sum M_A = V_B \times 60 - 3 \times 40 - 5.2 \times 70 = 0, \qquad V_B = 8.07 \text{ k},$$

$$\sum M_B = -V_A \times 60 + 3 \times 20 - 5.2 \times 10 = 0, \qquad V_A = 0.13 \text{ k},$$

$$\sum F_x = -H_A + 3 = 0, \qquad H_A = 3 \text{ k}.$$

The reactions at A of the cantilever beam of Fig. 5.3.2, which is loaded with a linearly varying load, consist of a vertical reaction V_A equal to the resultant W of the load:

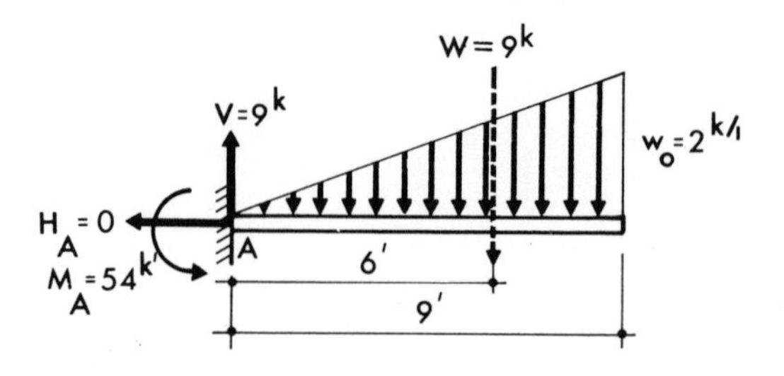

Fig. 5.3.2

$$V_A = \tfrac{1}{2} \times 2 \times 9 = 9\text{ k},$$

and of a moment M_A which, since W is applied at a section $\frac{2}{3}9 = 6$ ft from A (see Section 2.4), is given by:

$$\sum M_A = M_A - 9 \times 6 = 0, \qquad M_A = 54\text{ k ft}.$$

The horizontal reaction H_A equals zero, since no horizontal loads act on the beam.

The beam system A–B–C–D of Fig. 5.3.3 consists of a beam BC simply supported on the two cantilevers AB and CD. To determine the reactions at B and C, we split the load into a uniform load of intensity 1 k/ft with a resultant of 10 k, and a triangular load of intensity 1 k/ft at C and zero at B with a resultant of $\frac{1}{2}10 \times 1 = 5$ k at a distance of $\frac{2}{3}$ of the span from B:

$$V_B = \tfrac{1}{2}10 + \tfrac{1}{3}5 = 6.67\text{ k},$$
$$V_C = \tfrac{1}{2}10 + \tfrac{2}{3}5 = 8.33\text{ k}.$$

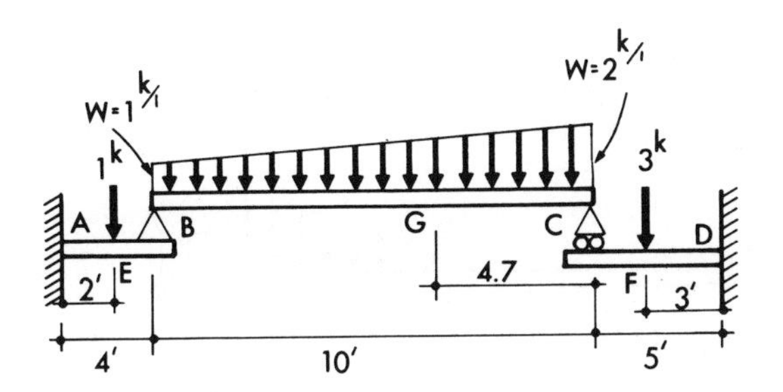

(a)

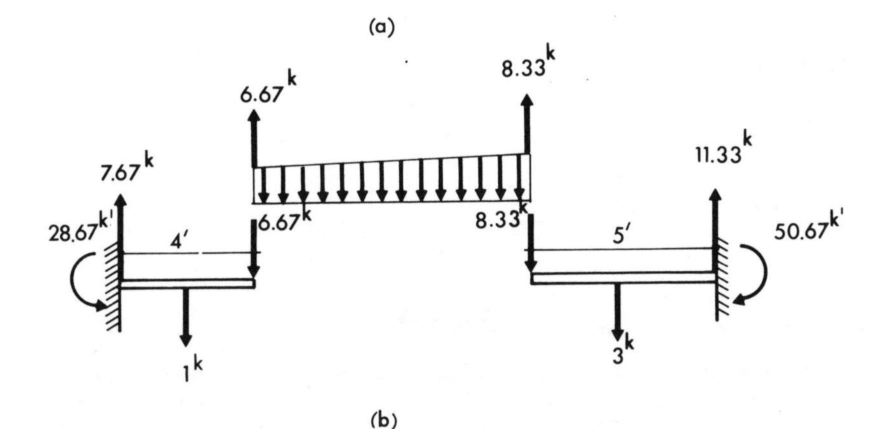

(b)

Fig. 5.3.3

The reactions at the root of the cantilevers are:

$$V_A = 6.67 + 1 = 7.67 \text{ k}, \qquad M_A = 6.67 \times 4 + 1 \times 2 = 28.67 \text{ k ft},$$
$$V_D = 8.33 + 3 = 11.33 \text{ k}, \qquad M_D = 8.33 \times 5 + 3 \times 3 = 50.67 \text{ k ft}.$$

PROBLEMS

5.3.1 Determine the reactions of the beam of Fig. 5.3.4.

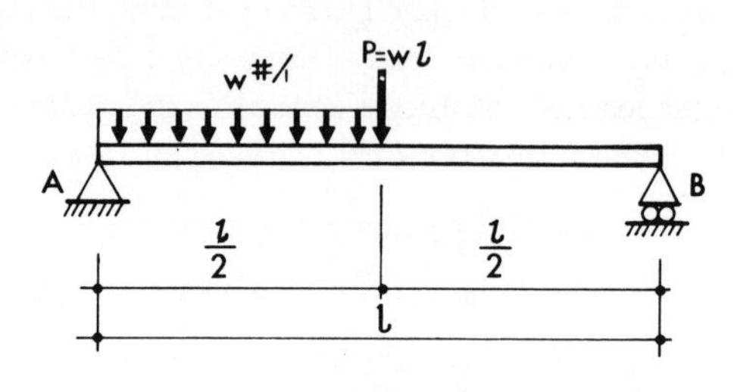

Fig. 5.3.4

5.3.2 Determine the reactions of the beam of Fig. 5.3.5.

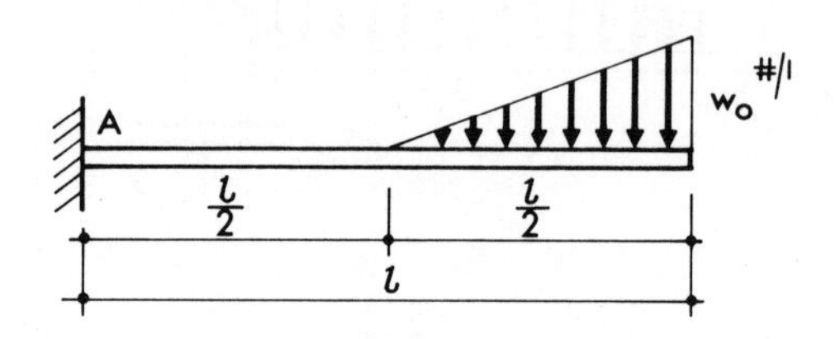

Fig. 5.3.5

5.3.3 Determine the reactions of the beam of Fig. 5.3.6.

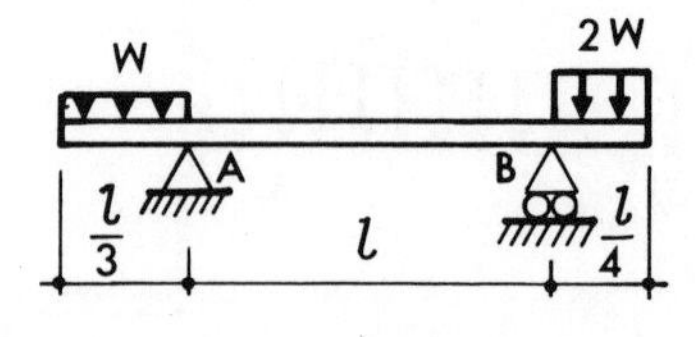

Fig. 5.3.6

5.3.4 The cantilever of Fig. 5.3.7 is loaded by a load W lbs at mid-span and is supported at its tip by the pull of a rope inclined by 45°, going over a pulley and supporting a weight of $\sqrt{2}\,W$ lbs. Determine the cantilever reactions.

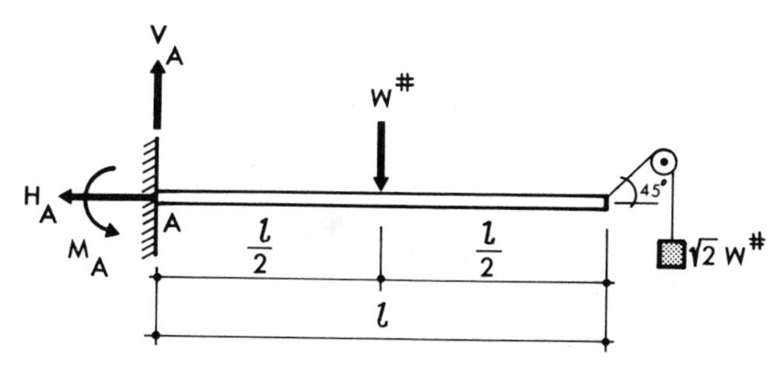

Fig. 5.3.7

5.3.5 Determine the reactions of the three beams in Fig. 5.3.8a, b and c.

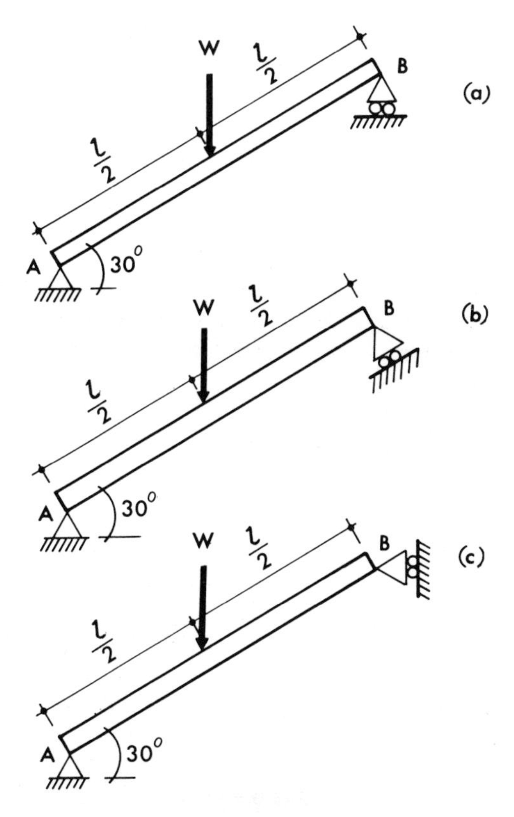

Fig. 5.3.8

5.3.6 Determine the reactions of the beams of Fig. 5.3.9a and b. Can you explain why the distance b does not influence the values of the reactions?

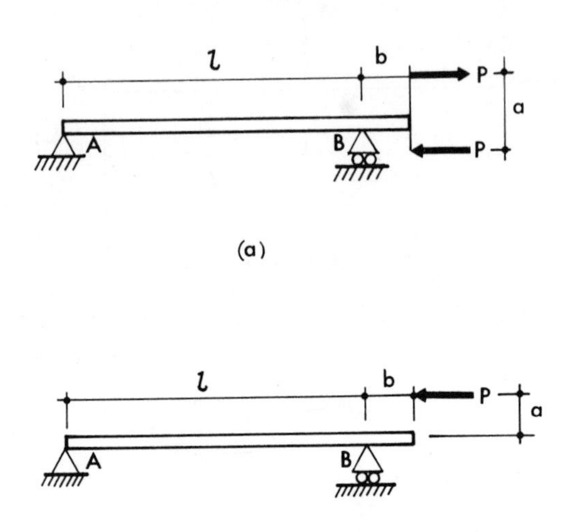

Fig. 5.3.9

5.3.7 The bridge beam of Fig. 5.3.10 carries a car with axle weights $\frac{2}{3}W$ and W. Determine the reaction V_A of the beam when the front axle is at a distance x from A, i.e., express V_A as a function of x/l as the front axle moves across the bridge from A to a point a distance a to the right of B, when the rear axle moves off the bridge. (Such a diagram is known as the *influence line* of the reaction V_A due to the moving axle loads.)

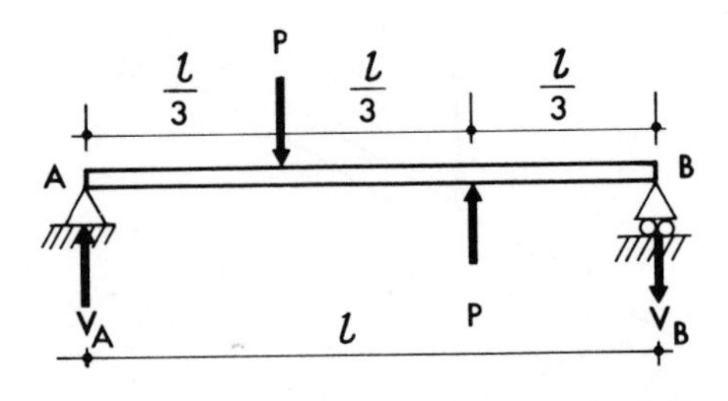

Fig. 5.3.10

5.3.8 Plot the values of the reaction V_A versus x/l in the beam of Fig. 5.3.11 as the load moves from A to C.

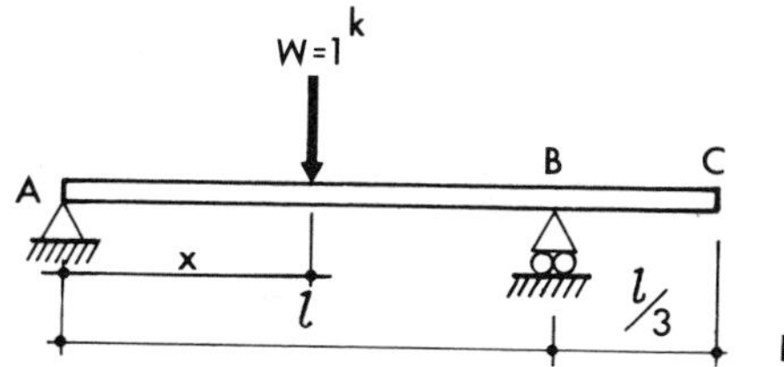

Fig. 5.3.11

5.3.9 For what value of the distance x is $V_A = V_B$ in the beam of Fig. 5.3.12, if the fixed distance between the loads is $l/4$? What is the value of $V_A = V_B$?

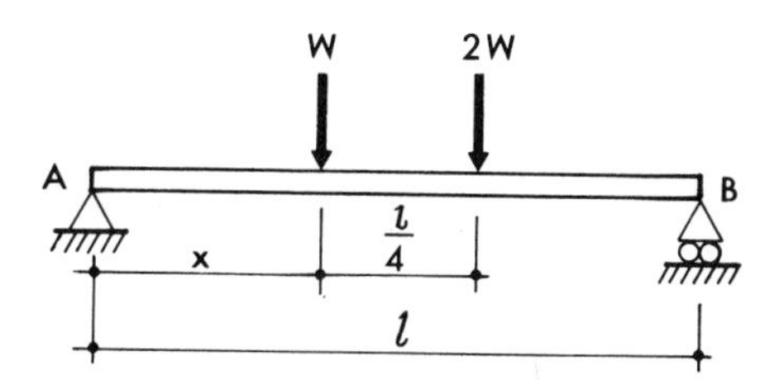

Fig. 5.3.12

5.3.10 For what values of x is V_A maximum and V_B maximum, respectively, in the beam of Fig. 5.3.12? What are these maximum values?

5.4 Shears and Axial Forces

In the preceding sections the values of the external reactions (forces and moments) of a loaded beam have been determined by stating that these reactions must maintain the entire beam in equilibrium. In so doing we have tacitly assumed that each and any part of the beam would also be in equilibrium. We are now going to check what *internal* forces and moments are needed to keep any portion of the beam in equilibrium. This knowledge will enable us to check later on (see Sections 5.7 and 5.8) whether the beam material can actually develop such internal forces and moments, i.e., whether the beam is properly designed.

Consider the beam of Fig. 5.4.1a, which carries a single load W at the left third point and is supported by reactions $V_A = \frac{2}{3}W$ and $V_B = \frac{1}{3}W$. Let us cut

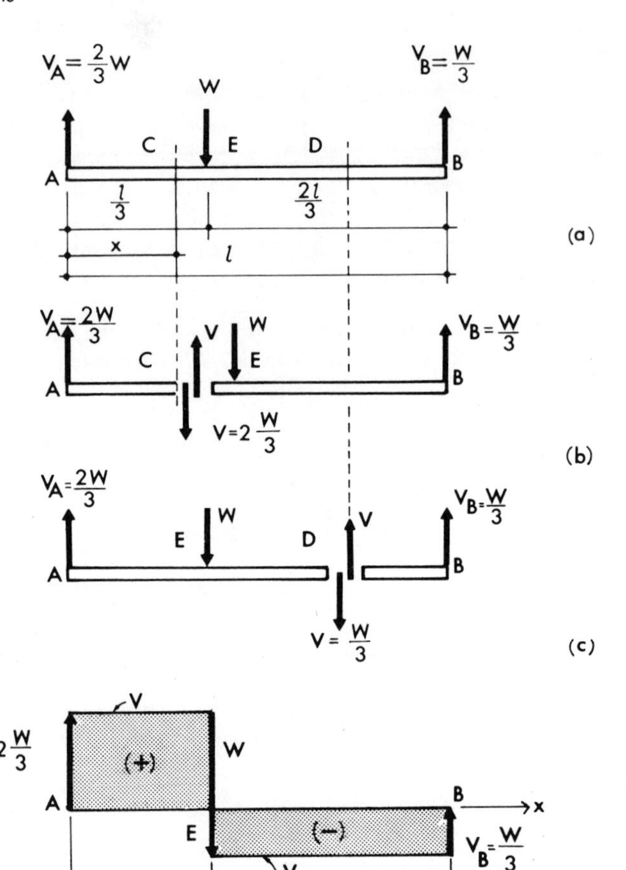

Fig. 5.4.1

out of the beam, by means of a section C to the left of E and a distance x from A, the *free body AC* (Fig. 5.4.1b). If the free body AC is to be in vertical equilibrium, the portion CB of the beam must exert on AC a force capable of equilibrating the upward reaction $\frac{2}{3}W$, i.e., a downward force V equal to $\frac{2}{3}W$. Such an internal force is called the *shear* at the section C, because it tends to cut or "shear off" the beam at C.

For any section C taken to the left of the load, the shear V is equal and opposite to the left reaction $V_A = \frac{2}{3}W$. But if we consider a free body BD obtained by means of a section D taken to the right of the load (Fig. 5.4.1c), the shear at D needed to keep the free body DB in vertical equilibrium must be equal and opposite to the reaction $V_B = \frac{1}{3}W$. (You will notice that the free bodies AC and BD are not in rotational equilibrium. This indicates that the sections at C and D must also be acted upon by *internal moments*. We shall discuss these moments in Section 5.5.)

In order to plot the value of V at all sections of the beam let us call a shear *positive when it acts downward on the face of the section facing to the right*, and *negative when it acts downward on the face of the section facing to the left.** The shear is then $+2W/3$ for sections between A and E and $-W/3$ for sections between E and B, and jumps by W, from $+2W/3$ to $-W/3$, at E, as shown in the diagram of Fig. 5.4.1d. This diagram is called the *shear diagram* of the beam and is required to check whether the beam material can safely develop such internal forces at all sections.

It is seen from Fig. 5.4.1d that *the shear V at any section is nothing else but the resultant of all the forces (including the reactions) normal to the beam axis from either end of the beam up to the section considered.* If the resultant is computed from the left end of the beam, V is positive if upward and negative if downward, and the shears at A and B equal the vertical beam reaction V_A and V_B.

With this definition of shear we can now draw the shear diagram for the beam of Fig. 5.4.2. Let us first evaluate V_A and V_B:

$$-V_A \times 10 + 10 \times 7 + 20 \times 4 = 0, \qquad V_A = 15\text{ k},$$
$$V_B \times 10 - 20 \times 6 - 10 \times 3 = 0, \qquad V_B = 15\text{ k}.$$

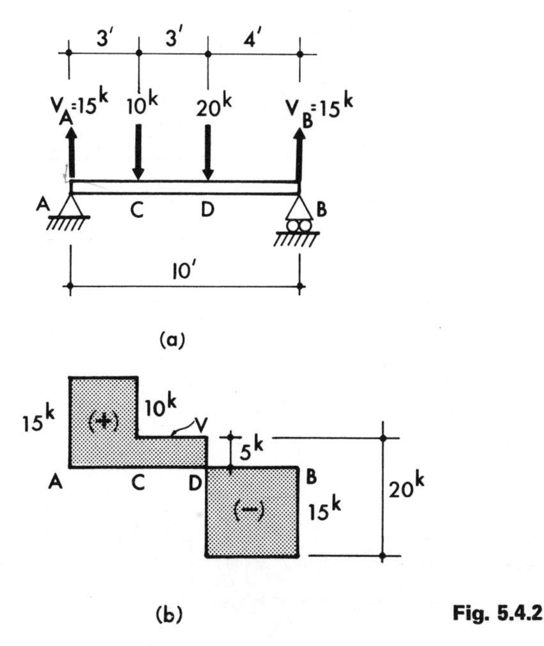

Fig. 5.4.2

*Since action equals reaction, the shear is also positive when acting upward on the face of a section facing to the left and negative when acting upward on the face of a section facing to the right (Figs. 5.4.1b, c).

The shear diagram is plotted by drawing consecutively an upward force of 15 k at A, a downward force of 10 k at C, a downward force of 20 k at D and an upward force of 15 k at B. The diagram starts and ends up at zero, since the beam is in vertical equilibrium and the vertical resultant of all the loads is zero. V is $+15$ k from A to C, $+5$ k from C to D and -15 k from D to B. It is thus seen that *the shear is constant between concentrated loads and its value jumps at each concentrated load by the value of that load.*

One determines the shear diagram for beams carrying distributed loads by the same procedure. Consider, for example, the beam of Fig. 5.4.3. Cutting a

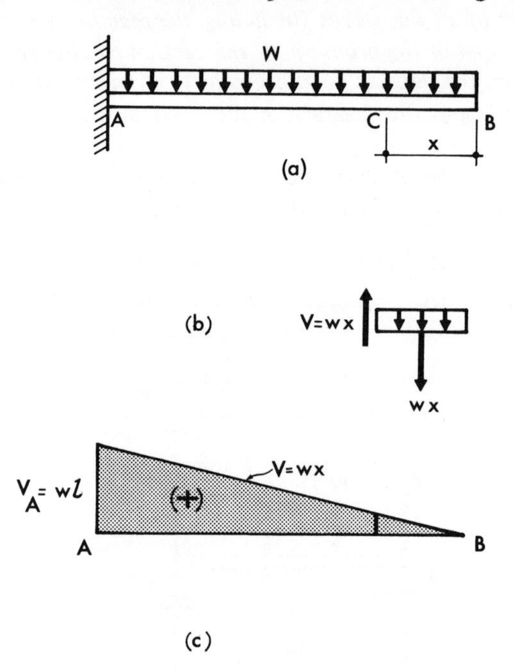

Fig. 5.4.3

section at C, we see that the free body BC carries a downward load wx; hence, the shear at C is up and has a value wx. The shear diagram $V = wx$ is zero at $x = 0$, the cantilever tip, and equals wl at $x = l$, the cantilever root. It is thus seen that *the shear due to a uniform load varies linearly.*

To determine the shear diagram of the beam of Fig. 5.4.4, we first compute the reactions $V_A = 25$ k, $V_B = 55$ k. The shear diagram has a left ordinate of 25 k, decreases linearly to $25 - 2 \times 10 = 5$ k to the left of C and to $5 - 20 = -15$ k to the right of C, decreases linearly to $-15 - 2 \times 10 = -35$ k to the left of B, grows to $-35 + 55 = +20$ k to the right of B and decreases linearly to $20 - 2 \times 10 = 0$ at D.

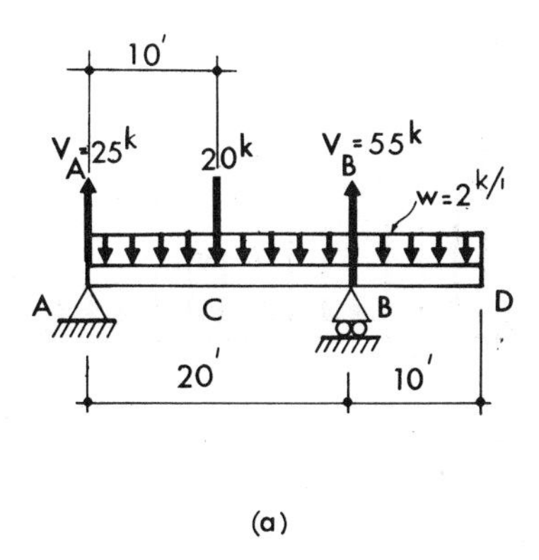

(a)

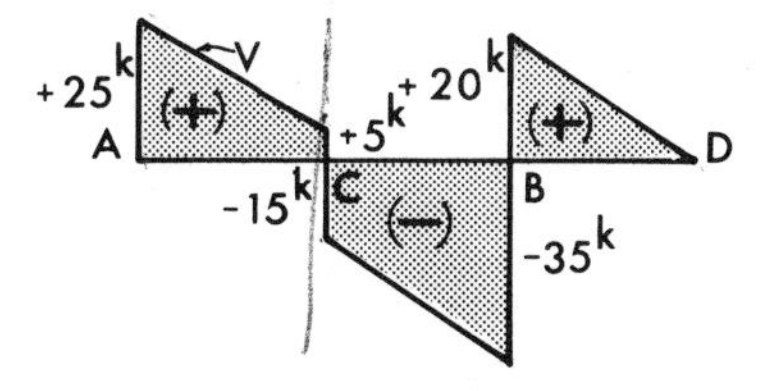

(b) **Fig. 5.4.4**

To evaluate the shear in the *linearly loaded* beam of Fig. 5.4.5, we cut a section at C, a distance x from B, and consider the vertical equilibrium of the free body CB, acted upon by the right upward reaction $w_0 l/6$ and the resultant of the downward triangular load:

$$\frac{1}{2}\left(w_0\frac{x}{l}\right)x = \frac{1}{2}\left(\frac{w_0}{l}\right)x^2.$$

The shear at x is thus:

$$V = \frac{1}{2}\left(\frac{w_0 x^2}{l}\right) - \frac{w_0 l}{6} = \frac{w_0 l}{2}\left[\left(\frac{x}{l}\right)^2 - \frac{1}{3}\right]$$

and varies *parabolically* with x/l, i.e., with the square of x/l. The shear is, at $x = l$:

$$V_A = \frac{w_0 l}{2}\left(1 - \frac{1}{3}\right) = \frac{2w_0 l}{6};$$

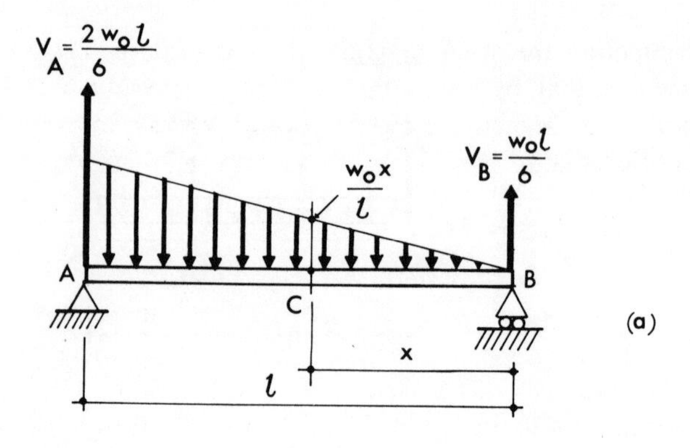

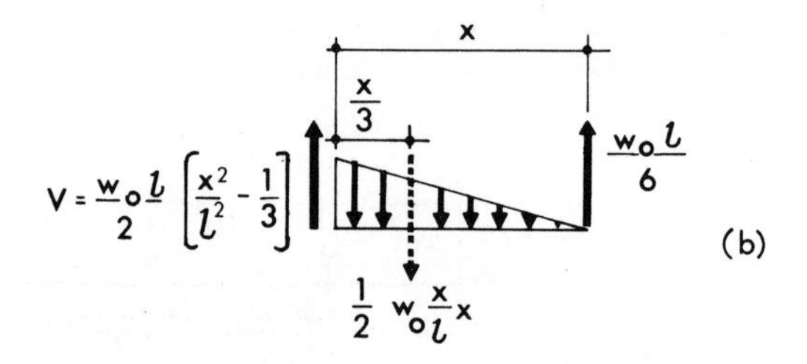

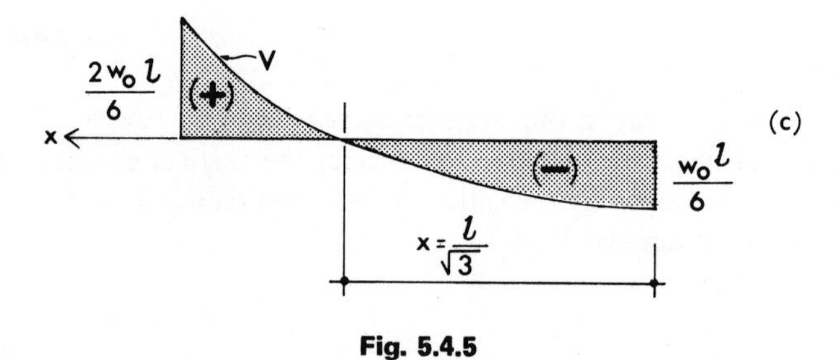

Fig. 5.4.5

it decreases parabolically to $-w_0 l/6$ at B, and it is zero where:

$$\left(\frac{x}{l}\right)^2 - \frac{1}{3} = 0,$$

i.e., at

$$\frac{x}{l} = \frac{1}{\sqrt{3}} = 0.58.$$

It is thus seen that *the shear due to a linearly varying load varies parabolically.*

In computing the shear diagram of the cantilever beam of Fig. 5.4.6, we must remember that, by definition, the shear is the resultant of the forces *normal* to the beam axis. Hence, taking the vertical and horizontal components of the forces, we find that:

$$V_A = 21.21 + 20 = 41.21 \text{ k},$$
$$H_A = 26.64 - 21.21 = 5.43 \text{ k},$$
$$M_A = 20 \times 7 + 21.21 \times 3 = 203.63 \text{ k ft},$$

so that the shear is 41.21 k from A to the left of B, $41.21 - 21.21 = 20$ k from the right of B to the left of C and $20 - 20 = 0$ from the right of C to D.

When the forces acting on the beam have components parallel to the beam axis, the beam will also develop *internal axial forces*. For example, Fig. 5.4.6c shows that, for the free body DE (cut out of the beam by a section at E) to be

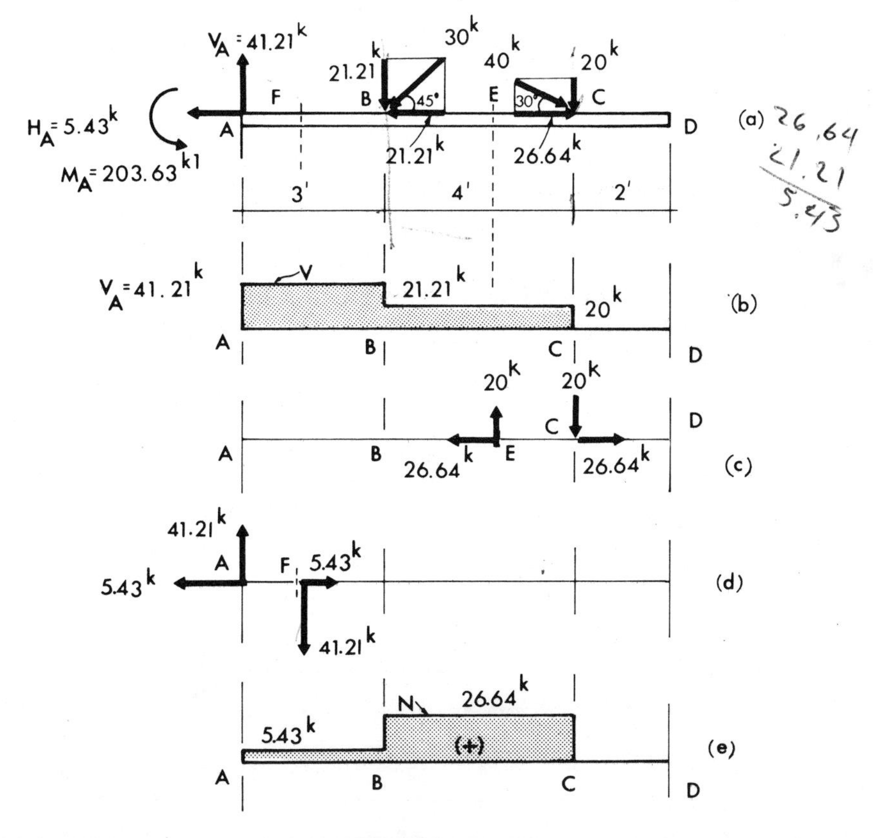

Fig. 5.4.6

in horizontal equilibrium, an internal axial force to the left, $N = 26.64$ k, must be exerted by AE on DE at E, so that the beam is acted upon by an internal tensile axial force of 26.64 k between C and B, while it has no axial force between D and C. The free body AF of Fig. 5.4.6d shows that the tension in the beam between A and B is 5.43 k. Figure 5.4.6e gives the *axial force diagram* of the beam, in which axial forces are considered positive when tensile.

PROBLEMS

5.4.1 Draw the shear diagram of the beam of Fig. 5.4.7.

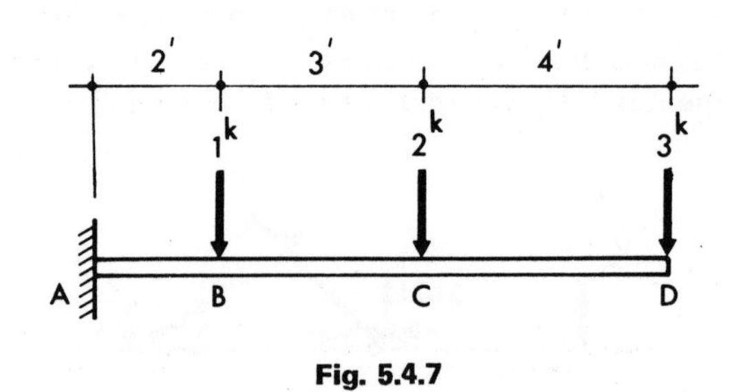

Fig. 5.4.7

5.4.2 Draw the shear diagram of the beam of Fig. 5.4.8.

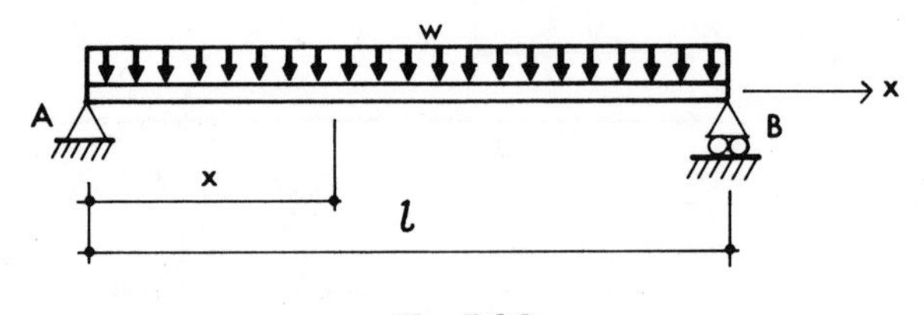

Fig. 5.4.8

5.4.3 Draw the shear diagram of the beam of Fig. 5.4.9.

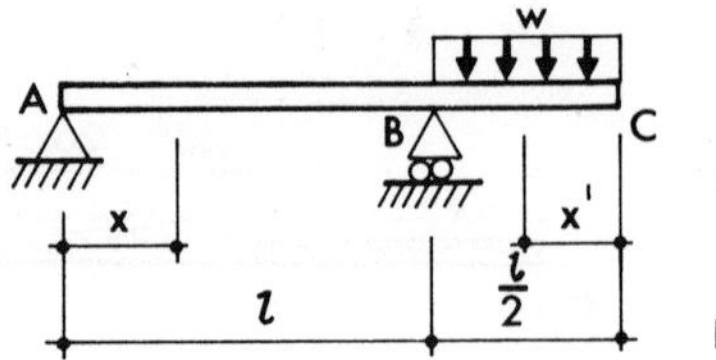

Fig. 5.4.9

5.4.4 Draw the shear diagram of the beam of Fig. 5.4.10.

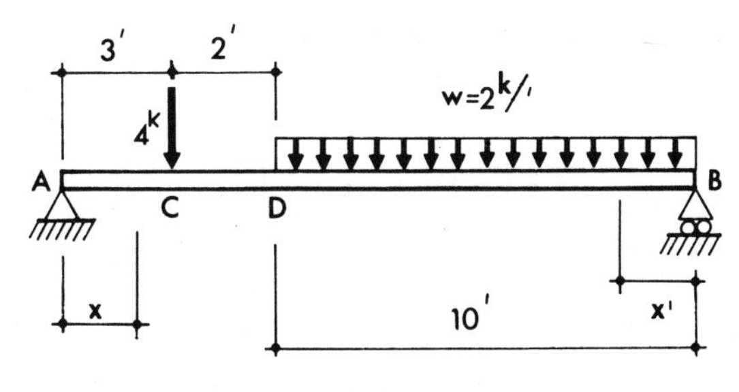

Fig. 5.4.10

5.4.5 Draw the shear diagram of the beam of Fig. 5.4.11.

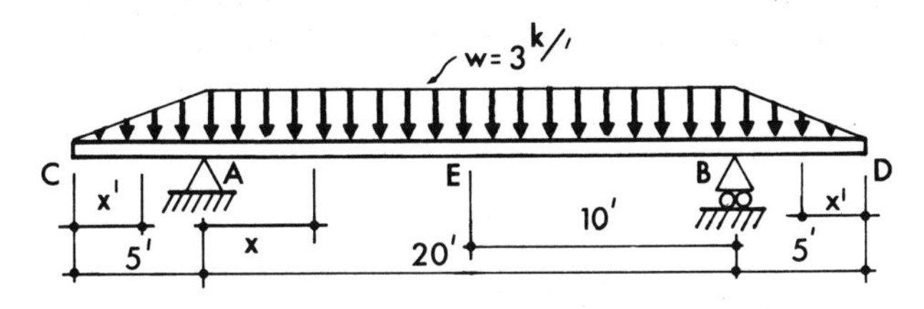

Fig. 5.4.11

5.4.6 Draw the shear diagram of the beam of Fig. 5.4.12.

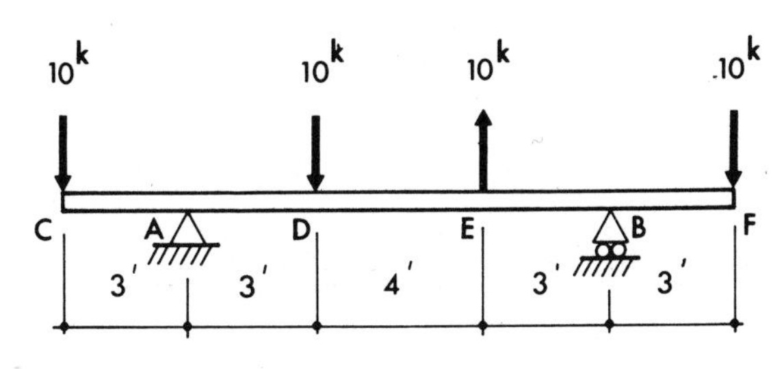

Fig. 5.4.12

5.4.7 Draw the shear and axial force diagrams of the beam of Fig. 5.4.13 after finding the values of W_1 and W_2 for which the beam is in equilibrium. What is the value of β?

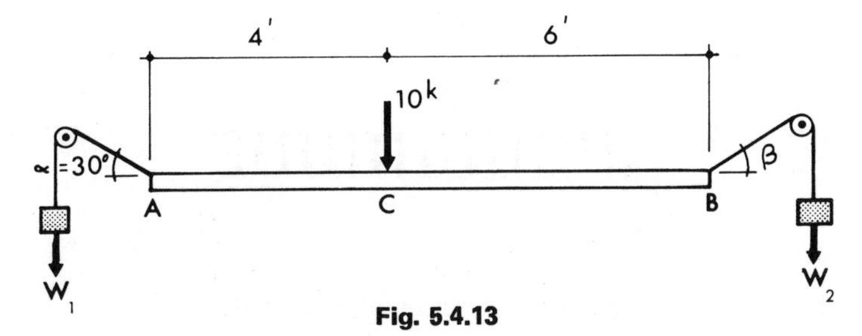

Fig. 5.4.13

5.4.8 Draw the shear diagram of the beam of Fig. 5.4.14.

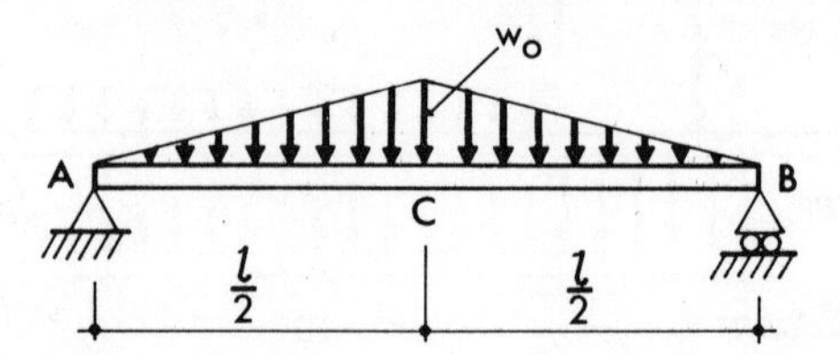

Fig. 5.4.14

5.4.9 A single concentrated load W travels on a simply supported bridge. For what locations x of the load is the shear, respectively, maximum and minimum? What are the maximum and minimum values of the shear?

5.4.10 The three beams of Fig. 5.4.15a, b and c carry the same total load $w_0 l/2$. Which beam develops the greatest shear? Which the smallest?

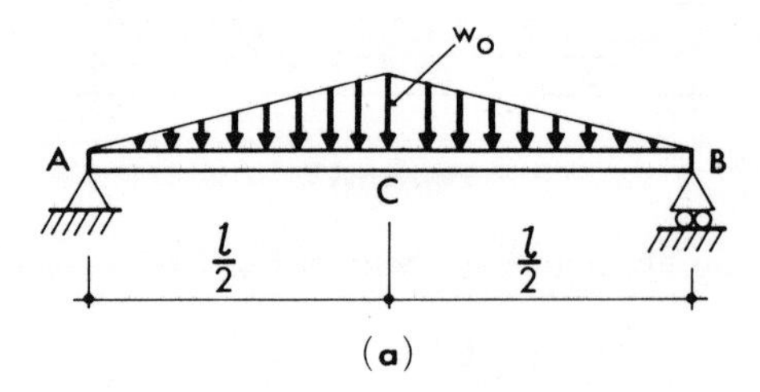

(a)

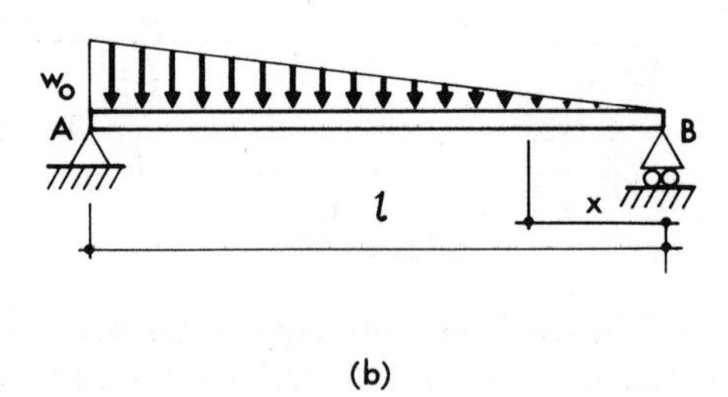

(b)

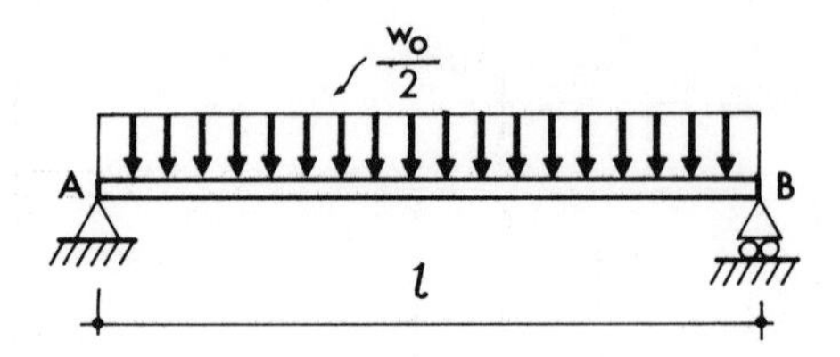

(c)

Fig. 5.4.15

5.4.11 At what section (i.e., for what value of x/l) does the shear in the beam of Fig. 5.4.16 become zero?

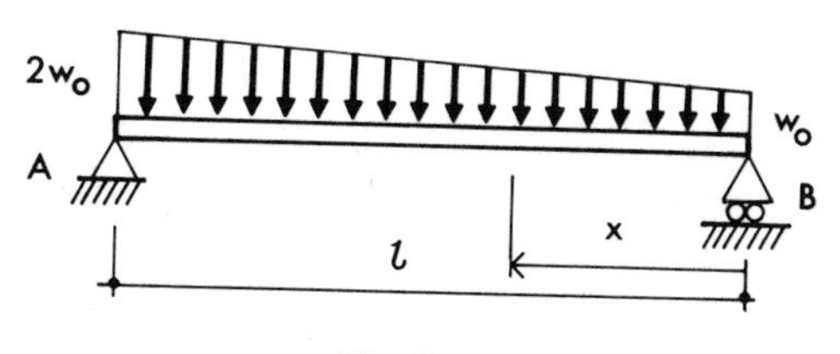

Fig. 5.4.16

5.4.12 At what section or sections of the beams of Fig. 5.4.17a, b, c and d does the shear become zero?

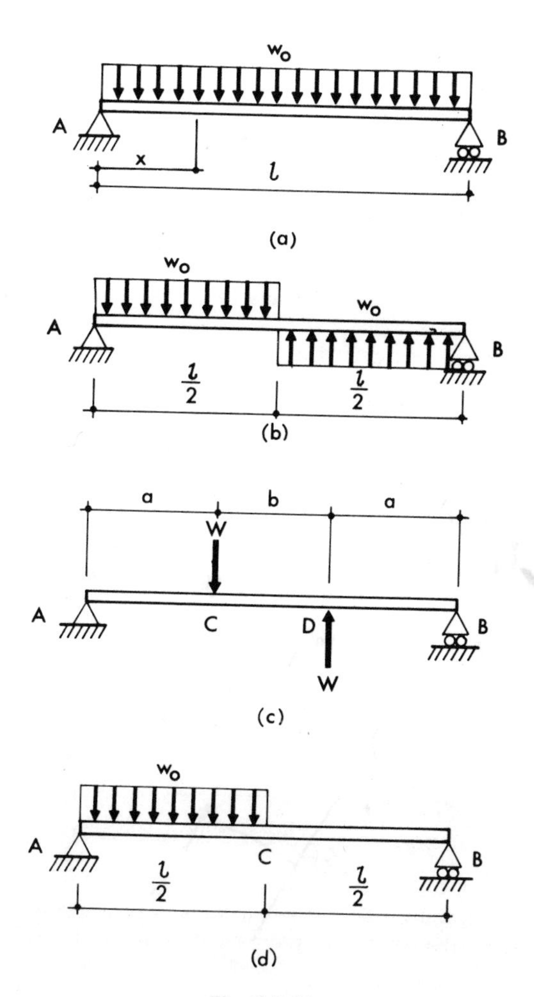

Fig. 5.4.17

5.4.13 For what value of a does the shear become zero at the section $x = l/3$ in the beam of Fig. 5.4.18?

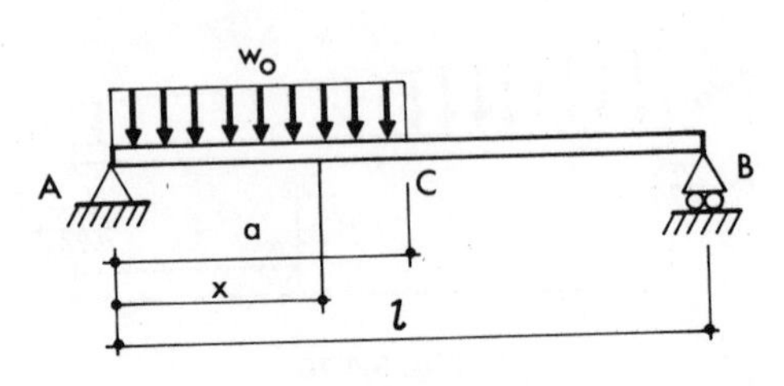

Fig. 5.4.18

5.4.14 Draw the shear and axial force diagrams of the beam of Fig. 5.4.19.

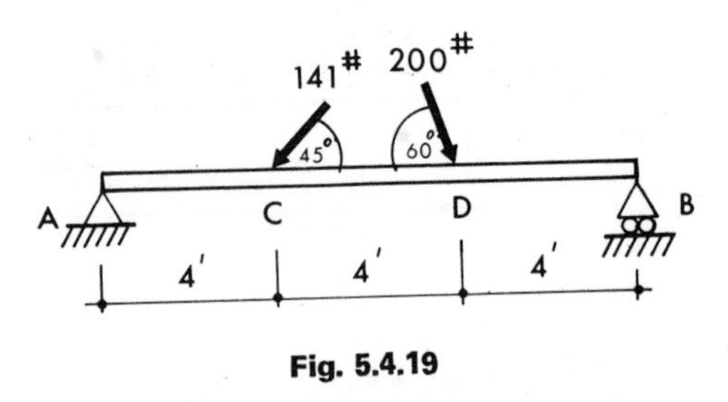

Fig. 5.4.19

5.4.15 Draw the shear and axial force diagrams of the inclined beam of Fig. 5.4.20.

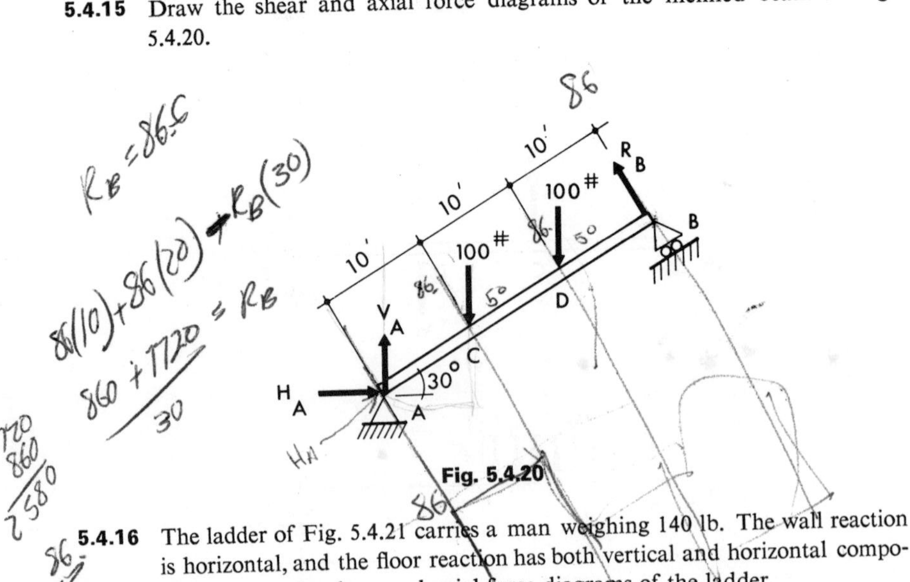

Fig. 5.4.20

5.4.16 The ladder of Fig. 5.4.21 carries a man weighing 140 lb. The wall reaction is horizontal, and the floor reaction has both vertical and horizontal components. Draw the shear and axial force diagrams of the ladder.

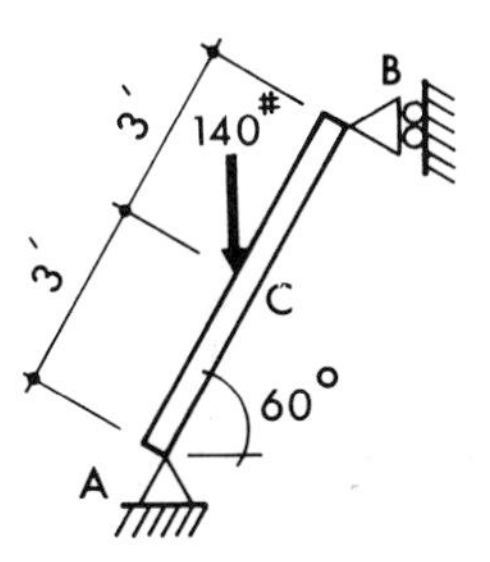

Fig. 5.4.21

5.5 Bending Moments

It was parenthetically noticed in the derivation of the shear diagram for the beam of Fig. 5.4.1 that under the action of the loads and the internal shears, the free bodies AC and DB were not in rotational equilibrium and that *internal moments* were required to guarantee such equilibrium. These moments M_C and M_D are called *bending moments* and are shown acting on sections C and D of the free bodies of the beam under consideration, which appears again in Fig. 5.5.1. Calling x the distance of D from B (Fig. 5.5.1b), a rotational equilibrium equation about D gives:

$$\frac{W}{3}x - M_D = 0 \quad \therefore \quad M_D = \frac{W}{3}x.$$

Similarly, calling x' the distance of C from A and taking moments about C, we obtain:

$$M_C - \frac{2W}{3}x' = 0 \quad \therefore \quad M_C = \frac{2W}{3}x'.$$

The bending moments M_C and M_D vary linearly from zero at the hinged ends to a maximum value under the load:

$$M_E = \left(\frac{2W}{3}\right)\frac{l}{3} = \left(\frac{W}{3}\right)\frac{2l}{3} = \frac{2}{9}Wl.$$

We shall call moments positive if they act counterclockwise on the face of a section facing right or clockwise on the face of a section facing left.* The moments in Fig. 5.5.1 are positive. Figure 5.5.1c gives the *bending moment diagram* of the beam, the knowledge of which is essential in beam design (see Section 5.8), and which is seen to vary linearly between concentrated loads.

*We shall investigate in Section 5.8 how such moments are developed inside the beam and find that *positive moments develop tension in the lower fibers of the beam and compression in its upper fibers.*

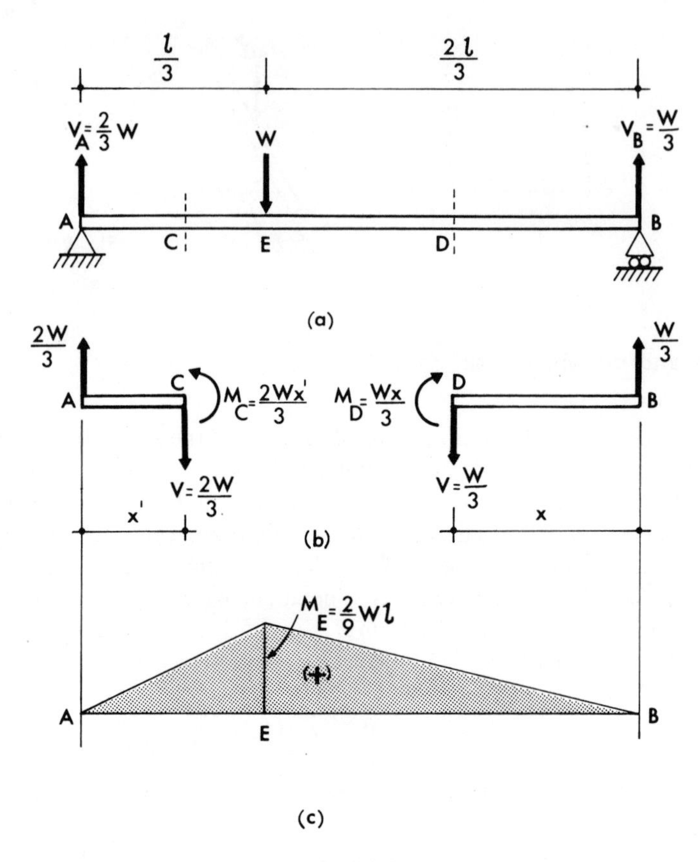

Fig. 5.5.1

It is seen from Fig. 5.5.1c that the *bending moment at a beam section is the moment about that section of all the forces* (*including the reactions*) *applied to the beam between one of its ends* (*either of them*) *and the section considered.*

Let us now derive by means of this definition the bending moment diagrams for the beams whose shear diagrams were derived in Section 5.4.*

*The numbers of the figures in Sections 5.4 and 5.5 are the same for the same beam.

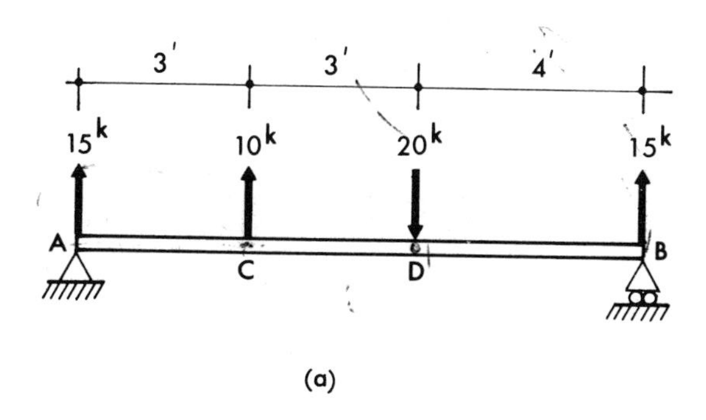

(a)

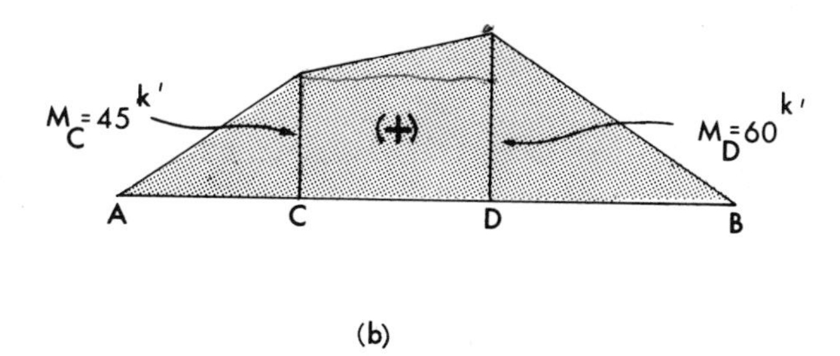

(b)

Fig. 5.5.2

Starting from B in Fig. 5.5.2, the bending moments at D and C are:

$$M_D = +15 \times 4 = +60 \text{ k ft},$$
$$M_C = +15 \times 7 - 20 \times 3 = +45 \text{ k ft},$$

which checks with the value of the same moment starting from A:

$$M_C = +15 \times 3 = +45 \text{ k ft}.$$

The moment varies linearly in between loads, and it is zero at the hinges A and B.

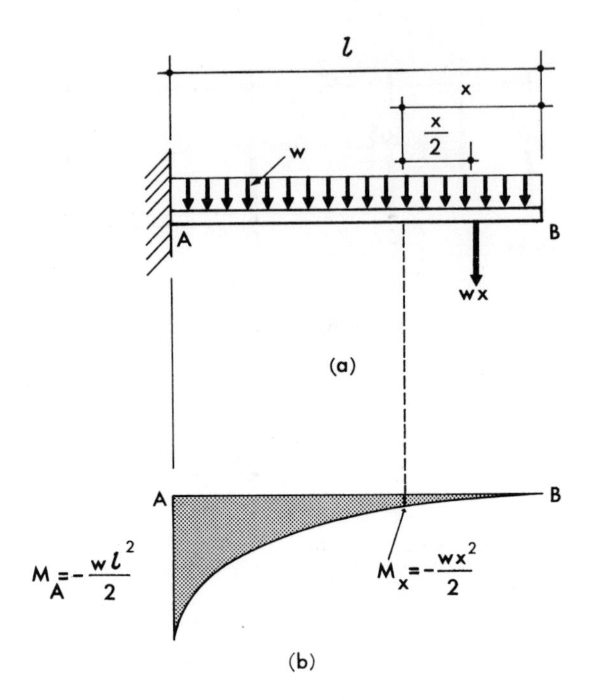

Fig. 5.5.3

In Fig. 5.5.3, the moment at a section a distance x from B is:

$$M_x = -wx\frac{x}{2} = -\frac{wx^2}{2}.$$

The moment has its largest value at A, where:

$$M_A = -\frac{wl^2}{2}.$$

It is thus seen that *the moment due to a uniform load varies parabolically*, i.e., varies with the square of the distance x.

In Fig. 5.5.4, the moments are:

$$M_D = 0, \qquad M_A = 0,$$

$$M_B = -2 \times 10 \times \frac{10}{2} = -100 \text{ k ft}$$

$$M_C = -2 \times 20 \times \frac{20}{2} + 55 \times 10 = +150 \text{ k ft}.$$

The moments vary parabolically between the concentrated loads because of the existence of the uniform load. Hence, the bending moment diagram is as shown in Fig. 5.5.4b.

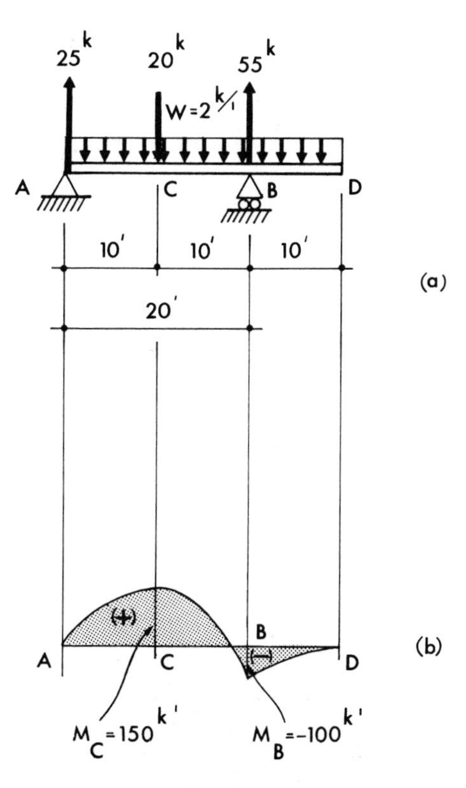

Fig. 5.5.4

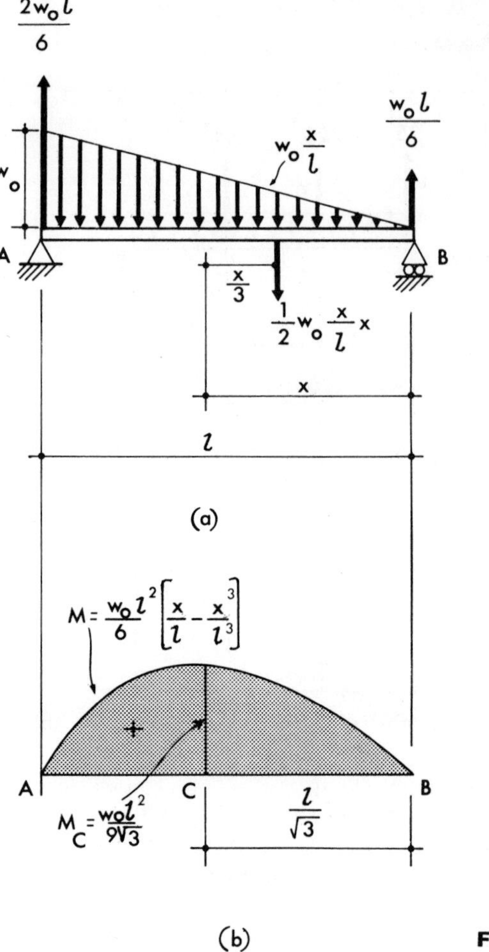

Fig. 5.5.5

In Fig. 5.5.5, the moment at a section a distance x from B is:

$$M_x = +\frac{w_0 l}{6}x - \frac{1}{2}\left(w_0 \frac{x}{l}\right)(x)\left(\frac{x}{3}\right) = \frac{w_0 l^2}{6}\left(\frac{x}{l} - \frac{x^3}{l^3}\right)$$

and is zero at $x = 0$ and $x = l$. The bending moment diagram of Fig. 5.5.5b shows that M_x is maximum at $x = l/\sqrt{3}$ or $x/l = 0.58$, where its value is:

$$M_C = +\frac{w_0 l^2}{6}\left[\frac{1}{\sqrt{3}} - \frac{1}{(\sqrt{3})^3}\right] = \frac{w_0 l^2}{6\sqrt{3}}\left(1 - \frac{1}{3}\right)$$

$$= \frac{1}{9\sqrt{3}}\, w_0 l^2 = 0.065 w_0 l^2.$$

The bending moment diagram of a linearly loaded beam is thus seen to be a cubic parabola.

Figure 5.5.6b gives the bending moment diagram of the beam of Fig. 5.5.6a, in which:

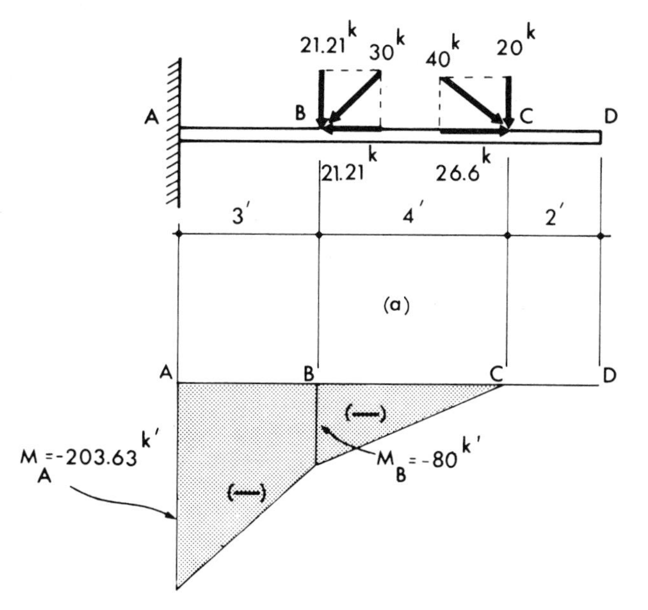

Fig. 5.5.6

$$M_D = 0, \qquad M_C = 0, \qquad M_B = -20 \times 4 = -80 \text{ k ft},$$

and:

$$M_A = -20 \times 7 - 21.21 \times 3 = -203.63 \text{ k ft},$$

and the moments vary linearly between the concentrated loads.*

An inspection of the shear and the bending moment diagrams *for the same beam* shows that an important relationship exists between them: *the bending moment diagram has its largest or smallest values at the points where the shear diagram crosses the x-axis.* In Figs. 5.4.1 and 5.5.1, this occurs at section E, in Figs. 5.4.2 and 5.5.2 at section D and in Figs. 5.4.4 and 5.5.4 at C (where M is largest) and at B (where M is smallest). In Fig. 5.4.3 the shear may be said to become zero only at A and in Fig. 5.5.3 the moment is largest at A, while in Fig. 5.4.6 the shear becomes zero at A and in Fig. 5.5.6 the moment is largest at A.

The fact that this relationship between shear and bending moment diagrams must subsist in all cases may be physically understood if we consider the beam of Fig. 5.5.7 and its shear and bending moment diagrams. The moment at a section F, computed from the support A, is given by:

$$M_F = V_A(a + b + c) - W_1(b + c) - W_2c,$$

which, rearranging terms, becomes:

$$M_F = V_Aa + (V_A - W_1)b + (V_A - W_1 - W_2)c.$$

Since the 3 terms of M_F are nothing else but the areas of the rectangles A_1, A_2, A_3 under the shear diagram, M_F is the area under the shear diagram from A to F. But the rectangular areas under the shear diagram change from positive to negative values where V crosses the x-axis (at D). Hence, the largest area under the shear diagram, i.e., the largest moment, is obtained by summing

*You will notice that the components of the forces parallel to the beam axis do not contribute to the value of the bending moments or the shears.

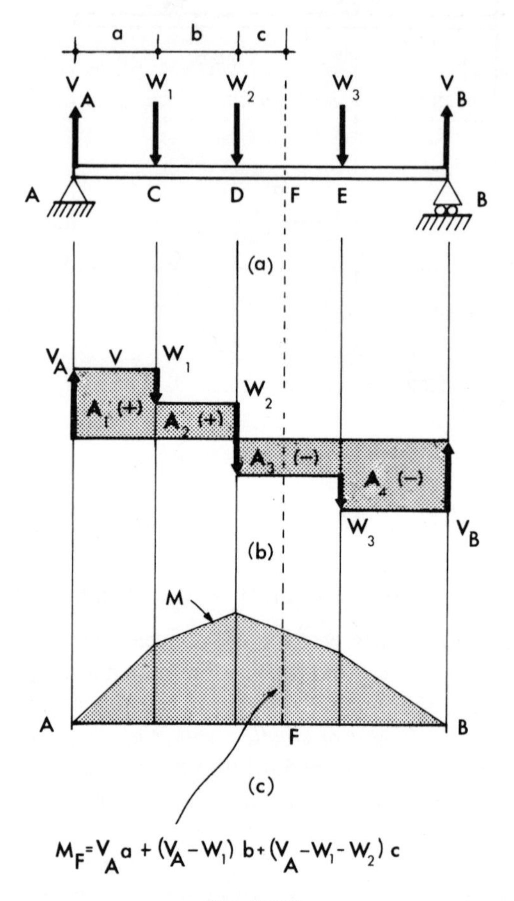

Fig. 5.5.7

all the positive rectangles and stopping when the next area would be negative, i.e., where the shear diagram crosses the x-axis from $+$ to $-$ values. Similarly, to obtain the smallest moment (i.e., the largest negative moment), we must add up all the negative shear diagram areas and stop where the next area would be positive, i.e., where the shear diagram crosses the x-axis from $-$ to $+$ values.*

*Since the ordinates of the bending moment diagram are the areas under the shear diagram from zero to x, $M(x)$ is the integral of $V(x)$ from zero to x:

$$M(x) = \int_0^x V(x)\,dx. \tag{a}$$

Hence, the maximum or minimum values of $M(x)$ occur where $dM/dx = V = 0$. Equation (a) also explains why, for a given polynomial load variation, the polynomial giving M is one degree higher than the polynomial giving V.

This result permits the location of the sections where the bending moment is largest or smallest by inspection of the shear diagram. The calculation and location of the largest and smallest moments are essential since these usually govern the beam design (see Section 5.8).

PROBLEMS

5.5.1-5.5.8 Draw the bending moment diagrams of the beams of Problems 5.4.1-5.4.8 (Figs. 5.4.7-5.4.14).

5.5.9 Which of the beams of Fig. 5.4.15a, b and c develops the largest and which the smallest maximum bending moment? Where? What are the values of these moments?

5.5.10 What is the maximum bending moment in the beam of Fig. 5.4.16? Where does it occur?

5.5.11 Locate the section, or sections, where the maximum moments occur and the value of the maximum moments for the beams of Fig. 5.4.17a, b, c and d.

5.5.12 Determine the values of the bending moment M_C at the mid-span section of the beam of Fig. 5.3.10 as the loads travel to the right over the beam. Plot the value of M_C versus x/l between $x = 0$ and $x = l + a$. (This diagram is called the *influence line* of M_C due to the given loads.)

5.5.13 Draw the bending moment diagram for the beam system of Fig. 5.3.3.

5.5.14 Draw the bending moment diagram for the beam of Fig. 5.5.8.

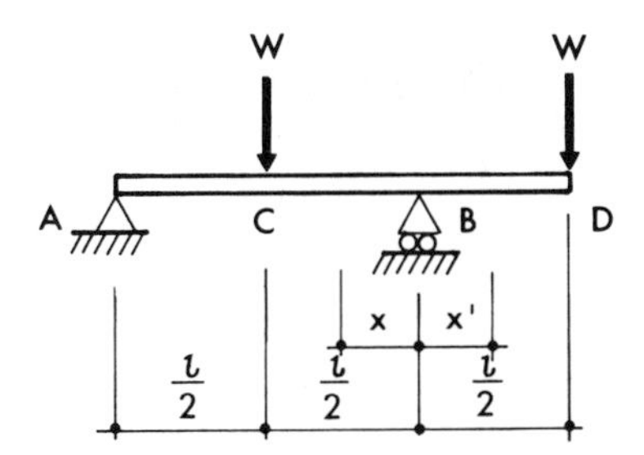

Fig. 5.5.8

5.5.15 Determine the length of the cantilevered portion a of the beam of Fig. 5.5.9, so that the moment at mid-span between A and B is of opposite sign but equal magnitude to the moment at B.

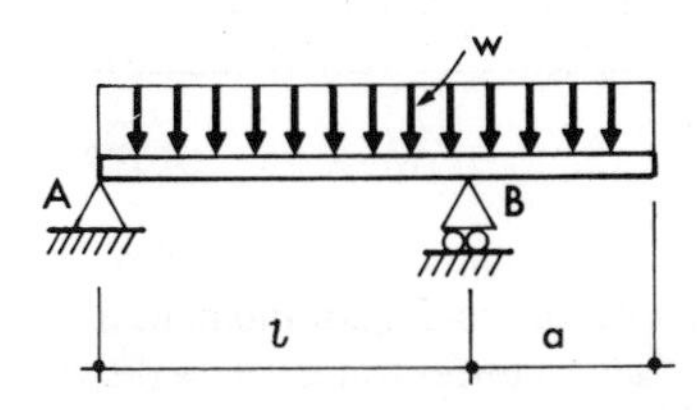

Fig. 5.5.9

5.5.16 Locate the supports under the beam of Fig. 5.5.10, i.e., choose a, so that the largest moment in the span l is equal to the negative moment at the supports, if $l + a$ is constant and equal to L.

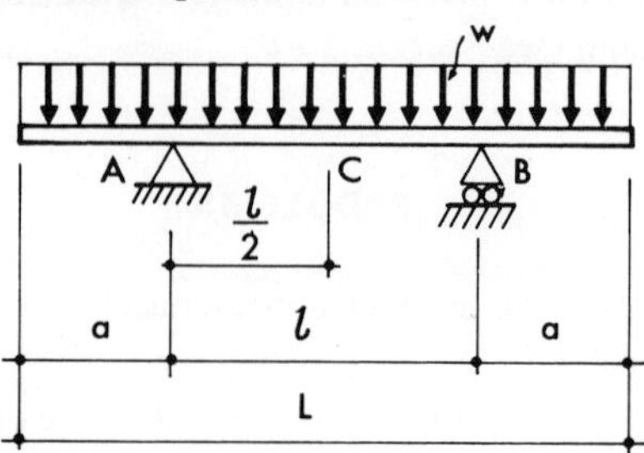

Fig. 5.5.10

5.5.17 Locate the supports under the beam of Fig. 5.5.10, i.e., determine a, so that the moment at mid-span between the supports has a magnitude equal to $-\frac{1}{2}$ that of the moments over the supports, keeping the span l constant. (It may be proved that for this value of a the sections over the supports do not rotate, so that the span AB behaves like a *fixed-end* beam.) Evaluate the moments at the supports and at mid-span.

5.5.18 Determine the cantilever length a for which the moment at C in the beam of Fig. 5.5.11a is equal to that at mid-span in the beam of Fig. 5.5.11b.

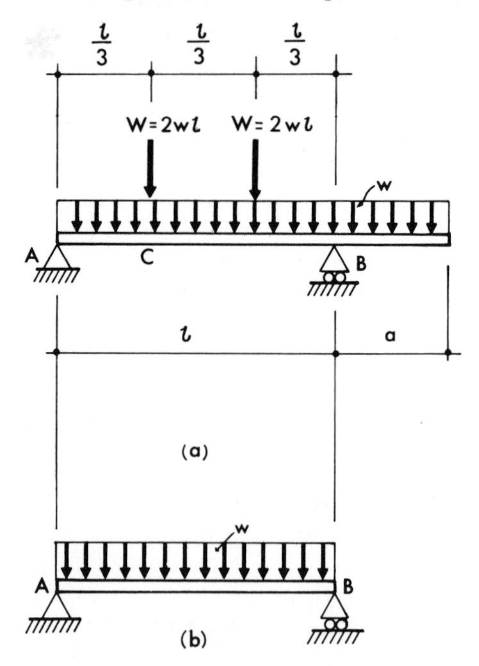

Fig. 5.5.11

5.5.19 Compare the mid-span moment $wl^2/8$ of a uniformly loaded, simply supported beam with the mid-span moment of the same beam loaded with: (a) a load $W_1 = wl/2$ concentrated at mid-span, (b) 2 loads $W_2 = wl/3$ concentrated at the third points, (c) 3 loads $W_3 = wl/4$ spaced by $l/4$ and (d) 4 loads $W_4 = wl/5$ spaced by $l/5$. What conclusion can you draw?

5.6. Bending Moment Diagrams by Graphics

The bending moment diagram of statically determinate beams may be conveniently obtained by a graphical construction which was used in Section 4.2, that of the *funicular polygon.*

Consider the simply supported beam of Fig. 5.6.1a, and draw the funicular polygon of its forces and reactions as shown in Fig. 5.6.1b and c. The pole P is chosen arbitrarily at a horizontal distance $s = 5$ in. from the force line 1–2–3. Starting at E, EG is drawn parallel to $1P$, GI to $2P$, IJ to $3P$, and $4P$ is then drawn parallel to EJ. The reactions V_A and V_B are represented by 0–1 and 3–4, where $0 \equiv 4$.*

Let us indicate by s_L the scale of lengths in Fig. 5.6.1a [say $s_L = 2$ ft/in. (1 in. = 2 ft)], and by s_F the force scale in Fig. 5.6.1b [say $s_F = 20$ k/in. (1 in. = 20 k)]. It is easy to prove that the segments $FG = m_1$ and $HI = m_2$ measure, in a certain scale, the bending moments of the beam at C and D, so

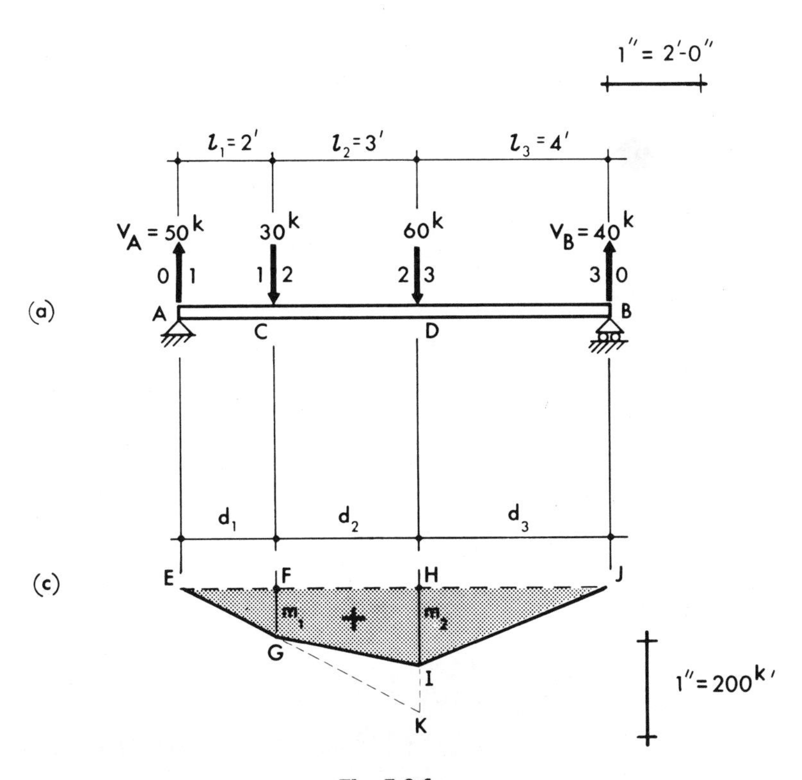

Fig. 5.6.1a–c

*In Section 4.2, P was chosen on the horizontal through 0 by first computing the reactions V_A and V_B, so that the base line EJ of the funicular polygon was horizontal. In order to avoid the previous evaluation of the reactions, one may locate P anywhere and refer the polygon to an inclined base line EJ.

that the diagram *EGIJ*, referred to the baseline *EJ*, is the bending moment diagram of the beam.

In fact, since the triangles *EFG* and *P*01, having parallel sides, are similar, their bases d_1 and s, and their vertical sides $FG = m_1$ and 01 are proportional:

$$\frac{m_1}{01} = \frac{d_1}{s},$$

from which:

$$01 = \frac{s}{d_1} m_1,$$

or, multiplying both sides by the force scale factor s_F:

$$(01) \times s_F = V_A = \frac{s}{d_1} s_F m_1.$$

The moment M_C at C equals $V_A \times l_1$, where $l_1 = d_1 \times s_L$, since l_1 is the real length *AC* and d_1 is the length *AC* on the scaled beam drawing. Hence:

$$M_C = V_A l_1 = \left(\frac{s}{d_1} s_F m_1\right)(d_1 s_L) = (s \times s_L \times s_F)\, m_1,$$

which proves that m_1 measures M_C in the scale $s \times s_L \times s_F = 5 \times 2 \times 20 =$ 200 k ft/in. In the drawing, $m_1 = 0.5$ in. and hence:

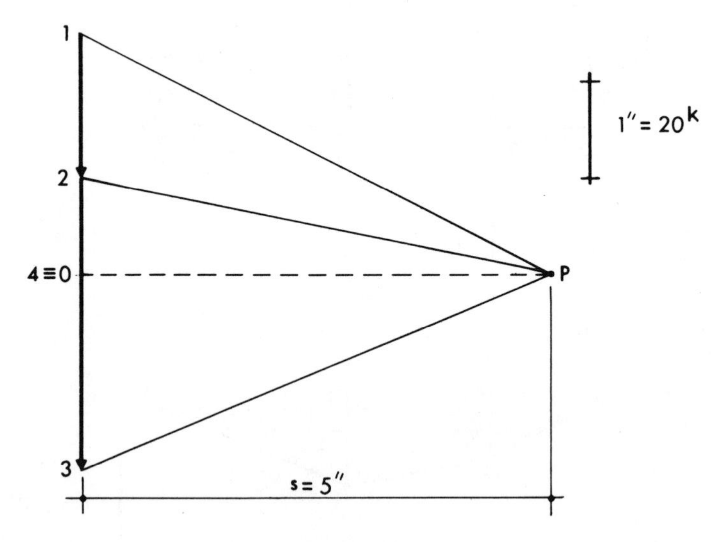

Fig. 5.6.1b

$$M_C = 0.5 \times 200 = 100 \text{ k ft}.$$

The moment M_D at D equals $V_A(l_1 + l_2) - W_1 l_2$. But *HK* measures the moment $V_A(l_1 + l_2)$ and *IK* the moment $W_1 l_2$ (since the triangle *GIK* is similar

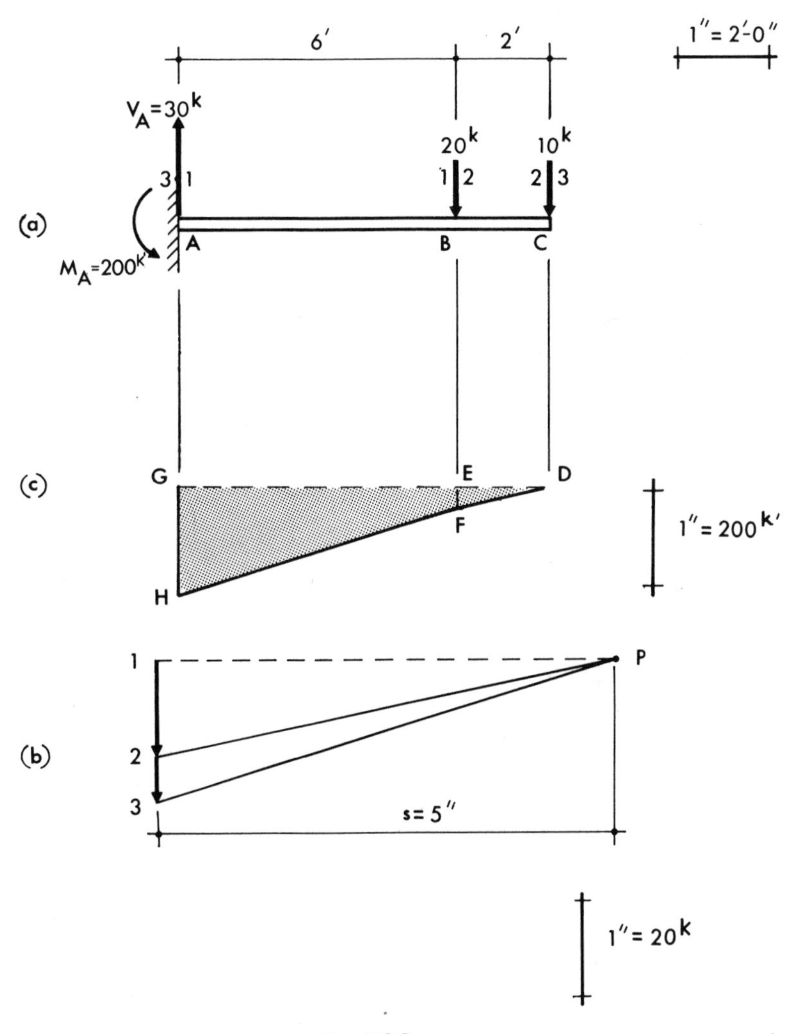

Fig. 5.6.2

to the triangle $P12$); therefore, M_D is measured by $m_2 = HK - IK = HI$. In the figure, $m_2 = 0.8$ in., so that:

$$M_D = 200 \times 0.8 = 160 \text{ k ft.}$$

Let us obtain graphically the bending moment diagram of the cantilever of Fig. 5.6.2 In this case, the point P may be taken on the horizontal through point 1, since we know that the single reaction $V_A = 30$ k is equal to the sum of all the loads. DF is drawn parallel to $P2$, FH to $P3$ and the baseline of the diagram is horizontal. EF measures M_B and GH measures M_A in the scale $s \times s_L \times s_F = 5 \times 2 \times 20 = 200$ k ft/in.

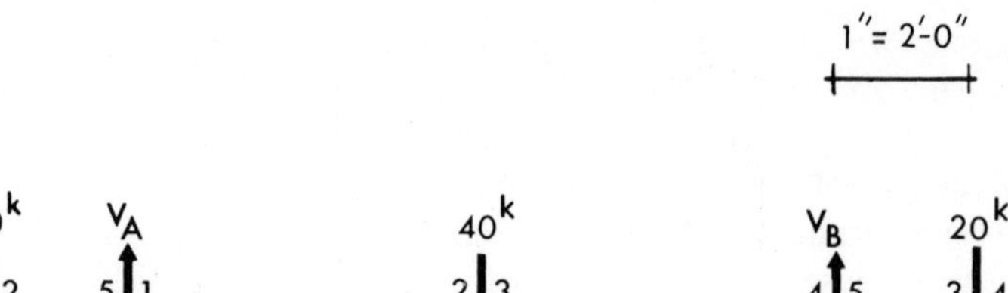
1″= 2′-0″

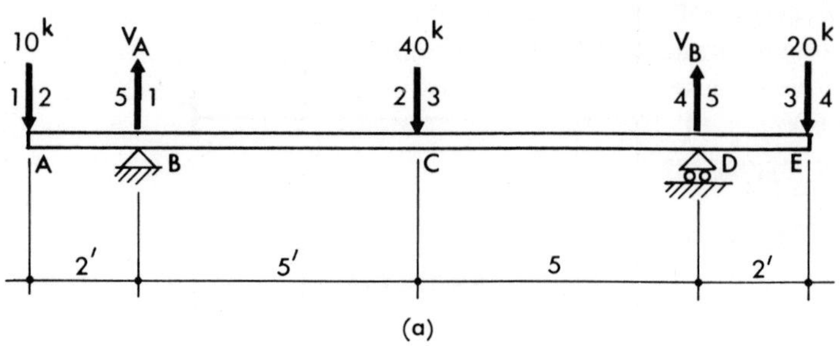
10k
VA
40k
VB
20k
1 2
5 1
2 3
4 5
3 4
A
B
C
D
E
2′
5′
5
2′
(a)

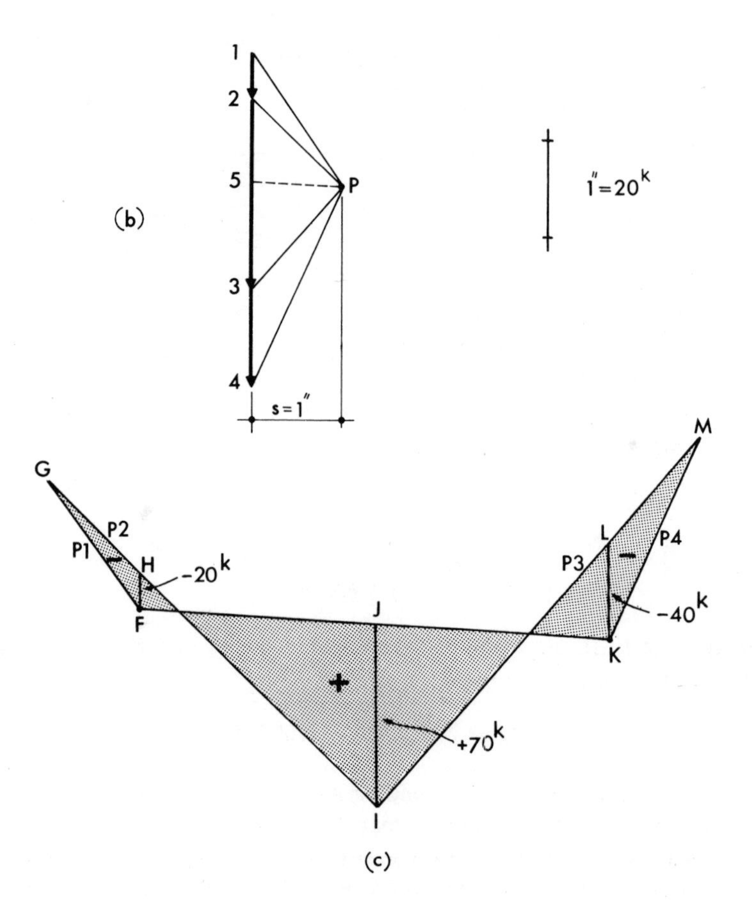
1
2
5
P
3
4
s = 1″
1″= 20k
(b)
G
P2
P1
H
−20k
F
J
+
+70k
I
M
L
P4
P3
−
−40k
K
(c)

Fig. 5.6.3

Figure 5.6.3 shows the construction of the bending moment diagram for a beam with overhangs. The scales are $s_L = 2$ ft/in., $s_F = 20$ k/in., $s = 1$ in. and $s \times s_L \times s_F = 40$ k ft/in. The diagram is started at F; FG is drawn parallel to $P1$, GI to $P2$, IM parallel to $P3$ and MK to $P4$. The base line is FK and $P5$ is drawn parallel to FK. The segment FH measures the moment at B and is negative because it is *above* the base line, as is the segment KL measuring the moment at D. The segment JI is *below* the base line and measures the positive moment at C.

PROBLEMS

5.6.1 Obtain graphically the bending moment diagram of the beam of Fig. 5.4.7 for $s = 5$ in., $s_F = 1$ k/in., $s_L = 3$ ft/in.

5.6.2 Obtain graphically the bending moment diagram of the beam of Fig. 5.4.8 for $s = 3$ in., $s_L = (l/5)$ ft/in., $s_F = (wl/5)$ k/in., substituting 4 concentrated loads for the uniform load. Compare the moment at mid-span with that obtained analytically in Problem 5.5.2.

5.6.3 Obtain graphically the bending moment diagram of the beam of Fig. 5.4.10 for $s = 3$ in., $s_F = 8$ k/in., $s_L = 3$ ft/in., substituting for the uniform load 2 concentrated loads of 10 k each, 2.5 ft and 7.5 ft from B. Compare this diagram with the diagram obtained analytically in Problem 5.5.4.

5.6.4 Obtain graphically the bending moment diagram of the beam of Fig. 5.4.12. Choose proper values for s, s_L and s_F.

5.6.5 Obtain graphically an approximation to the bending moment diagram of a uniformly loaded, simply supported beam by substituting for the uniform load 1, 2 and 3 evenly spaced, concentrated loads of intensity $wl/2$, $wl/3$ and $wl/4$.

5.6.6 Obtain graphically the bending moment diagram for the beam of Fig. 5.6.4.

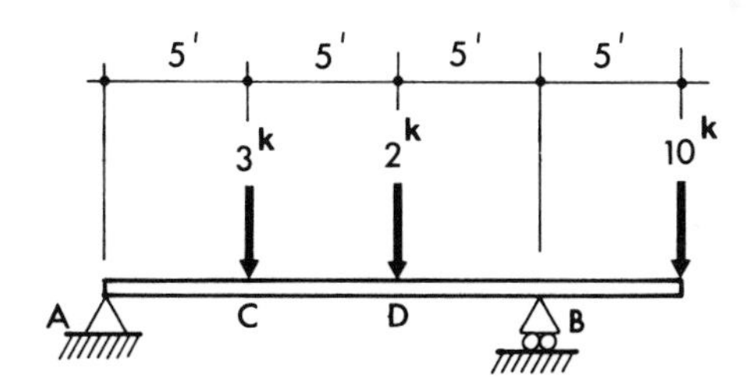

Fig. 5.6.4

5.6.7 The balcony beam of Fig. 5.6.5 must be designed for a uniform load of 0.4 k/ft and a concentrated load of 2 k at its tip. Obtain its bending moment diagram graphically by substituting 3 concentrated loads for the uniform load.

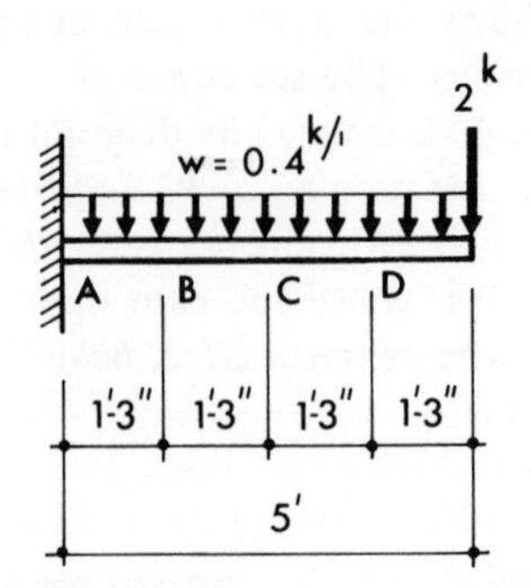

Fig. 5.6.5

5.6.8 The beam *AB* of the floor system of Fig. 5.6.6 carries joists like *CD* 3 ft on center and is one of a system of parallel beams set 20 ft apart. The total load on the floor is 200 psf. Determine graphically the bending moment diagram of the beam.

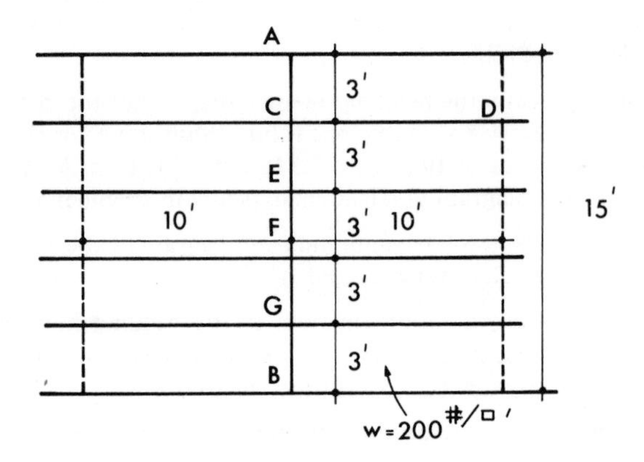

Fig. 5.6.6

5.7. Shear Stresses

We have seen in Section 5.4 that the vertical equilibrium of a free body cut out of a beam requires the development of internal shears. Just as tensile or compressive internal forces were seen to be the resultants of tensile and compressive stresses evenly distributed over the cross section of a truss bar, shears are the resultants of *shear stresses* distributed over the cross section of a beam. But there is a basic difference between tensile or compressive stresses and shear stresses: in general, shear stresses are *not* evenly distributed over the beam cross section. For the case of a rectangular cross section $b \times h$, for example, the shear stresses v are constant across the width b of the section, but vary from zero at top and bottom to a maximum at mid-height, where the shear stress $v_{\max}$ is 1.5 times the average stress:

$$v_{\max} = 1.5 v_{\text{av}} = 1.5 \frac{V}{bh}, \tag{5.7.1}$$

as shown in Fig. 5.7.1. On the other hand, in the I-section of Fig. 5.7.2, the shear is almost entirely taken by the web through practically constant shear stresses, and the shear stress is approximately:

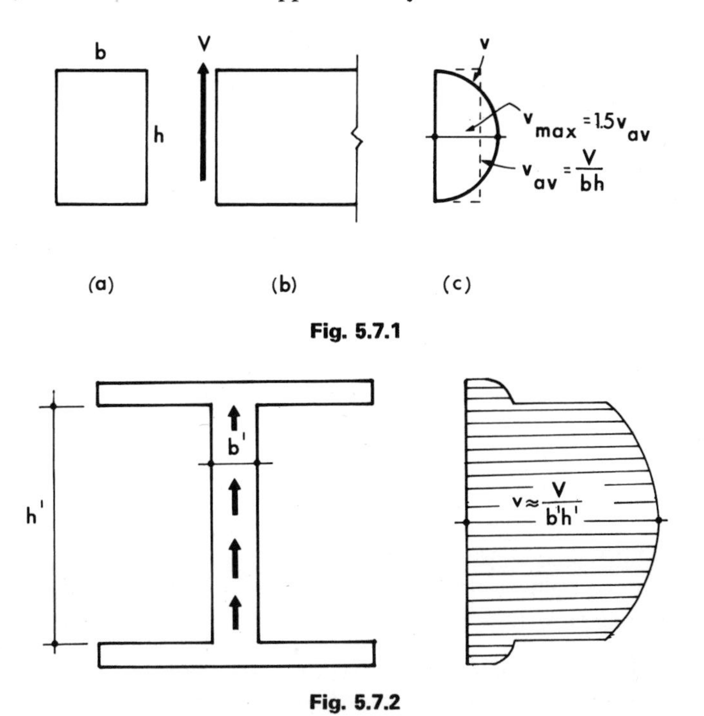

Fig. 5.7.1

Fig. 5.7.2

$$v = \frac{V}{b'h'}. \tag{5.7.2}$$

The vertical sides of a boxed beam also take most of the vertical shear by means of uniform shear stresses, while the horizontal sides contribute only in a minor way (Fig. 5.7.3). Hence, the shear stress in boxed beams is approximately given by:

$$v = \frac{V}{2b'h'}. \tag{5.7.3}$$

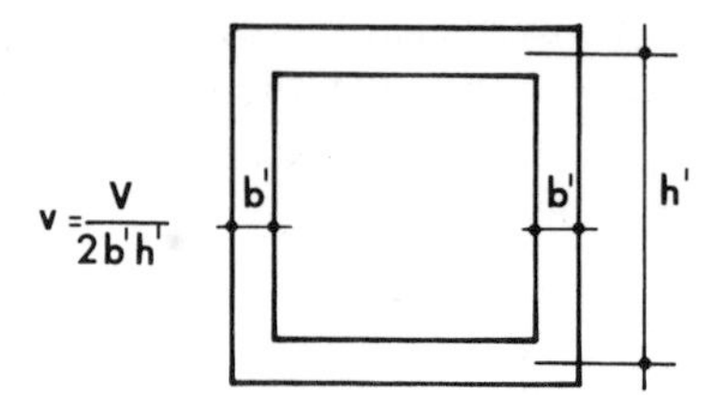

Fig. 5.7.3

The maximum shear stress in a circular bar of radius r may be proved to be:

$$v = \frac{4}{3}\left(\frac{V}{\pi r^2}\right) = \frac{4}{3}\left(\frac{V}{A}\right), \tag{5.7.4}$$

and in a circular pipe of radius r and small thickness t, it is:

$$v = \frac{V}{\pi rt} = \left(\frac{r}{t}\right)\frac{V}{A}, \tag{5.7.5}$$

where A is the area πr^2 of the full cross section.*

Another essential characteristic of the shear stresses v must be noted here. If a square element 1 in. by the side is cut out of the web (t in. thick) of an I-beam at a point where the shear stress is $+v$, the two shears acting on the vertical sides of the square are a force $v \times 1 \times t = vt$ acting down on its right side and, for vertical equilibrium, a force $v \times 1 \times t = vt$ acting up on its left side (Fig. 5.7.4a). If no shears acted on the two horizontal sides of the square element, the element would not be in rotational equilibrium because acted upon by the clockwise couple $vt \times 1$. For the element to be in rotational equilibrium, shears must also develop on the horizontal sides of the square element, which: (a) to satisfy horizontal equilibrium must be equal and opposite, and (b) to satisfy rotational equilibrium must have values vt to the left on the upper side and vt to the right on the lower side (Fig. 5.7.4a), thus creating a counterclockwise couple $vt \times 1$.

*The basic formula for shear stresses is derived in Section 5.8. Equations (5.7.1)-(5.7.5) are particular cases of this formula, equation (5.8.9).

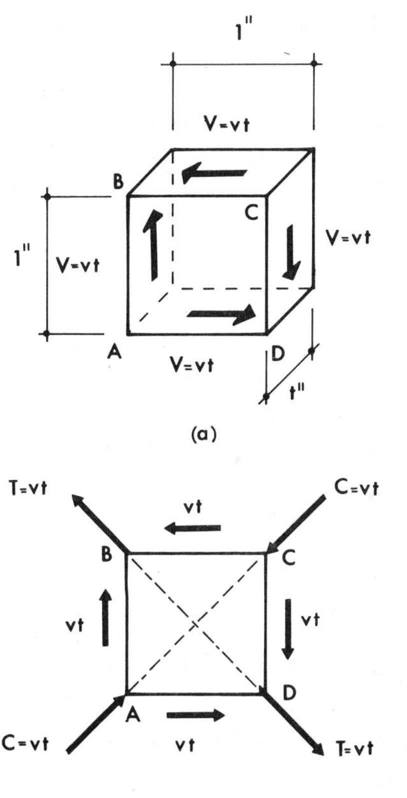

Fig. 5.7.4

This result shows that: (a) *the development of vertical shear stresses implies the development of identical horizontal shear stresses*, and (b) *shear is a state of stress equivalent to tension and compression* of magnitude equal to the shear and at 45° to it, since the resultants of the vt forces meeting at the corners of the square are forces of magnitude:

$$\sqrt{(vt)^2 + (vt)^2} = \sqrt{2}\, vt,$$

tensile at B and D and compressive at A and C (Fig. 5.7.4b), which produce on the diagonal sections AC and BD, of area $(\sqrt{1^2 + 1^2})\, t = \sqrt{2}\, t$, stresses:

$$f_t = \frac{\sqrt{2}\, vt}{\sqrt{2}\, t} = v, \qquad f_c = \frac{\sqrt{2}\, vt}{\sqrt{2}\, t} = v.$$

The shear stresses of equations (5.7.1)–(5.7.5) must be compared with the *allowable shear stress* v_{all} for the given material. For example, v_{all} may be taken equal to 14.5 ksi for structural steel, to 12 ksi for aluminum, to 75 psi for reinforced concrete without shear reinforcement and 300 psi for reinforced concrete with special shear reinforcement,* and to 100 psi for wood (taking into account the actual rather than the nominal sizes of wood sections).

It is customary to design beams on the basis of resistance to bending moments (see Section 5.8) and then to check their shear resistance, since shear usually governs design only in fairly short, i.e., deep beams.

PROBLEMS

5.7.1 Check the maximum allowable shear developed by a reinforced concrete beam 10 in. × 20 in. with and without special shear reinforcement.

5.7.2 Determine the maximum allowable shear developed by a 14WF426 beam which has a web $1\frac{7}{8}$ in. thick and $11\frac{3}{8}$ in. deep.

5.7.3 A square box beam, made out of steel and 2 ft by the side, has a constant wall thickness of 1 in. Determine its maximum allowable shear.

5.7.4 Determine the maximum allowable shear on a 2 in. × 4 in. lumber beam (actual size $1\frac{5}{8}$ in. × $3\frac{5}{8}$ in.).

5.7.5 An American Standard beam 24 × $7\frac{7}{8}$, weighing 120 lb/ft, has a web $\frac{13}{16}$ in. thick and $20\frac{1}{8}$ in. high. Determine its maximum allowable shear.

5.7.6 A steel beam is built by means of two 13 × 4 channels with webs $\frac{13}{16}$ in. thick and $10\frac{3}{8}$ in. high. Determine its maximum allowable shear.

5.7.7 Structural square tubing 12 in. × 12 in. has a wall thickness of $\frac{1}{2}$ in. Determine its maximum allowable shear.

5.7.8 Can a reinforced concrete beam 15 in. × 45 in. absorb a shear of 90 k without special shear reinforcement?

5.7.9 What is the maximum allowable shear in the beam of Problem 5.7.8 with special shear reinforcement?

5.7.10 A steel beam spans 3 ft and carries a concentrated load of 300 k. Determine the WF beam of least weight capable of carrying this load if shear governs.

5.7.11 Determine the maximum allowable shear in a steel pipe of radius $r = 4$ in. and thickness $t = 0.237$ in.

5.7.12 A concentrated load of 300 k hangs from the mid-span point of a horizontal, circular cross section steel rod 8 in. in diameter and 2 ft long. Is the rod safe in shear?

5.7.13 Determine the maximum allowable shear in a square steel rod 4 in. by the side.

*Such reinforcement absorbs essentially the tensile stress due to shear, to avoid cracking of the concrete which is weak in tension. The allowable stress in shear for concrete sections is referred to the *average* and not to the peak shear stress.

5.8 Bending Stresses

As was seen in Section 5.5, the rotational equilibrium of any portion or free body cut out of a beam requires the development of internal bending moments to equilibrate the moments of the external forces. In order to understand how these internal moments are developed, one must consider the deformation of a beam bent by loads, which is illustrated in Fig. 5.8.1a for the case of a cantilevered rectangular beam.

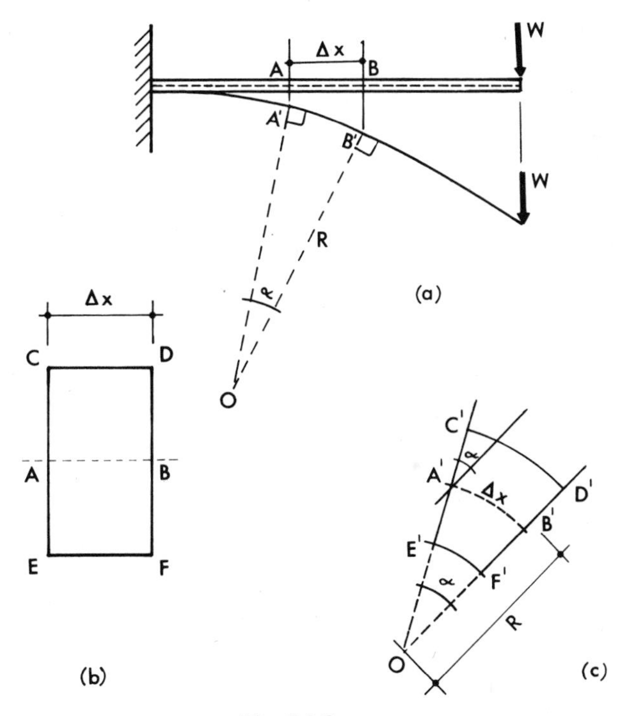

Fig. 5.8.1

As the beam bends, experiments show that: (1) a rectangular element $CDEF$ of length Δx, which is cut out of the beam (Fig. 5.8.1b), takes the wedge shape of Fig. 5.8.1c, and (2) the segment AB becomes the arc of circle $A'B'$ of radius R *and length* $A'B' = AB$, while the sides CE and DF become $C'E'$ and $D'F'$, i.e., rotate, but *remain straight*. In other words, sections which were parallel and plane before bending remain plane after bending, but do not remain parallel. This implies that the fibers above AB stretch ($C'D' > CD$) and those below AB shorten ($E'F' < EF$). The middle axis of the beam, whose

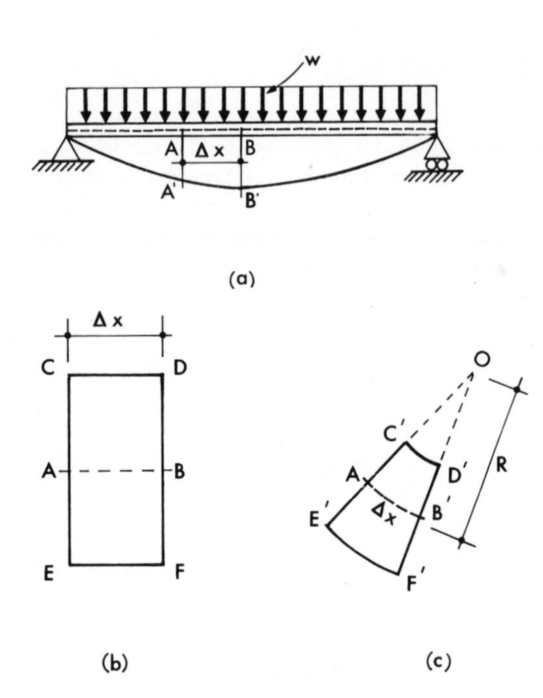

Fig. 5.8.2

length is unchanged by bending, is called its *neutral axis*. The fibers above the neutral axis stretch and are under tension, while those below the neutral axis shorten and are under compression. Hence, we find that in a bent beam like that of Fig. 5.8.1, the so-called *bending stresses*, which act on the face of its cross sections, are tensile above and compressive below the neutral axis. In the beam of Fig. 5.8.2a, b, and c, however, the lower fibers are clearly in tension and the upper fibers in compression.

Experiments also show that structural materials, when not excessively stressed, behave in a *linearly elastic* fashion. In the case of beams, this means that the *elongation of a beam fiber is proportional to its stress*. Since plane sections remain plane (i.e., fiber elongations vary linearly along the beam depth) and the middle axis of the beam is the neutral axis, the bending stresses on the cross sections of a beam made out of a linearly elastic material are zero at the neutral axis and vary *linearly* from a maximum tensile stress f_b to a maximum compressive stress $-f_b$ at the extreme fibers (Fig. 5.8.3).

Once the bending stress distribution across the depth of the beam sections is thus established experimentally, it is easy to evaluate the *internal bending moment*, i.e., the moment of the bending stresses. Indicating by b the width of the section and noticing that bending stresses are constant across its width, we see in Fig. 5.8.4a that the resultant F_t of the tensile triangular stress dia-

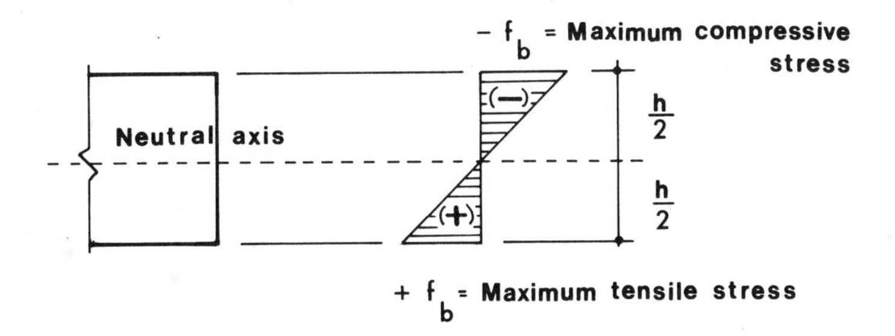

Fig. 5.8.3

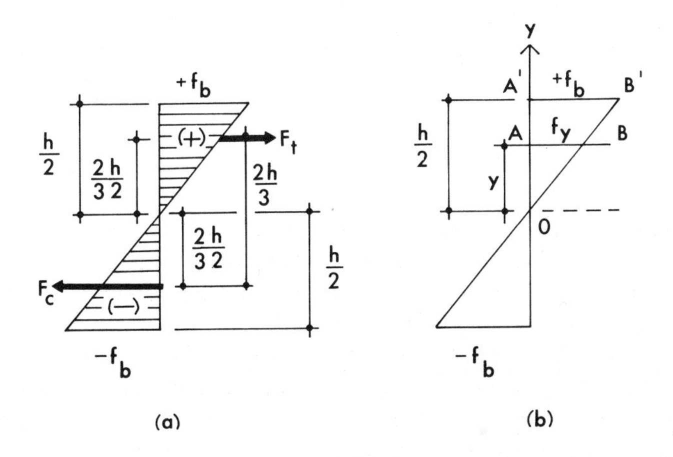

Fig. 5.8.4

gram above the neutral axis 0 and the resultant F_c of the compressive stress diagram below the neutral axis are given by:

$$F_t = F_c = \frac{1}{2} b\left(\frac{h}{2}\right) f_b \equiv F$$

and are located at a distance $(2/3)(h/2)$ from 0 (see Section 2.4). Hence, the bending stresses are equivalent to a couple with forces of magnitude F and lever arm $(2/3)(h/2) + (2/3)(h/2) = (2/3)\,h$, i.e., of moment:

$$M_b = \tfrac{2}{3} Fh = \tfrac{2}{3}(\tfrac{1}{4} f_b bh) = \tfrac{1}{6} bh^2 f_b.$$

Equating M_b to the bending moment M of the external forces at a given section, taken from the bending moment diagram, we obtain the extreme fiber stress at that section:

$$f_b = \frac{M}{bh^2/6}. \qquad (5.8.1)$$

The fiber stress f_y at a distance y from the neutral axis (Fig. 5.8.4b) is obtained from the consideration of the similar triangles $0AB$ and $0A'B'$:

$$\frac{f_y}{f_b} = \frac{y}{h/2} \quad \therefore \quad f_y = f_b \frac{y}{h/2} = \frac{My}{bh^3/12}. \qquad (5.8.2)$$

It is seen from (5.8.2) that f_y is proportional to M and to y and is inversely proportional to the quantity:

$$I = \tfrac{1}{12}bh^3, \qquad (5.8.3)$$

called the *moment of inertia of the rectangular cross section*, by means of which:

$$f_y = \frac{My}{I}. \qquad (5.8.4)$$

The moment of inertia of a cross section depends on its shape (see Appendix A.2). Handbooks with tables of rolled steel sections give the moments of inertia I_x and I_y about the two neutral axes x and y corresponding to the two orientations of the section shown in Fig. 5.8.5.

It may be noticed from equation (5.8.4) that, if the extreme beam fibers develop a stress f_b equal to the allowable bending stress for the material, all other fibers are *understressed*: bending is a most useful, but unfortunately, not a very efficient mechanism for carrying vertical loads horizontally to the supports.

The extreme fiber stress f_b may be obtained from equation (5.8.4) for f_y by setting in it $y = h/2$:

$$f_b = \frac{M(h/2)}{I} = \frac{M}{I/(h/2)}. \qquad (5.8.5)$$

The quantity:

$$S = \frac{I}{(h/2)} = \frac{bh^3/12}{h/2} = \frac{bh^2}{6} \qquad (5.8.6)$$

is called the *section modulus* of the rectangular cross section $b \times h$. By means of the section modulus, the extreme fiber stress becomes:

$$f_b = \frac{M}{S}. \qquad (5.8.7)$$

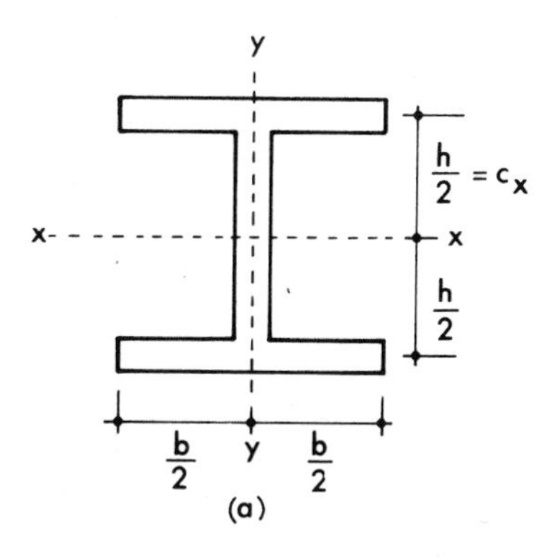

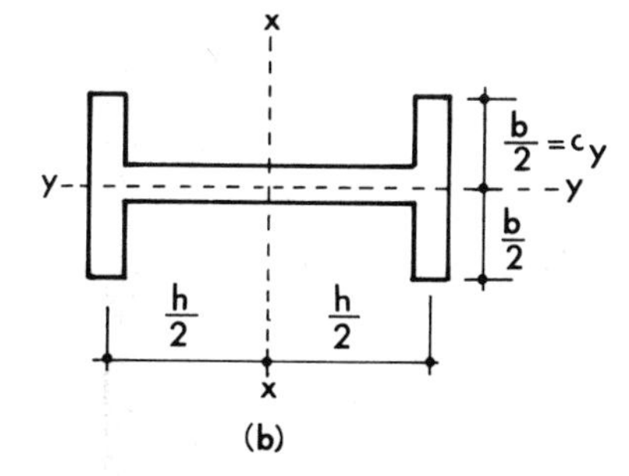

Fig. 5.8.5

This result can be generalized. Indicating by c_x and c_y the distance of the extreme fibers from the neutral axes x and y, we define the section moduli for the orientations of the section in Fig. 5.8.5 as:

$$S_x = \frac{I_x}{c_x}, \qquad S_y = \frac{I_y}{c_y} \tag{5.8.6a}$$

and obtain the corresponding extreme fiber stress as:

$$f_b = \frac{M}{S_x} \quad \text{or} \quad f_b = \frac{M}{S_y}. \tag{5.8.7a}$$

Values of S_x and S_y appear in tables of rolled steel sections and are given in Table A.1 of the Appendix for the most common cross-sectional shapes.

The formulas of this section allow the dimensioning of beams in bending and the checking of bending stresses (or the load capacity) in dimensioned beams, as shown by the following examples, in which the allowable bending stress for structural steel or aluminum may be taken as $F_b = 20$–24 ksi, that for wood as $F_b = 1{,}500$ psi and the allowable compressive bending stress in concrete as $F_c = 1{,}800$ psi (for 4,000 psi concrete).

The maximum bending moment in a floor steel beam is 200 k ft. We wish to determine the lightest WF section capable of developing this moment for an allowable stress $F_b = 20$ ksi. By (5.8.7):

$$S_x = \frac{M}{F_b} = \frac{200 \times 12}{20} = 120 \text{ in.}^3.$$

A 14WF78 with $S_x = 121.1$ is satisfactory, but a 21WF62 with $S_x = 126.4$ is lighter, although deeper.

By (5.8.7a), the maximum bending moment M developed by a WF beam equals $S_x F_b$. For $F_b = 24$ ksi, a 36WF300 which weighs 300 lb/ft and has an $S_x = 1105$ in.^{3}, can develop a moment:

$$M = 24 \times 1105 = 26{,}520 \text{ k in.} = 2{,}210 \text{ k ft.}$$

What is the maximum uniform live load this section can carry over a 60 ft span? Its maximum total load moment is $wl^2/8$, which, equated to the capacity moment $M = 2{,}210$ k ft, gives a total allowable w:

$$w = \frac{8M}{l^2} = \frac{8 \times 2{,}210}{60^2} = 4.61 \text{ k/ft.}$$

Subtracting from the total load the dead load of 0.3 k/ft, we obtain a maximum live load of 4.61 k/ft.

What is the maximum uniform load that can be carried by a 10 ft long 2 in. $\times$ 4 in. wood beam (a so-called 2 $\times$ 4)? A nominal 2 $\times$ 4 has:

$$b = 1\tfrac{5}{8} = 1.625 \text{ in.,} \qquad h = 3\tfrac{5}{8} = 3.625 \text{ in.}$$

With:

$$F_b = 1{,}800 \text{ psi}$$

and:

$$S_x = \frac{bh^2}{6} = \frac{(1.625)(3.625)^2}{6} = 3.56 \text{ in.}^3,$$

we obtain:

$$M = F_b S_x = 1{,}800 \times 3.56 = 6{,}408 \text{ lb in.} = 534 \text{ lb ft,}$$

and:

$$w = \frac{8 \times 534}{10^2} = 42.7 \text{ lb/ft.}$$

A simply supported steel beam spans 30 ft and carries 2 concentrated loads of 10 k at the third points. We wish to choose a WF section for this beam on the basis of its bending stresses and check its shear stresses. The beam reactions are 10 k each; its shear and bending moment diagrams appear in Fig. 5.8.6b and c. The maximum bending moment is 100 k ft = 1,200 k in., and for an $f_b = 20$ ksi, $S_x = 1{,}200/20 = 60$ in.^{3}. From the AISC manual we can choose a 10WF54 with an $S_x = 60.4$ in.^{3}. The maximum shear is 10 k. The web depth $T = 7\frac{7}{8} = 7.875$ in., its width is $\frac{3}{8}$ in. = 0.375 in., its area $7.85 \times 0.375 = 2.95$ in.^{2}. The maximum shear stress is $v = 10/2.95 = 3.39$ ksi < 14.5 ksi, the allowable shear stress.

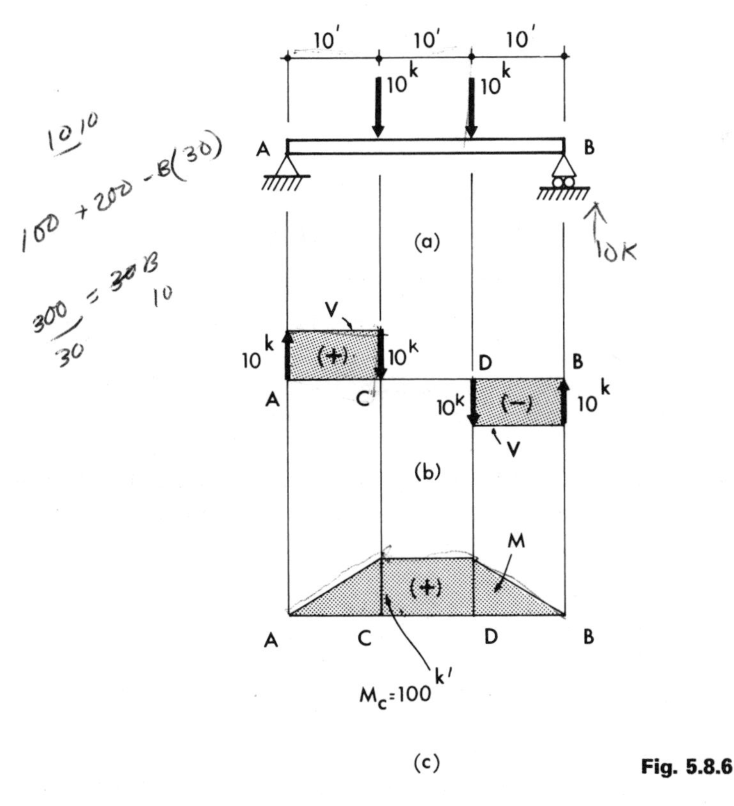

Fig. 5.8.6

We are now in a position to determine the variation of the shear stress along the depth of the rectangular section, a question we could not answer until we knew the distribution of the bending stress along the depth of the section, i.e., until we had derived equation (5.8.4). To this purpose let us consider the rectangular cross section beam of Fig. 5.8.7 and derive by statics the value v_y of the horizontal shear stress at a distance y from its neutral axis, which was seen in Section 5.7 to be equal to the vertical shear stress at the same point.

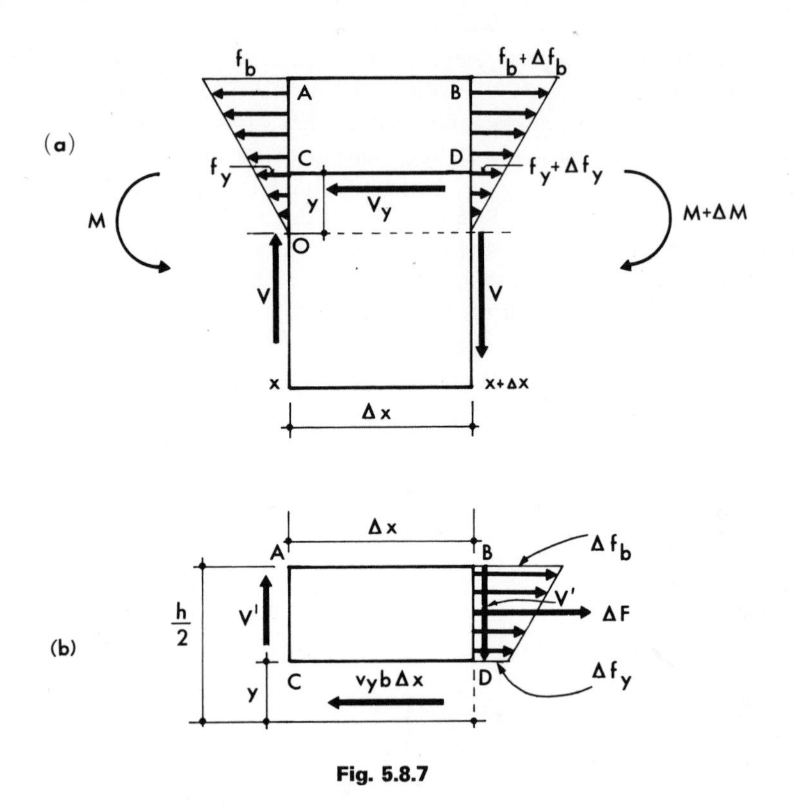

Fig. 5.8.7

If we cut from the beam an unloaded free body of length Δx at a section x (Fig. 5.8.7a), call V the equal and opposite shears on its faces, M the bending moment on its left face and $M + \Delta M$ the bending moment on its right face, we see that vertical equilibrium is satisfied and that for rotational equilibrium about 0:

$$-M - V\Delta x + M + \Delta M = 0 \quad \therefore \quad \Delta M = V\Delta x. \qquad (5.8.8)$$

Let us now cut from the free body just considered a new free body by means of a horizontal cut a distance y from the neutral axis (Fig. 5.8.7b). This new free body is acted upon by: (a) the bending stresses f_y due to M on AC; (b) the bending stresses due to $M + \Delta M$ on BD, which are the sum of the stresses f_y due to M and the stresses Δf_y due to ΔM; (c) the equal and opposite shears $V'(< V)$ on AC and BD; and (d) the resultant of the horizontal shear stresses v_y on CD, which are equal to the vertical shear stresses at C and D, as shown in Section 5.7. The horizontal bending stresses due to M on AC and to M on BD cancel, so that the resultant ΔF of the horizontal bending stress on BD is only due to ΔM. ΔF equals the area $A_y = (h/2 - y)b$ of the section DB times the average bending stress $\bar{f} = \frac{1}{2}(\Delta f_b + \Delta f_y)$, which by (5.8.4) equals

$(1/2)[\Delta M(h/2)/I + \Delta My/I]$, so that, taking into account (5.8.8):

$$\Delta F = \frac{\Delta M}{2I}\left(\frac{h}{2} + y\right) A_y = \left(\frac{V\Delta x}{I}\right)\left(\frac{1}{2}\right)\left(\frac{h}{2} + y\right) A_y.$$

For horizontal equilibrium of the free body *ABCD*:

$$\Delta F - v_y b \Delta x = 0,$$

or:

$$\left(\frac{V\Delta x}{I}\right)\left(\frac{1}{2}\right)\left(\frac{h}{2} + y\right) A_y = v_y b \Delta x,$$

from which:

$$v_y = \frac{V \times \frac{1}{2}(h/2 + y)A_y}{Ib} \tag{a}$$

Since $(1/2)(h/2 + y)$ is the distance $\bar{y}$ of the centroid of the area of the section *BD* from the neutral axis (see Appendix A.1), equation (a) is usually written as:

$$v_y = \frac{VA_y\bar{y}}{Ib}. \tag{5.8.9}$$

Equation (5.8.9) was derived for a rectangular cross section but may be shown to be valid for any cross section. For the rectangular cross section, with $I = bh^3/12$ and $A_y = (h/2 - y)b$, (5.8.9) becomes:

$$\begin{aligned} v_y &= \frac{V(h/2 - y)b \times \frac{1}{2}(h/2 + y)}{(bh^3/12)b} = \frac{1}{2}\frac{V(h^2/4 - y^2)}{bh^3/12} \\ &= \frac{6V}{bh}\left(\frac{1}{4} - \frac{y^2}{h^2}\right), \end{aligned} \tag{5.8.10}$$

and shows that v_y varies parabolically with y, is zero at $y = \pm h/2$ and equals $\frac{3}{2}(V/bh)$ at $y = 0$, where it is maximum. [This result was indicated in equation (5.7.1).]

The role of the horizontal shears is to transfer the bending stresses from one beam fiber to the adjoining fibers. If the two flanges of an I-section were not connected by the web, they would act as two separate, shallow rectangular sections $b \times t$ with a total moment of inertia $\frac{2}{12}bt^3$. Instead, the web connecting the flanges gives to the section a much larger moment of inertia. Even if we neglect the contribution of the web to the value of the moment of inertia and approximate I by the moment of inertia $Ah^2/4$ (see Appendix A.2) of a so-called *ideal I-beam* with two flanges of area A and a web of depth h and negligible width, we must not forget that without the shear capacity of the web, this moment of inertia could not be developed.

PROBLEMS

In the following problems assume all moments to be in the elastic range, the dead load of the beam to be negligible and refer to the AISC handbook for the properties of rolled steel sections.

5.8.1 Determine the lightest WF section capable of developing the following bending moments for $F_b = 22$ ksi:
(a) 100 k ft, (b) 180 k ft, (c) 300 k ft, (d) 425 k ft,
(e) 2,000 k ft.

5.8.2 Determine the maximum moment that can be developed by a 2 in. × 6 in. wood beam (actual size $1\frac{5}{8}$ in. × $5\frac{1}{2}$ in.): (a) with the 6 in. side oriented vertically, (b) with the 6 in. side oriented horizontally.

5.8.3 Determine by the tables in the AISC manual the maximum moment developed by light steel beams (B beams) of the following types for $F_b =$ 20 ksi:
(a) 16B31, (b) 12B19, (c) 6B12.

5.8.4 Determine by the tables in the AISC manual the maximum moment developed by the following American Standard beams for $F_b = 20$ ksi:
(a) 24 × 7(100 lb); (b) 12 × 5(35 lb); (c) 3 × $2\frac{3}{8}$(5.7 lb).

5.8.5 Determine the nominal depth of a wood beam 2 in. wide (actual size $1\frac{5}{8}$ in.) capable of developing a moment of 700 lb ft.

5.8.6 A wood beam must develop a moment of 2,200 lb ft but cannot be deeper than 6 in. Determine its nominal width.

5.8.7 What is the ratio between the maximum moments developed by a rectangular beam of sides b and h when the side b is horizontal and when it is vertical?

5.8.8 An I-beam with two flanges, each A sq in. in area and b in. wide, is h in. deep. What is the ratio between the maximum bending moments when b is horizontal and when b is vertical, if one neglects the moment of inertia of the web, i.e., considers the beam as an ideal I-beam?

5.8.9 A 4 in. × 4 in. wood column (actual size $3\frac{5}{8}$ in.) carries a load of 15 k. The column is not straight and bulges out by 1 in. at mid-height. What are its maximum and minimum compressive stresses? *Note:* The bending stresses due to the crookedness must be added and subtracted to the compressive stresses due to the centered load.

5.8.10 A simply supported steel rod 2 in. × 2 in. spans 20 ft. What is the maximum bending stress due to its dead load? *Note:* Steel weighs 0.3 lb/cu in.

5.8.11 A rectangular cross section beam $b \times h$ has a span l and is simply supported. What is its maximum span under dead load only if its weight per unit volume is ρ and its allowable bending stress is F_b? Determine the span for a wood beam with $\rho = 62$ lb/cu ft and $F_b = 1{,}800$ psi for $l/h = 10$ and $l/h = 20$.

5.8.12 What is the maximum span for the beams of Problem 5.8.11 when they are cantilevered?

5.8.13 What is the maximum span under dead load only of a simply supported ideal I-beam of steel with a total flange area of $2A$ and a depth h for an allowable stress F_b? How much is the span reduced if the beam is cantilevered?

5.8.14 A rectangular cross section beam $b \times h$ carries a total load w (dead plus live load) per unit length and is simply supported. The span-depth ratio l/h is limited to a value r. What is the ratio b/h if the allowable bending stress is F_b?

5.8.15 The beam of Problem 5.8.14 has given dimensions b and h. Plot the value of the uniform live load w_l that can be carried by the beam versus the span l if its dead load w_0 equals cl^2, where c is a given constant. Apply the result for $c = 0.001$ lb ft^3, $F_b = 1.8$ ksi, $b = 2$ ft and $h/l = 1/10$.

5.8.16 Derive the value of the total maximum uniform live load $w_l l$ carried by an ideal I-beam of specific weight ρ, total flange area $2A$, depth h and span l.

5.8.17 The 10 ft wood joists of a floor are 2 × 6's (actual size $1\frac{5}{8}$ in. × $5\frac{1}{2}$ in.). The floor carries a total load of 40 psf. What should the spacing c of the joists be?

5.8.18 The wood joists of a floor are 2 × 6's (actual size $1\frac{5}{8}$ in. × $5\frac{1}{2}$ in.) spanning 10 ft, 2 ft on center. What total uniform load w can they carry? If the load is increased by 50%, by how much must the span of the joists be reduced?

5.8.19 An aluminum and a steel beam are acted upon by their dead load only. Their cross sections are identical. The F_b for aluminum is the same as that for steel, but the weight of aluminum is 1/3 that of steel. What is the ratio between maximum spans for the aluminum and the steel beams? Does this ratio depend on the support conditions?

5.8.20 Two cantilevered beams of rectangular cross section carry the same total load, one uniformly distributed, the other concentrated at its tip. The beams are made of the same material and have the same depth. What percentage increase in material is needed in the beam carrying the concentrated load in comparison with the other?

5.8.21 Two beams made out of the same material carry the same total load wl, uniformly distributed over their span l, and have the same depth h. What is the ratio of their weights, if both are ideal I-beams of flange area $2A$ and $2A'$, respectively, but one is simply supported and the other is cantilevered?

5.8.22 A simply supported beam can carry a uniform load w over a span l. What concentrated load W_1 can it carry at mid-span? What equal concentrated loads W_2 at the third points?

5.8.23 A wood floor can carry a load w psf on 2 × 4's (actual size $1\frac{5}{8}$ in. × $3\frac{5}{8}$ in.), 3 ft on center. How many feet on center would 2 × 6 joists ($1\frac{5}{8}$ in. × $5\frac{1}{2}$ in.) be set to carry the same load? Which joist system requires less lumber?

5.8.24 A bridge steel truss may be considered an ideal I-beam with the upper and lower chords representing the flanges, and the diagonals and verticals representing the webs. Determine the area of the chords for a simply supported bridge truss spanning 200 ft and carrying a total load of 1 ton/ft with a depth of 20 ft at mid-span, for $F_b = 22$ ksi. Can you explain why in many trusses the height decreases towards the supports?

5.8.25 A square steel building 100 ft by the side and 200 ft high has 20 stories weighing 250 psf each. Sixty percent of the weight of the building is supported by 4 peripheral trusses resting on 4 corner columns and 40% on a central core. The peripheral trusses are 10 ft deep, i.e., one floor high. Determine the area A_1 of the chords of the trusses for $F_b = 22$ ksi. If the chords are of constant cross section, how many tons of steel would one save in the chords if the trusses were two stories high?

5.9 Reinforced Concrete Beams and Columns

In reinforced concrete design, concrete is assumed to be unable to develop tensile stresses, and, hence, to crack and be totally ineffective on the tensile side of a bent section; the compressive stresses due to bending are taken by the concrete, while the tensile stresses are totally absorbed by the reinforcing steel. Moreover, as confirmed by experiments, plane sections are assumed to remain plane (i.e., the steel and the concrete around it are stretched or shortened by the same amount, since there is no slippage between concrete and steel). It must be noticed that, depending on the composition of the concrete, the stress in the steel required to stretch or shorten it as much as the surrounding concrete is between 7 and 15 times that developed in the concrete. Hence, if we indicate by n the ratio of steel to concrete stress, which is the same as the ratio of the so-called *moduli of elasticity* E_s and E_c for steel and concrete, the stress f_s in the reinforcing steel is n times the theoretical stress $\bar{f}_c$ in the adjoining concrete, which is the stress shown by the linear stress distribution at the depth where the steel is (Fig. 5.9.1).

In order to determine the maximum compressive stress f_c in the concrete and the moment capacity of the beam, we must first locate the neutral axis of the section. Calling d the distance between the extreme compressed fiber and the steel,* let us indicate the depth of the neutral axis as a fraction kd of d (Fig. 5.9.1). Hence, the resultant C of the compressive concrete stresses is:

*A layer of concrete of depth c must be added to d in order to protect the steel from corrosion. The total depth h of the section is the sum of the *steel cover* c and the depth d.

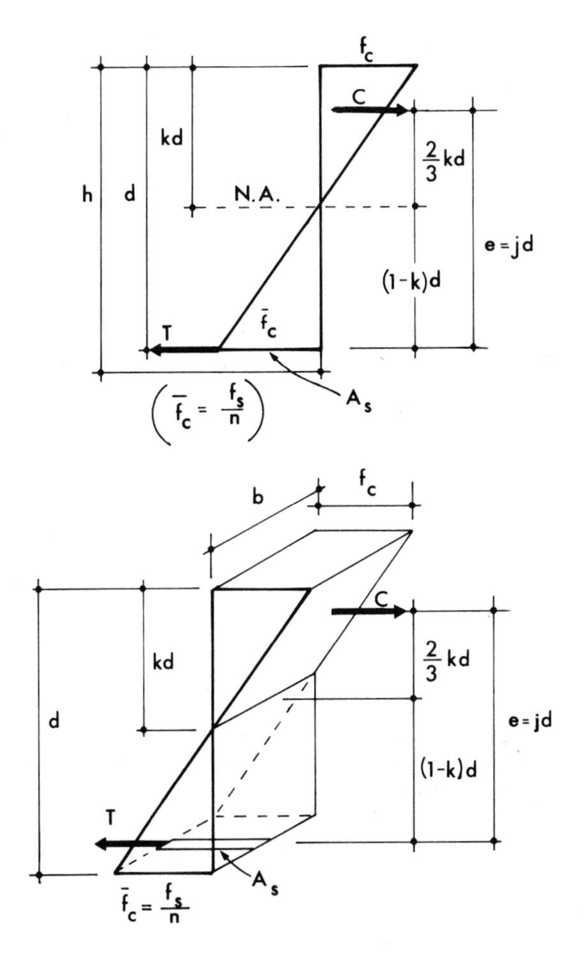

Fig. 5.9.1

$$C = \frac{1}{2}(kd)bf_c = \frac{k}{2}bdf_c. \tag{5.9.1}$$

The steel area A_s is usually expressed as a percentage $p/100$ of the cross section area bd:

$$A_s = \frac{pbd}{100}. \tag{a}$$

The linear stress distribution gives (Fig. 5.9.1):

$$\frac{\bar{f}_c}{f_c} = \frac{(1-k)d}{kd} = \frac{1-k}{k};$$

substituting:

$$\bar{f}_c = \frac{f_s}{n}$$

in this equation, we obtain:

$$\frac{f_s}{nf_c} = \frac{1-k}{k}, \tag{b}$$

from which:

$$k = \frac{1}{1 + f_s/nf_c}. \tag{5.9.2}$$

For a given d, (5.9.2) locates the neutral axis as soon as f_s and f_c are chosen. The total tensile steel force T, by (a) and (b), is:

$$T = f_s A_s = n\frac{1-k}{k}f_c \times \frac{p}{100}bd = \frac{np}{100}\frac{1-k}{k}bdf_c. \tag{c}$$

Since C and T must be a couple equilibrating the external bending moment $M, C = T$ and by (5.9.1) and (c):

$$\frac{k}{2}\,bdf_c = \frac{np}{100}\frac{1-k}{k}bdf_c, \tag{5.9.3}$$

from which:

$$p = \frac{50}{n}\frac{k^2}{1-k}. \tag{5.9.4}$$

Once the *concrete strength* f'_c is chosen, say 4,000 psi, n and $f_c(=0.45f'_c)$ are known; for a given f_s, equation (5.9.2) gives k and equation (5.9.4) gives the steel percentage p. The internal moment M_i equals Ce (Fig. 5.9.1), where the lever arm e of the couple C, T is usually expressed as a fraction jd of d, and is given by:

$$e \equiv jd = \left[(1-k) + \frac{2k}{3}\right]d = \left(1 - \frac{k}{3}\right)d, \tag{5.9.5}$$

so that:

$$M_i \equiv Ce = \left(\frac{k}{2}bdf_c\right)\left(1 - \frac{k}{3}\right)d = \left[\frac{k}{2}\left(1 - \frac{k}{3}\right)f_c\right]bd^2,$$

or:

$$M_i = Kbd^2 \qquad \text{with} \qquad K = \frac{k}{2}\left(1 - \frac{k}{3}\right)f_c. \tag{5.9.6}$$

Table 5.9.1 gives k, j, p and K in terms of f_s for $f'_c = 4{,}000$ psi, and hence for $n = 8$ and $f_c = 0.45 \times 4{,}000 = 1{,}800$ psi.

Table 5.9.1

$f'_c = 4{,}000$ psi ($n = 8$, $f_c = 1{,}800$ psi)

f_s (psi)	16,000	18,000	20,000	22,000	24,000	27,000
k	0.474	0.444	0.419	0.396	0.375	0.348
j	0.842	0.852	0.860	0.868	0.875	0.884
$p\%$	2.66	2.22	1.88	1.62	1.41	1.16
K	359	341	324	309	295	277

It will be noticed from Table 5.9.1 that the lever arm coefficient j of the internal moment is not very sensitive to f_s; hence, in preliminary design it is often assumed equal to $\frac{7}{8} = 0.875$. Table 5.9.1 also shows that the moment capacity, expressed by K, does not grow rapidly with p: while p almost doubles from 1.41 to 2.66 as f_s decreases from 24 ksi to 16 ksi, the moment capacity grows only by 22%. It is therefore usual to keep the steel percentage around 1% in preliminary design. Table 5.9.1 allows the design of rectangular, reinforced concrete sections with tensile steel only (i.e., the design of certain beams and of slabs), as shown by the following examples.*

Given a reinforced concrete beam with a rectangular cross section 10 in. × 22 in. and with 1.5% tensile steel, we want to compute its moment capacity for $f_c = 1{,}800$ psi. Interpolating at sight from Table 5.9.1 between $p = 1.41$ and $p = 1.62$, we obtain $f_s = 23{,}000$ psi and $K = 300$. Hence, with $d = h - 2 = 20$ in.:

$$M = 300 \times 10 \times (20)^2 = 12 \times 10^5 \text{ lb in.} = 100 \text{ k ft.}$$

A reinforced concrete beam 12 in. × 32 in. is required to develop a

*More complete tables, similar to Table 5.9.1, appear in the *Reinforced Concrete Design Handbook, Working Stress Method*, American Concrete Institute Publication SP-3, in which beams with tensile and compressive steel, T-section beams and columns are also considered.

moment of 300 k ft. Determine its steel percentage if $f_c = 1{,}800$ psi. From (5.9.6), with $d = 32 - 2 = 30$ in.:

$$K = \frac{M}{bd^2} = \frac{300 \times 12{,}000}{12 \times (30)^2} = 333;$$

from Table 5.9.1, $p \doteq 2\%$ and $A_s = \frac{2}{100} 12 \times 30 = 7.2$ sq in., while $f_s \doteq 19{,}000$ psi.

A beam with $d = 20$ in. and $p = 1.4\%$ must develop a moment $M =$ 100 k ft. Determine its width if $f_c = 1{,}800$ psi. From Table 5.9.1, for $p =$ 1.4% we obtain $K = 295$; by (5.9.6):

$$bd^2 = \frac{M}{K} = \frac{100 \times 12{,}000}{295} = 4{,}080$$

$$\therefore \quad b = \frac{4{,}080}{20^2} = 10.2 \text{ in.}$$

If in a reinforced concrete beam $f_c = 1{,}800$ psi and $f_s = 20{,}000$ psi, what is its steel percentage? Table 5.9.1, which is only valid for $f_c = 1{,}800$ psi, gives for $f_s = 20{,}000$, $p = 1.88\%$.

Reinforced concrete columns, which are not so slender as to buckle under compressive axial loads, are designed on the basis of the same experimental results which govern beam design. In such columns plane sections remain plane and the ratio of the compressive stress in the reinforcing steel to the compressive stress in the surrounding concrete is n, a number varying between 7 and 15 depending on the concrete strength f'_c. Hence, indicating by A_s the area of the reinforcing steel, by A_c the area of the concrete and by f_c the allowable compressive stress in the concrete, we find that the load on the column is given by:

$$P = f_c A_c + (nf_c)A_s. \tag{d}$$

Expressing A_c in terms of the area A of the column cross section and of A_s:

$$A_c = A - A_s,$$

we may write equation (d) as:

$$P = f_c[A + (n - 1)A_s], \tag{5.9.7}$$

or, representing A_s in terms of the steel percentage $p = \frac{1}{100}A_s/A$, as:

$$P = f_c A\left(1 + \frac{n-1}{100}p\right). \tag{5.9.8}$$

For example, a rectangular column 20 in. $\times$ 30 in. with 2% steel reinforcement made out of 3,000 psi concrete, with $n = 10$ and $f_c = 0.45 \times 3 = 1.35$ ksi, can carry a load:

$$P = 1.35 \times 20 \times 30\left(1 + \frac{10-1}{100} \times 2\right) = 956 \text{ k}.$$

For the same column to carry a load of 1,200 k, the steel percentage must be such that:

$$1{,}200 = 1.35 \times 20 \times 30\left(1 + \frac{9}{100}p\right) \quad \therefore \quad p = 4.33\%.$$

PROBLEMS

5.9.1 A reinforced concrete, simply supported beam spans 20 ft and carries a total uniform load of 2 k/ft. Determine its depth d for $b = 12$ in., $f_c = 1.8$ ksi and $f_s = 22$ ksi.

5.9.2 A reinforced concrete cantilever beam 10 ft long carries a total distributed load of 1 k/ft. It has 2% tensile steel. Plot d versus b for $f_c = 1{,}800$ psi and $b = 5, 6, 7$ and 8 in.

5.9.3 Determine the depth d of a fixed-end, reinforced concrete beam spanning 30 ft and carrying a live load of 3 k/ft. In order to evaluate its dead load, assume at first the beam to be 12 in. $\times$ 36 in., and determine d for $f_s = 20$ ksi and $f_c = 1.8$ ksi. Check the assumed dead load and correct it if necessary. (*Note:* The maximum fixed end moments occur at the supports and have a value $M = -wl^2/12$. See Problem 5.5.17.)

5.9.4 A simply supported beam must span 30 ft and carry a live load of 2 k/ft. First choose for this beam the lightest WF steel section with $F_b = 22$ ksi. Then design the beam in reinforced concrete for $f_c = 1{,}800$ psi, $f_s = 22{,}000$ psi and $b = 18$ in. Determine which beam is more economical if steel costs \$400/ton and concrete \$100/cu yd including reinforcing steel and form work.

5.9.5 A reinforced concrete beam cantilevers 20 ft, is 1 ft wide and carries a total uniform load of 2 k/ft. Assuming $f_c = 1{,}800$ psi and $j = 0.875$, what is the required reinforcing steel area?

5.9.6 A one-way, simply supported 5 in. slab spans 15 ft and carries a 100 psf live load. Determine its tensile reinforcement per foot width if $f_c = 1.8$ ksi. (*Note:* Consider a 1 ft width of slab as a beam with $b = 1$ ft.)

5.9.7 A slab is 12 in. deep and has a span $l = 25$ ft. It is built-in at the boundary so that its maximum moment per foot width is $-wl^2/12$, where w is the total load per square foot of slab. Determine the live load per square foot it can carry if $f_c = 1{,}800$ psi and $p = 1.16\%$.

5.9.8 A foundation beam in reinforced concrete supports a large number of 10 in. $\times$ 10 in. columns 20 ft on center, which carry 100 k each. The soil reaction is assumed to be uniform. The beam is 10 in. wide, has $p = 2\%$ and $f_c = 1{,}800$ psi. Determine its depth h, inclusive of a steel cover of 2 in., and the steel area at the sections under the columns. (*Note:* Because of symmetry the 20 ft beam spans are built-in and their maximum moments $-wl^2/12$ occur at their ends.)

5.9.9 Determine the diameter of a circular concrete column with 2% steel reinforcement capable of supporting an axial load of 500 k if $f'_c = 3{,}000$ psi.

5.9.10 A rectangular column of 3,000 psi concrete ($n = 10$) with sides b and $2b$ has 3% steel reinforcement and must support an axial load of 1,500 k. Determine its dimensions and the steel area.

5.9.11 A 24 in. $\times$ 36 in. column of 4,000 psi concrete must carry an axial load of 2,000 k. Determine its steel area if $f_c = 1.8$ ksi and, hence, $n = 8$.

Chapter Six

6.1 Arch Action

In the preceding chapters we have considered two basic structures which transfer vertical loads horizontally to the supports: trusses, whose bars develop essentially axial (tensile and compressive) stresses uniformly distributed across the bar cross section; and beams that carry loads by means of bending stresses linearly distributed across the beam cross section.

Arches carry loads to the supports by a combination of axial and bending stresses, but are so shaped as to develop a relatively minor amount of bending. Just as cables develop inward thrusts through their sag, arches, through their *rise*, develop *outward thrusts*, which are resisted in compression by the abutments (Fig. 6.1.1a) or in tension by a tie-rod (Fig. 6.1.1b). The development of thrusts at the arch supports and of a combination of axial and bending stresses in its sections is typical of *arch action.*

Figure 6.1.2a shows the total stresses developed at an arch section by compression and bending. If $f_b < f_c$, as it should be in a well designed arch, the outer and inner extreme fiber stresses f', f'', although different, are both compressive. Hence, arches can usually be built of materials weak in tension, like

Arches

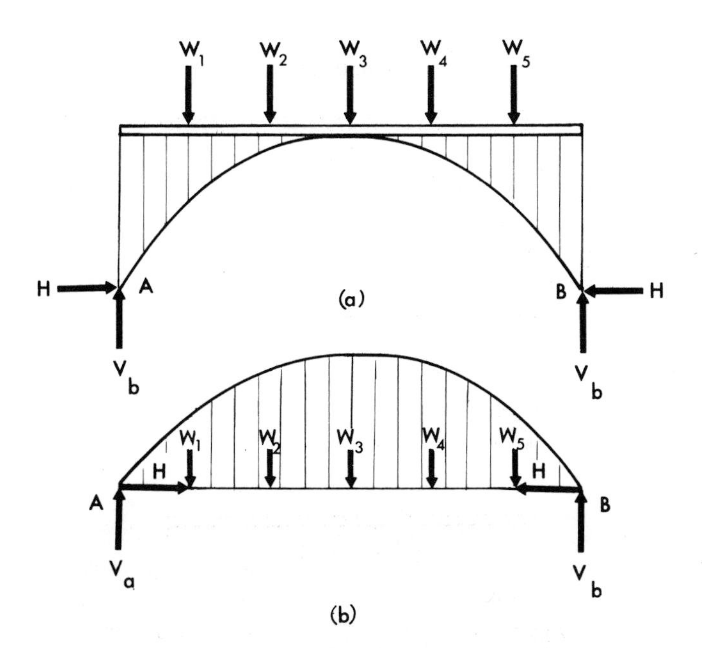

Fig. 6.1.1

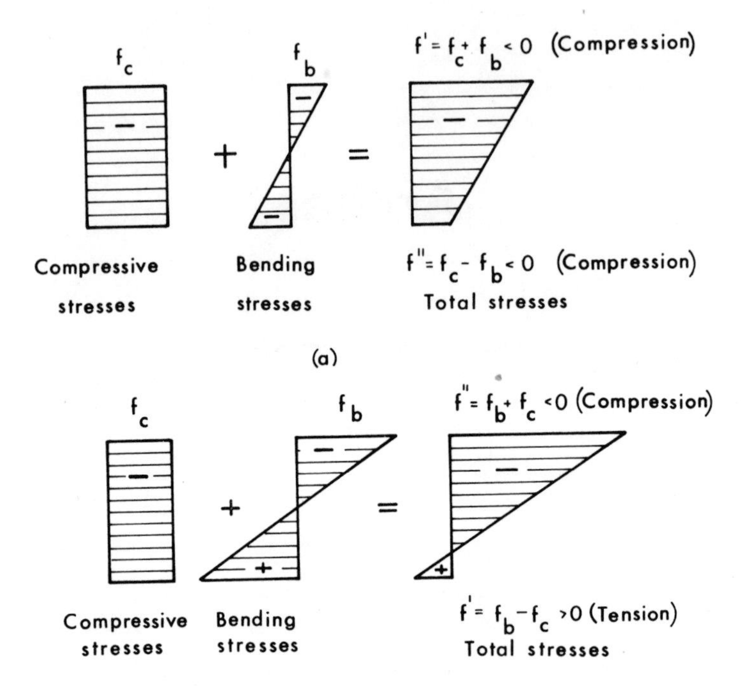

(b)

Fig. 6.1.2

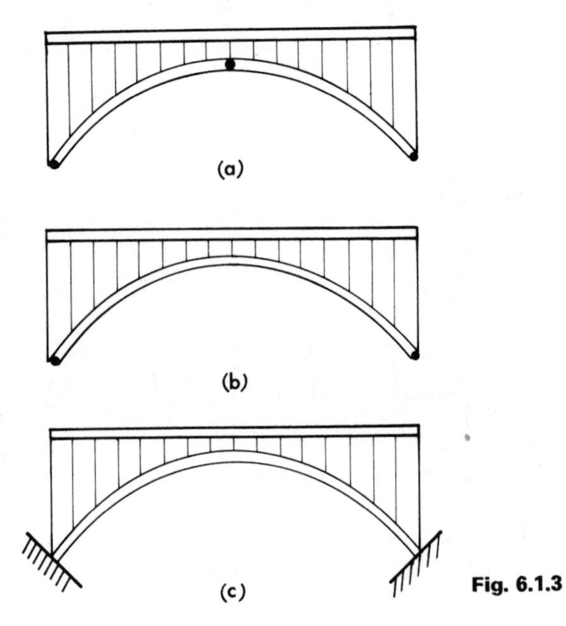

Fig. 6.1.3

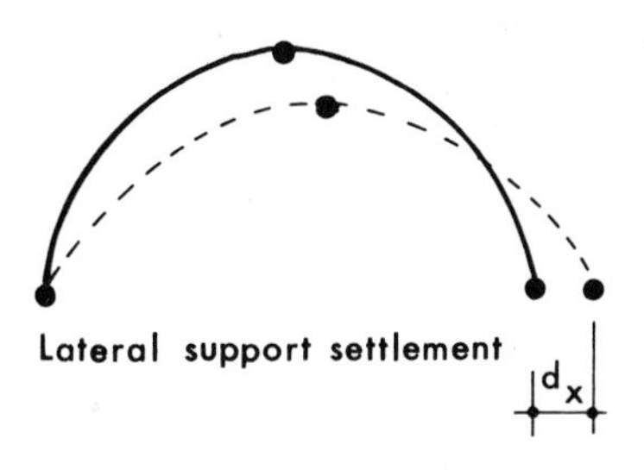

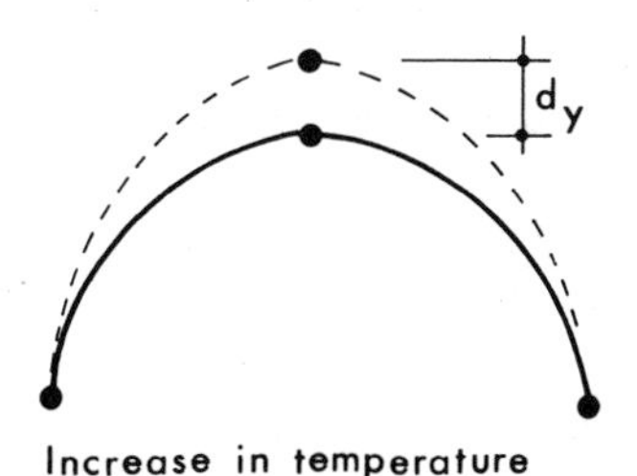

Fig. 6.1.4

masonry or concrete, even though they develop some bending. Of course, if, for certain loads, $f_b > f_c$, then the arch develops tensile stresses (Fig. 6.1.2b) and must be properly reinforced whenever its material is incapable of developing tension.

Since an arch carries loads mostly by compression and bending, its analysis requires the determination at each of its sections of the axial compressive force N (as in the analysis of truss bars), as well as of the bending moment M and the shear V (as in the analysis of beams). We shall see that N, M and V can be determined by statics in so-called *3-hinge arches*, i.e., arches supported on 2 *fixed* hinges and with a third hinge, usually at their crown section (Fig. 6.1.3a). Arches with only 2 support hinges and arches with fixed supports (Fig. 6.1.3b, c) are, instead, statically indeterminate. Three-hinge arches, like all determinate structures, are insensitive to support settlements and temperature variations, since they can deform freely under such conditions without becoming stressed (Fig. 6.1.4).

Unless otherwise stated, only *symmetrically shaped*, 3-hinge arches will be considered at first in the following sections.

6.2 Three-Hinge Arches

Let us first determine the maximum values of N, M and V at the sections of a *symmetrical* 3-hinge arch of span l and rise f, loaded by a single load W at a horizontal distance a from the right support B and a distance $b = l - a$ from the left support A (Fig. 6.2.1a).

The vertical reactions V_a and V_b are evaluated by taking moments about B and A, respectively:

$$-V_a l + Wa = 0, \qquad V_b l - Wb = 0;$$
$$\therefore \quad V_a = \frac{a}{l} W, \qquad V_b = \frac{b}{l} W. \tag{6.2.1}$$

Equations (6.2.1) show that the vertical arch reactions are identical with those of a simply supported beam of span l identically loaded.

To determine the thrust H, we consider the loaded right half of the arch as a free body (Fig. 6.2.1b) and apply to the hinge C at the crown the compression N_C and the shear V_C needed to maintain the free body in vertical and rotational equilibrium. (No moment M_C is added at C since a hinged section is free to rotate and cannot develop a moment.) For vertical equilibrium:

$$V_C - W + \frac{b}{l} W = 0 \quad \therefore \quad V_C = W\left(1 - \frac{b}{l}\right) = \frac{a}{l} W = V_a.$$

The shear V_C is seen to be identical with that in the simply supported beam of

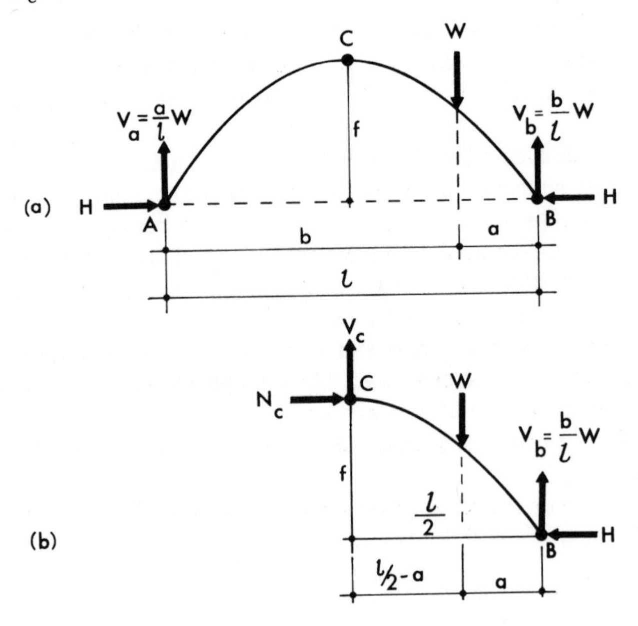

Fig. 6.2.1a–b

span l. For rotational equilibrium of the free body about C:

$$-Hf + V_b\frac{l}{2} - W\left(\frac{l}{2} - a\right) = 0,$$

$$\therefore \quad Hf = V_b\frac{l}{2} - W\left(\frac{l}{2} - a\right).$$

Noticing that $V_b(l/2) - W(l/2 - a)$ is the mid-span bending moment $M_{b,C}$ in the simply supported beam of span l, we see that the last equation may be written as:

$$H = \frac{M_{b,C}}{f}. \tag{6.2.2}$$

Equation (6.2.2) shows that the thrust is proportional to the mid-span beam moment and inversely proportional to the rise. Finally, by horizontal equilibrium:

$$N_C = H. \tag{6.2.3}$$

It is seen from (6.2.2) and (6.2.3) that the arch resists the mid-span beam moment $M_{b,C}$ as if it were an ideal I-section of depth f developing a compressive force $N_C = H$ in its upper flange, represented by the arch section, and developing a tensile force H in its lower flange, represented by the tie-rod, or an opposite compressive force in the abutments. Since $N_C = H$, $V_C = V_a$ and $Hf = M_{b,C} = V_a(l/2)$, the free body sketch of the unloaded half of the arch (Fig. 6.2.1c) shows, as a check, that this free body is also in equilibrium.

Once V_a, V_b and H are known, the maximum compressive force N in the arch is given by the larger of the two reactions R_a, R_b (in this example R_B):

$$N_{\max} = R_b = \sqrt{V_b^2 + H^2} \tag{6.2.4}$$

or:

$$N_{\max} = R_a = \sqrt{V_a^2 + H^2}, \tag{6.2.4'}$$

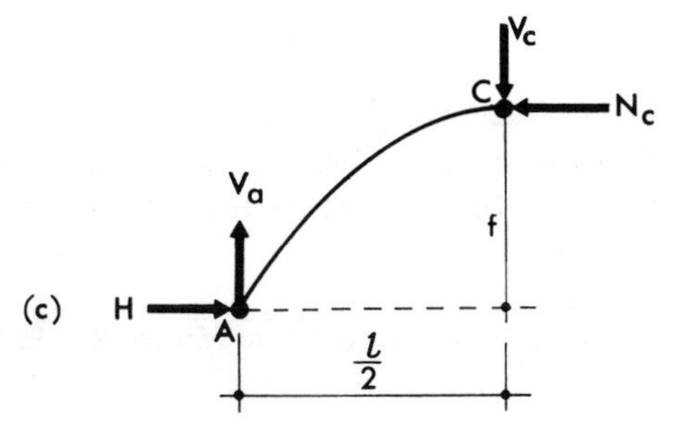

Fig. 6.2.1c

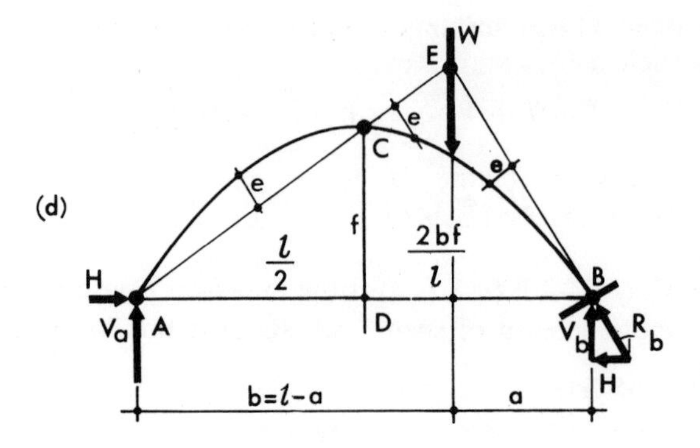

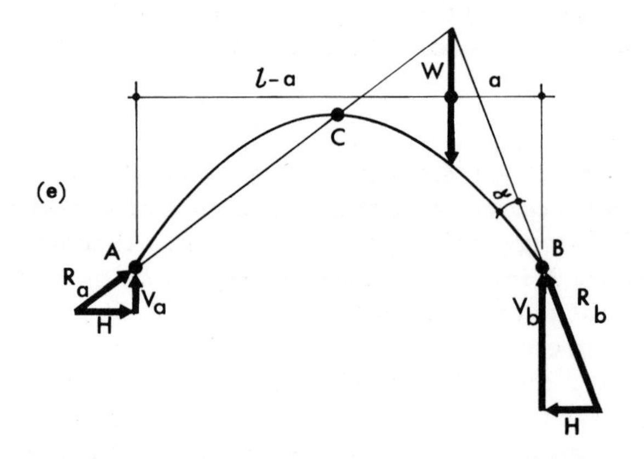

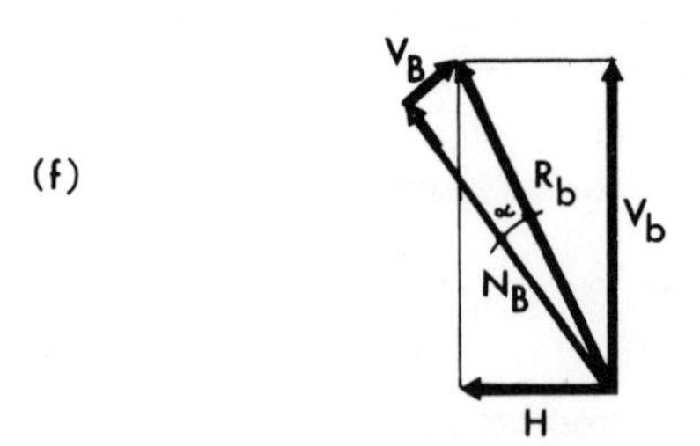

Fig. 6.2.1d–f

and occurs at the section where the line tangent to the arch is parallel to the larger reaction (at B in Fig. 6.2.1d). When R_B is so inclined that such a section does not exist, as in Fig. 6.2.1e, $N_{\max}$ occurs at B and equals the component of R_b along the tangent to the arch at B:

$$N_{\max} = N_B = (\sqrt{V_b^2 + H^2}) \cos \alpha. \tag{6.2.5}$$

N_{max} may be easily evaluated graphically as shown in Fig. 6.2.1f, but for small values of the angle α between R_b and the tangent to the arch at B, N_{max} may be conservatively evaluated by (6.2.4). The minimum value of N is always equal to H.

The maximum shear is either V_C or, for arches with a small rise, the component of the larger reaction, say R_b, in the direction perpendicular to the arch at B:

$$V_B = (\sqrt{V_b^2 + H^2}) \sin \alpha, \tag{6.2.6}$$

which may be also determined graphically, as shown in Fig. 6.2.1f. Shear seldom governs arch design, since beam bending is minor in a well designed arch.

To evaluate the bending moment M_x at a section of the arch of abscissa x and ordinate y (Fig. 6.2.2), we notice that M_x equals the bending moment $M_{b,x}$,

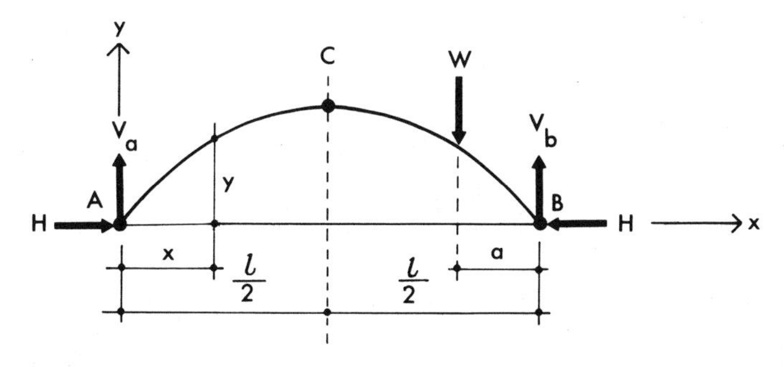

Fig. 6.2.2

due to the vertical loads and reactions only, plus the bending moment due to the horizontal thrust. As the vertical reactions are identical with those in the simply supported beam, $M_{b,x}$ is the moment at the section x of the simply supported beam of span l. The moment due to the thrust is $-Hy$. Hence, with the value of H given by (6.2.2), the *arch moment* M_x becomes:

$$M_x = M_{b,x} - Hy = M_{b,x} - M_{b,C}\left(\frac{y}{f}\right). \tag{6.2.7}$$

Since, for a given arch shape, y is proportional to f, equation (6.2.7) shows that, for a given arch shape, the arch moment M_x is independent of the rise.

It is also seen from (6.2.7) that, by the action of the thrust, the positive arch moment is always smaller than the corresponding beam moment. Let us evaluate this reduction for a parabolic arch of rise f, a shape commonly used in arch design (Fig. 6.2.3), for which:

$$y = 4f\frac{x}{l}\left(1 - \frac{x}{l}\right). \tag{a}$$

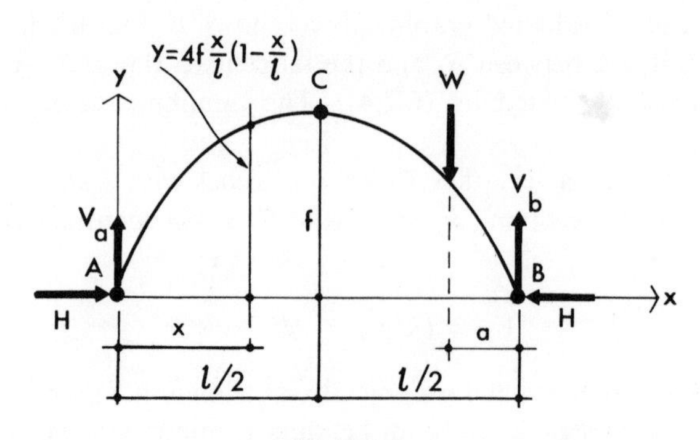

Fig. 6.2.3

The beam moment due to W at a section x to the left of W is:

$$M_{b,x} = V_a x = Wa\left(\frac{x}{l}\right), \tag{b}$$

and the mid-span beam moment is:

$$M_{b,C} = Wa\frac{l/2}{l} = \frac{Wa}{2}, \tag{c}$$

so that, by (6.2.7) and (a), the arch moment becomes:

$$M_x = Wa\left(\frac{x}{l}\right) - \frac{Wa}{2}\left[4\frac{x}{l}\left(1-\frac{x}{l}\right)\right] = -Wa\left[\frac{x}{l} - 2\left(\frac{x}{l}\right)^2\right], \tag{d}$$

which, as noticed above, only depends on the abscissa x and not on y/f. For example, when the load W is applied at the crown (Fig. 6.2.4a), $a = l/2$ and:

$$M_x = -\frac{Wl}{2}\left[\frac{x}{l} - 2\left(\frac{x}{l}\right)^2\right].$$

Table 6.2.1 gives the ratio of the arch moment M_x to the beam moment $M_{b,x} = Wa(x/l) = (Wl/2)(x/l)$, as well as the ratio of M_x to $M_{b,\max} = M_{b,C} = Wl/4$, for x/l between 0 and $\frac{1}{2}$. Table 6.2.1 and Fig. 6.2.4b show that the maximum

Table 6.2.1

x/l	0	0.1	0.2	0.25	0.3	0.4	0.5
$M_x/M_{b,x}$	−1.0	−0.80	−0.60	−0.50	−0.40	−0.20	0
$M_x/M_{b,C}$	0	−0.16	−0.24	−0.25	−0.24	−0.16	0

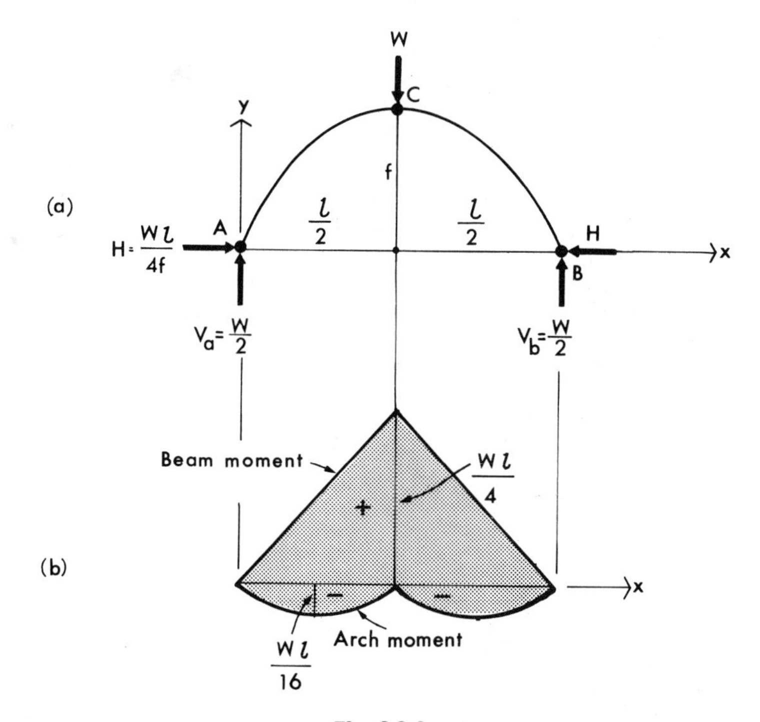

Fig. 6.2.4

arch moment, which occurs at the quarter point $x/l = 0.25$, is 50% of the beam moment at $x/l = 0.25$ and only 25% of the maximum beam moment. The minus sign of M_x indicates that M_x develops tension in the outer fibers of all arch sections.

Equations (6.2.7) and (6.2.4) allow the evaluation of the moments and the maximum compression in any symmetrical 3-hinge arch for any loading condition, as soon as H is known. For example, given a circular arch of radius r (i.e., with $f = r$ and $l = 2r$), loaded uniformly in horizontal projection (Fig. 6.2.5), the value of H is obtained by (6.2.2):

$$H = \frac{M_{b,C}}{f} = \frac{wl^2}{8f} = \frac{w(2r)^2}{8r} = \frac{1}{2}wr. \tag{e}$$

With the x-, y-axes of Fig. 6.2.5a, the arch shape is given by:

$$(x - r)^2 + y^2 = r^2$$

$$\therefore \quad y = \sqrt{r^2 - (x - r)^2} = r\sqrt{1 - \left(\frac{x}{r} - 1\right)^2}.$$

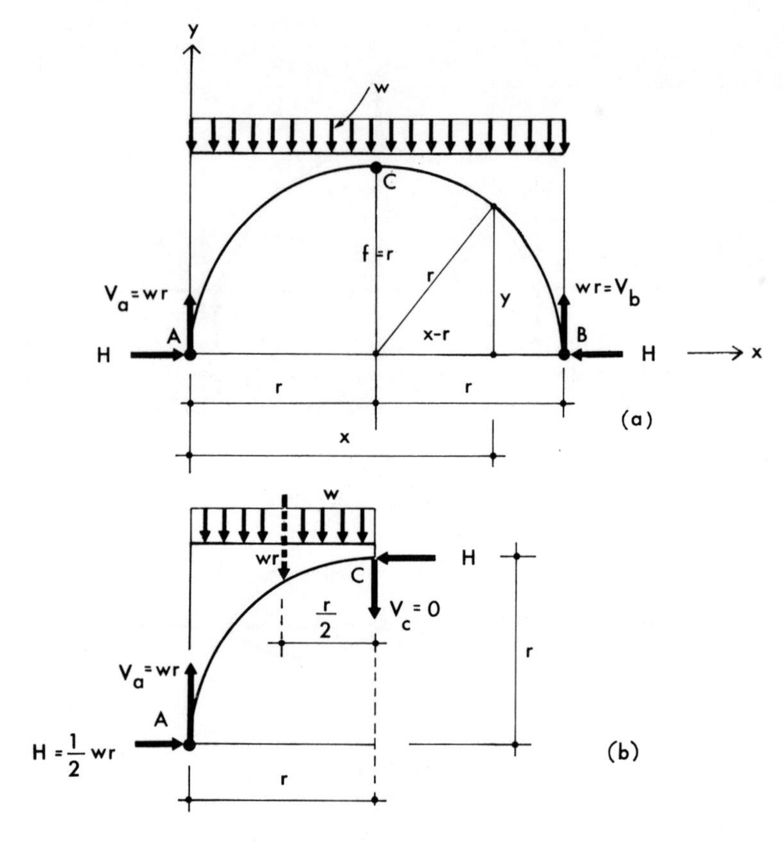

Fig. 6.2.5

With $V_a = wr$ and the beam moment $M_{b,x} = (wr)x - wx^2/2 = (wr^2/2)(2x/r - x^2/r^2)$, (6.2.7) and (e) give:

$$M_x = M_{b,x} - Hy = \frac{wr^2}{2}\left(\frac{2x}{r} - \frac{x^2}{r^2}\right) - \left(\frac{wr^2}{2}\right)\sqrt{1 - \left(\frac{x}{r} - 1\right)^2}$$

$$= \frac{wr^2}{2}\left[\left(2\frac{x}{r} - \frac{x^2}{r^2}\right) - \sqrt{2\frac{x}{r} - \frac{x^2}{r^2}}\right], \tag{f}$$

while by (6.2.4) and (e):

$$N_{\max} = \sqrt{(wr)^2 + \left(\frac{wr}{2}\right)^2} = \frac{\sqrt{5}}{2}\,wr = 1.12\,wr. \tag{g}$$

Table 6.2.2 gives $M_x/M_{b,C} = M_x/(wr^2/2)$ for x/r between 0 and 1, i.e., for sections between A and C.

Table 6.2.2

x/r	0.	0.134	0.2	0.4	0.5	0.6	0.8	1.0
$\dfrac{M_x}{wr^2/2}$	0.	−0.25	−0.24	−0.16	−0.12	−0.075	−0.02	0.

The table shows that the maximum arch moment, which occurs at $x/r = 0.134$, is 25% of the maximum beam moment and is of opposite sign. For this arch, $V_{\max} = V_A = wr/2$, $N_{\max} = V_a = V_b = wr$ and $N_{\min} = H = wr/2$.

PROBLEMS

Note: All arches in the following problems are 3-hinge arches.

6.2.1 Determine the thrust, the bending moment at D, $N_{\max}$ and $N_{\min}$, and V_C for the arch of Fig. 6.2.6.

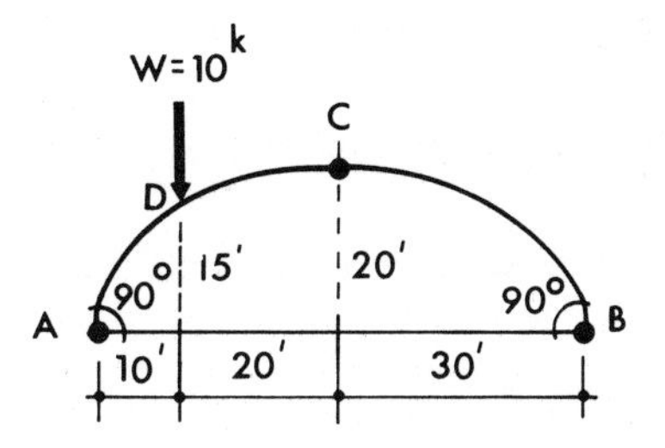

Fig. 6.2.6

6.2.2 Determine the thrust, the moment at D, $N_{\max}$ and $N_{\min}$ for the arch of Fig. 6.2.7.

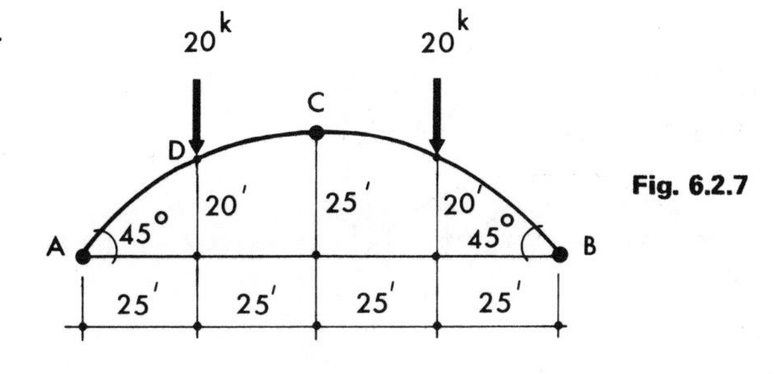

Fig. 6.2.7

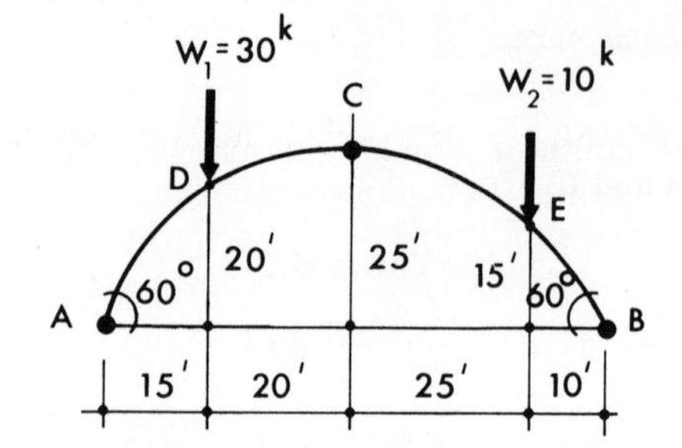

Fig. 6.2.8

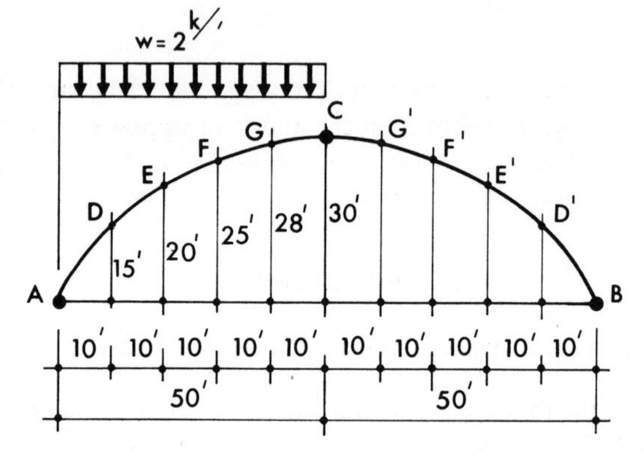

Fig. 6.2.9

6.2.3 Determine the thrust, the moments at D and E, N_{max} and V_{max} for the arch of Fig. 6.2.8.

6.2.4 Determine the thrust and the moments at D, E, F, G, G', F', E' and D' for the arch of Fig. 6.2.9.

6.2.5 Two arches have the same span l and are loaded uniformly in horizontal projection with a load w. The first has a rise f; the second a rise $f/2$. What is the ratio between the thrusts H_1 and H_2 of the two arches? Which has the larger moments at $x = l/4$ if the ordinates of the two arches at $x = l/4$ are $y_1 = \frac{2}{3}f$ and $y_2 = \frac{1}{4}f$?

6.2.6 Determine the thrust of the circular arch in Fig. 6.2.10, and compute a table of moments at $x/r = 0.$-0.2-0.4-0.6-0.8-1.0.

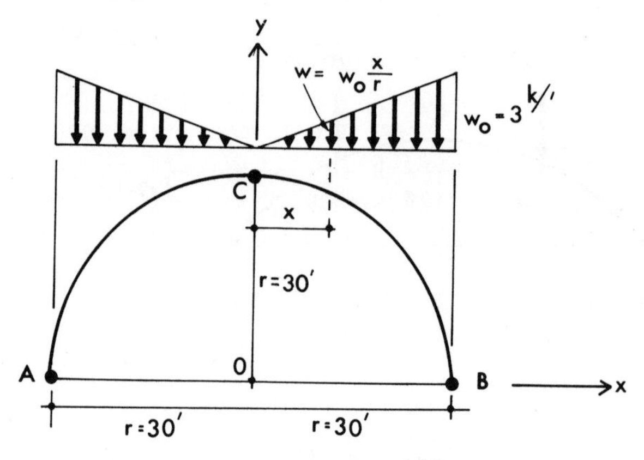

Fig. 6.2.10

6.2.7 Determine the thrusts H_a and H_b and the moment at $x = 25$ ft due to the horizontal wind load of 10 k in the circular arch of Fig. 6.2.11.

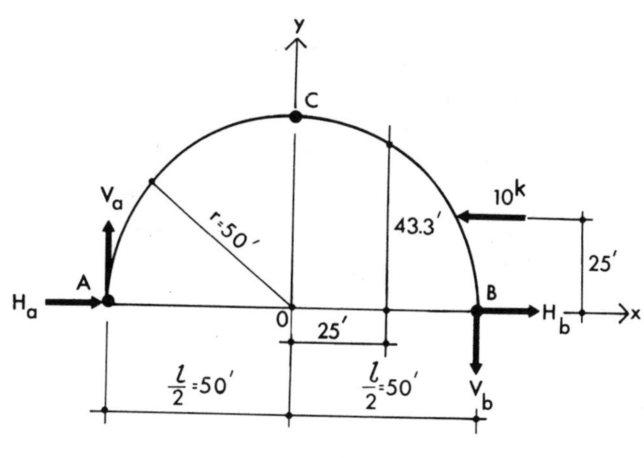

Fig. 6.2.11

6.3 Arch Moment Diagram by Graphics

The bending moment diagram for a 3-hinge arch of given shape may be conveniently obtained graphically, once the vertical reactions and the thrust are evaluated.

Consider first the simple case of the arch in Fig 6.3.1. Since the reaction R_a cannot develop a moment at the hinge C, R_a must go through C and its line of action is the line AC. The lever arm of R_a with respect to any section E is the perpendicular distance e between the line AC and the section; hence, the arch moment at any section between A and D is $M = R_a e$.

The load W is equilibrated by the two reactions R_a and R_b; hence, R_a and R_b must meet on the line of action of W and the line of action of R_b is BD'. Therefore, the moment at any section between D and B is $M = R_b e$.

It is thus seen that the hatched diagram in Fig. 6.3.1a measures the bending moments M at any arch section, provided its ordinates e are multiplied by R_a between A and D and by R_b between D and B, i.e., provided the ordinates are "read" in the scales R_a and R_b, respectively. For example, for a circular arch of radius 50 ft (i.e., for $l = 100$ ft and $f = 50$ ft) with a load $W = 100$ k at $a = 25$ ft:

$$V_a = 25 \text{ k}, \qquad V_b = 75 \text{ k}, \qquad H = \frac{V_a l/2}{f} = 25 \text{ k},$$

$$R_a = \sqrt{(25)^2 + (25)^2} = 35.36 \text{ k},$$

$$R_b = \sqrt{(25)^2 + (75)^2} = 79.06 \text{ k}.$$

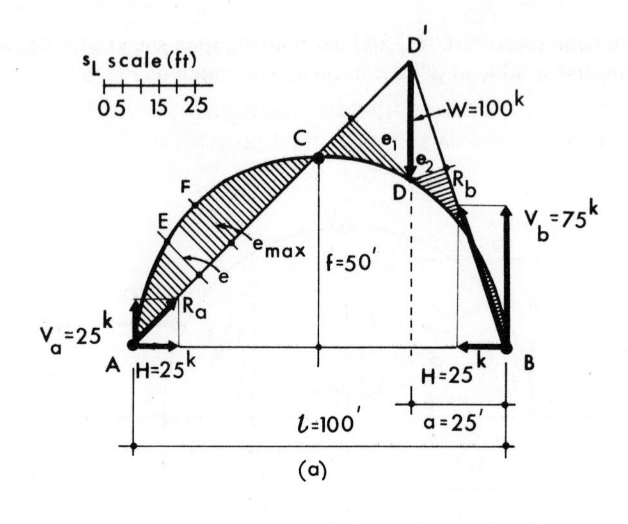

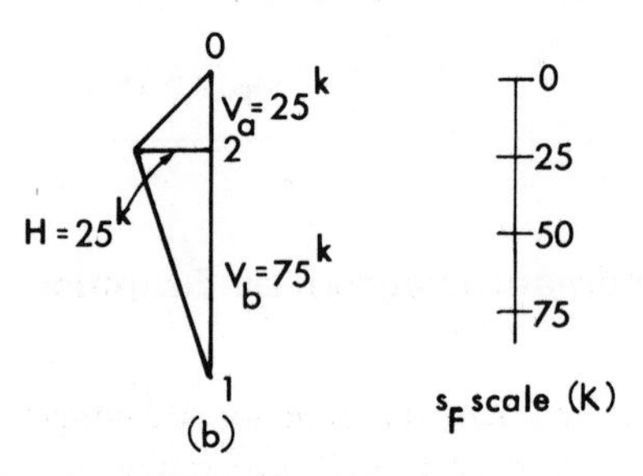

Fig. 6.3.1

Reading the ordinates e from Fig. 6.3.1 in the scale of the drawing, the maximum negative moment at F equals:

$$-R_a e = -35.36 \times 14.65 = -518 \text{ k ft},$$

and the maximum positive moment at D equals:

$$+R_a e_1 = +\ 35.36 \times 22.4 = +\ 792 \text{ k ft}.$$

The moment at D may be checked by:

$$+R_b e_2 = +\ 79.06 \times 10 = +\ 791 \text{ k ft}.$$

We finally notice that $AD'B$ is the shape of the inverted cable passing through the points A, C, B and carrying the load $-W$ at D. Hence, the bending moment diagram for the arch may be obtained by drawing in a scale s_F, say 1 in. = 100 k, the force polygon of Fig. 6.3.1b, with $V_a = 2\text{–}0 = 25$ k, $V_b =$

1–2 = 75 k and P–2 = H = 25 k, and by constructing $AD'B$ as the corresponding funicular polygon.

Let us obtain by the same graphical procedure the bending moment diagram for the arch in Fig. 6.3.2a carrying the 2 loads $W_1 = 20$ k and $W_2 = 8$ k at

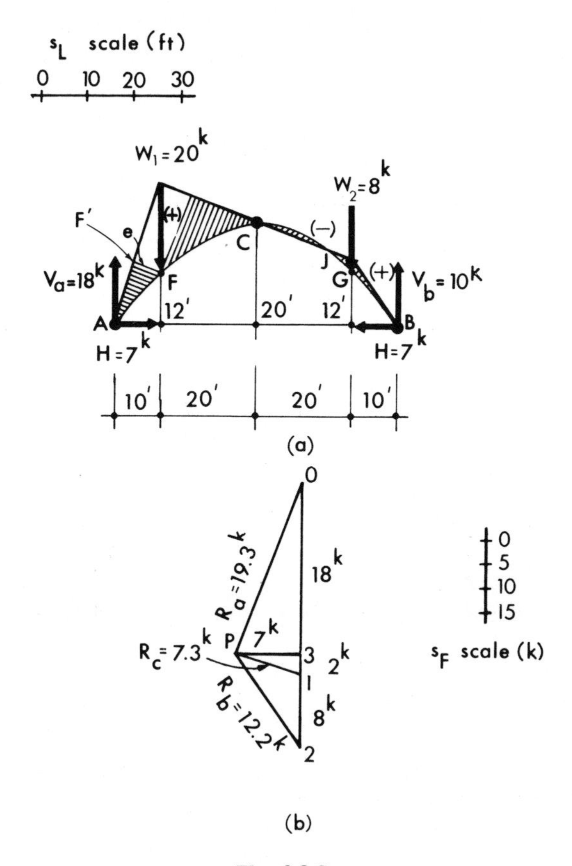

Fig. 6.3.2

the indicated sections. We determine first:

$$V_a = 18 \text{ k}, \qquad V_b = 10 \text{ k}, \qquad H = 7 \text{ k}$$

(check these results), and then draw in a scale s_F the force diagram of Fig. 6.3.2b in which 3–0 = 18 k, 2–3 = 10 k, 0–1 = 20 k, 1–2 = 8 k and P–3 = 7 k. If the scale of the drawing in Fig. 6.3.2a is s_L, the bending moments are obtained by multiplying the lever arms e, read in the scale s_L, by $R_a = P$–0 from A to F, by $R_c = P$–1 from F to G and by $R_b = P$–2 from G to B read in the scale s_F. For example, if Fig. 6.3.2a is drawn in the scale $s_L = 20$ ft/in.

(1 in. = 20 ft) and the forces in Fig. 6.3.2b are drawn in the scale s_F = 10 k in. (1 in. = 10 k), the moment at F is given by:

$$M_F = 10(P\text{–}0) \times 20(F\text{–}F') = 10(1.93) \times 20(0.25) = 96.5 \text{ k ft.}$$

The correct value 18 × 10 − 7 × 12 is 96 k ft. The moments are positive from A to C, negative from C to J and positive from J to B. (Why?)

PROBLEMS

6.3.1 Draw the bending moment diagrams for the circular arches of:
(a) Fig. 6.3.3,

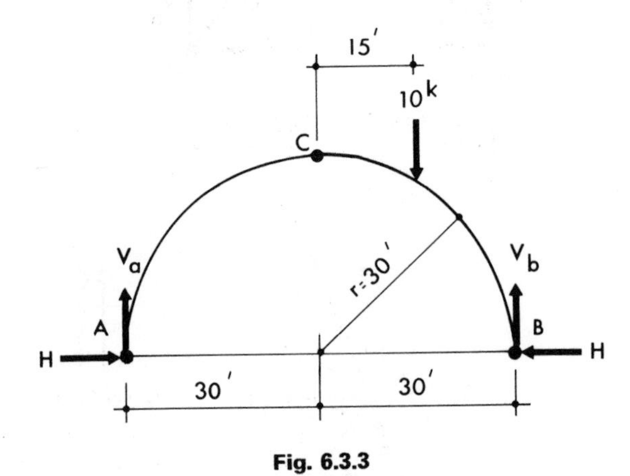

Fig. 6.3.3

(b) Fig. 6.3.4, (Can you draw the bending moment diagram without using the funicular polygon construction?)

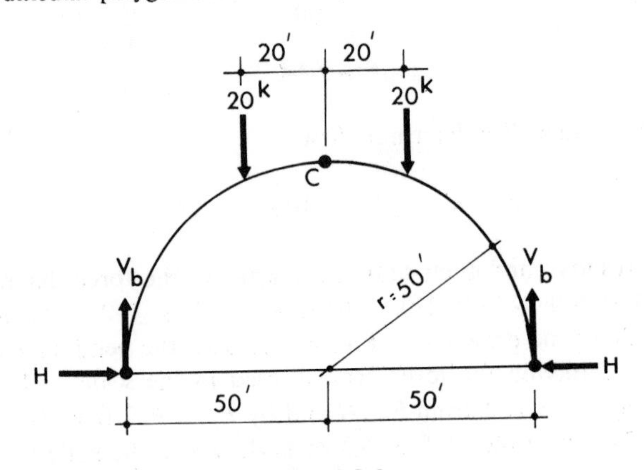

Fig. 6.3.4

(c) Fig. 6.3.5,

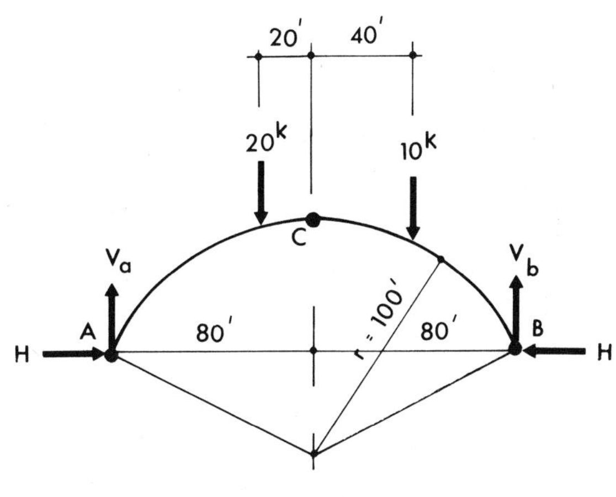

Fig. 6.3.5

(d) Fig. 6.3.6.

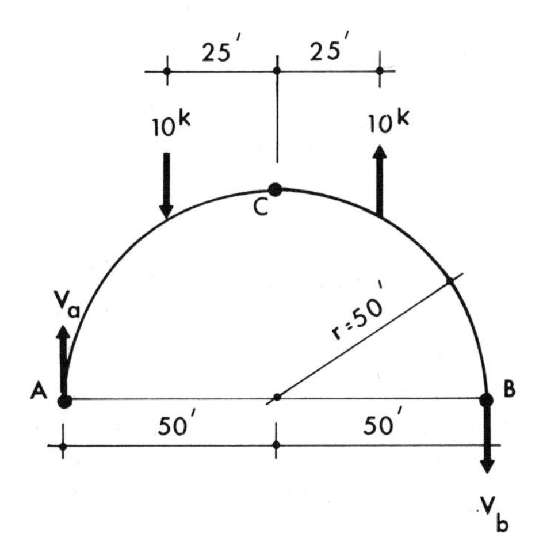

Fig. 6.3.6

Evaluate the maximum and minimum bending moments in each arch, locating the corresponding sections visually.

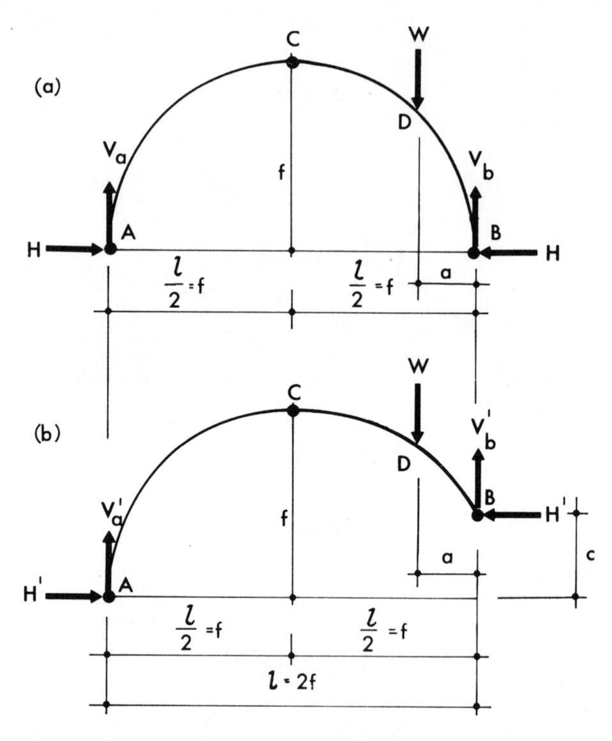

Fig. 6.3.7

6.3.2 The two arches of Fig. 6.3.7a and b have the same span and the same rise. Draw the bending moment diagrams for the two arches, and determine whether their vertical reactions are equal. Are their thrusts equal? Are the bending moments at D equal? If not, which is larger? *Note:* Draw free body diagrams for AC and CB in Fig. 6.3.7b.

6.3.3 Determine V'_a, V'_b and H' if the arch of Fig. 6.3.7b carries 2 loads W, one a distance a from B and one a distance a from A. Assume $W = 100$ k, $l = 100$ ft, $f = 50$ ft, $a = 25$ ft and $c = 20$ ft. Draw the bending moment diagram for this arch. (*Note:* Draw free body diagrams for AC and BC.)

6.4 Funicular Arches

Since well designed arches develop relatively small moments, one may wonder whether the shape of a symmetrical arch, carrying a given set of loads, could be chosen so that the arch will not develop bending moments and shears but only axial compression at all sections. That this is possible may be seen by first hanging the given loads from a cable, that will naturally take a funicular shape in pure tension (Fig. 6.4.1a), and then by flipping the cable over and "freezing it" (Fig. 6.4.1b). The frozen cable becomes a *segmental arch*, in

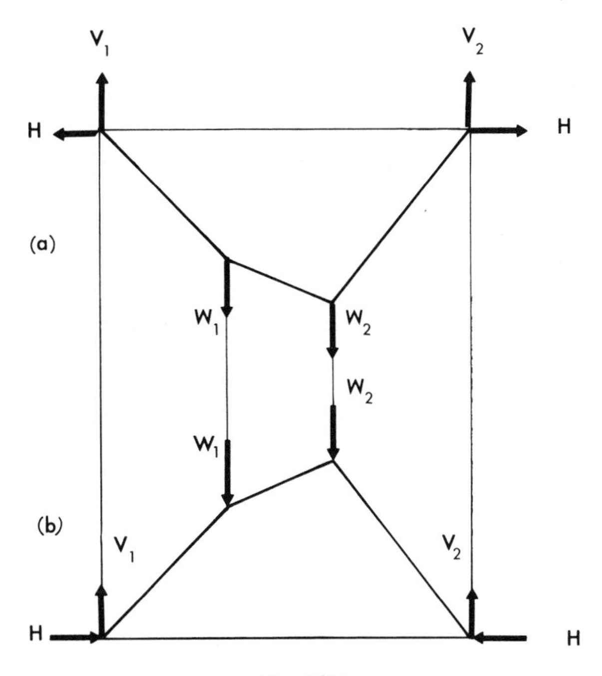

Fig. 6.4.1

which each segment develops only compression and which, therefore, is momentless. Such momentless arch is also called *funicular*.

The shape of a symmetrical funicular arch is obtained analytically by setting equal to zero the arch moment $M_x = M_{b,x} - M_{b,C}(y/f)$ of equation (6.2.7). If M_x is to be zero for all values of x, the ordinate y of the arch at x must be such that:

$$y(x) = f\frac{M_{b,x}}{M_{b,C}}, \tag{6.4.1}$$

where $M_{b,x}$ is the simply supported beam moment at x and $M_{b,C}$ its mid-span moment. The equation shows that the *funicular arch shape* is the shape of the moment diagram of the simply supported beam for the given loads, i.e., their *funicular polygon* read in the scale $f/M_{b,C}$ (see Section 5.6).

For example, the concentrated load W at mid-span of the "arch" of Fig. 6.4.2 produces in the left half of the arch the moments:

$$M_x = \frac{W}{2}x - M_{b,C}\frac{y}{f} = \frac{Wl}{4}\left(\frac{2x}{l}\right) - M_{b,C}\frac{y}{f} = M_{b,C}\left(2\frac{x}{l} - \frac{y}{f}\right).$$

M_x is zero at all sections x if:

$$y = 2\frac{f}{l}x, \tag{a}$$

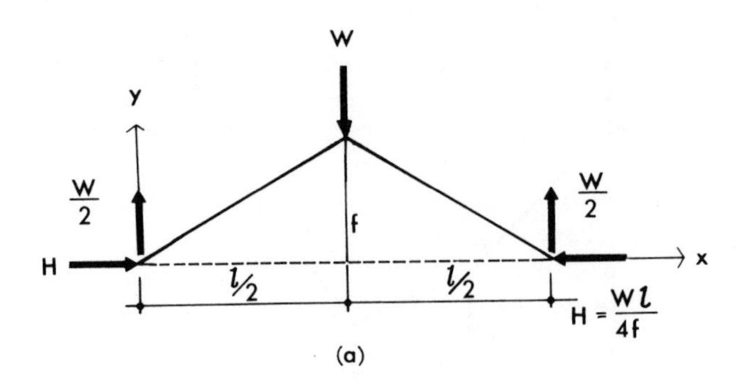

(a)

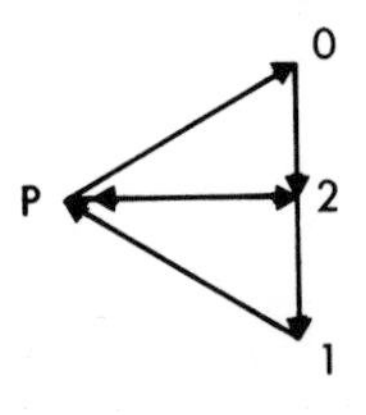

(b)

Fig. 6.4.2

that is, for the "arch" with the straight sides of Fig. 6.4.2a. Such shape is nothing else but the inverted funicular polygon due to the load W drawn by means of a force diagram with a distance P–2 $= H = Wl/4f$ (Fig. 6.4.2b). Similarly, since for a uniformly loaded, simply supported beam:

$$M_{b,x} = \frac{wl}{2}x - \frac{wx^2}{2} = \frac{wl^2}{8} 4\frac{x}{l}\left(1 - \frac{x}{l}\right) = M_{b,C}\left[4\frac{x}{l}\left(1 - \frac{x}{l}\right)\right],$$

(6.2.7) shows that M_x is equal to zero for all values of x if the shape of an arch uniformly loaded in horizontal projection is chosen to be the parabola:

$$y = 4f\frac{x}{l}\left(1 - \frac{x}{l}\right). \tag{b}$$

Hence, a parabolic arch of shape (b) is funicular for a uniform load in horizontal projection. Referring, in general, to the graphical examples of Section 6.3, we may also add that, if the shape of the arch is the funicular polygon drawn by means of a force diagram with a horizontal reaction equal to the thrust H, the lever arm e is zero and hence, M is also zero at all arch sections.

Since each specific set of loads leads to a specific funicular polygon, an arch that is funicular for one set of loads cannot be funicular for any other set of loads. If the shape of an arch is chosen so as to be funicular for the most critical or most common loading condition, the arch will develop only minor moments for other less critical or less common loading conditions. For example, the bending moments in a parabolic arch, loaded by a uniform load w in horizontal projection and by a concentrated moving load W, are only due to W, since the parabolic arch is funicular for the load w. This is the condition developed in a shallow steel arch bridge, where w may be the heavy weight of the roadway and (approximately) of the arch itself, and W the much lesser weight of a traveling truck.

The funicular shape for an arch of constant cross section under its own dead load is that of an inverted heavy cable or chain, i.e., a *catenary* (from the latin *catena* for chain) and is very near a parabola for shallow arches (Fig. 6.4.3).

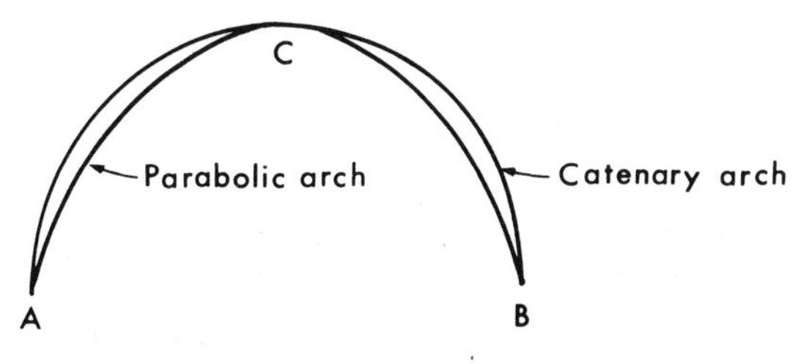

Fig. 6.4.3

Since a funicular arch develops only compression, its design requires the evaluation of N_{max} and N_{min} only. Its maximum and minimum sectional areas A_{max} and A_{min} are established on the basis of the allowable stress in compression F_c by the compression formulas [see equation (3.4.2)]:

$$A_{max} = \frac{N_{max}}{F_c}, \qquad A_{min} = \frac{N_{min}}{F_c}. \tag{6.4.2}$$

For example, a parabolic arch with $l = 200$ ft and $f = 20$ ft, carrying a total load $w = 10$ k/ft develops reactions:

$$V_a = V_b = \frac{10 \times 200}{2} = 1{,}000 \text{ k},$$

$$H = \frac{10 \times (200)^2}{8 \times 20} = 2{,}500 \text{ k} = N_{min}$$

$$R_a = R_b = \sqrt{(2{,}500)^2 + (1{,}000)^2} = 2{,}693 \text{ k} = N_{max}.$$

If the arch is made out of concrete with an $F_c = 1$ ksi:

$$A_{min} = \frac{2{,}500}{1} = 2{,}500 \text{ in.}^2 = 17.4 \text{ ft}^2 \simeq 3 \text{ ft} \quad \text{by} \quad 5 \text{ ft-}2\tfrac{1}{2} \text{ in.},$$

$$A_{max} = \frac{2{,}693}{1} = 2{,}693 \text{ in.}^2 = 18.7 \text{ ft}^2 = 3 \text{ ft} \quad \text{by} \quad 6 \text{ ft-}3 \text{ in.}$$

PROBLEMS

Note: All arches in the following problems are 3-hinge arches.

6.4.1 A parabolic concrete arch of span $l = 100$ ft and rise $f = 20$ ft carries a uniform load in horizontal projection $w = 5$ k/ft, which includes its dead load. Determine the maximum depth of the arch sections (at the supports) and the minimum depth (at the crown), if the rectangular cross sections of the arch have a constant width of 1 ft and $F_c = 1{,}000$ psi.

6.4.2 The rise of the arch of Problem 6.4.1 is reduced to 10 ft. How much uniform load carrying capacity is lost with respect to the arch with a rise $f =$ 20 ft?

6.4.3 Determine the depth of the funicular arch of Problem 6.4.1 at $x = l/4$ by noticing that the portion of the arch above the sections at $x = l/4$ and $x = 3l/4$ behaves like a parabolic arch supported on hinges at these sections. (*Note:* Obtain the rise for this arch as the difference between $f = 20$ ft and the value of y at $x = l/4$.)

6.4.4 The parabolic arch of Problem 6.4.1 has a cross section of width $b = 1$ ft and depth $h = 3$ ft and carries a concentrated load $W = 50$ k at its crown. The maximum bending moment due to W is absorbed by the compressive and tensile forces in two groups of steel reinforcing bars set 2.5 ft apart in the depth of the cross section $x = l/4$, where the maximum moment occurs. Determine the area of the tensile and compressive reinforcing bars for $F_s =$ 20 ksi.

6.4.5 What is the funicular shape of a 3-hinge arch of span l and rise f carrying a uniform load w from $x = 0$ to $x = l/2$? Derive the two expressions for y valid for $0 < x \leq l/2$ and for $l/2 \leq x < l$.

6.4.6 (a) Draw the shape of a funicular arch of span l and rise $f = l/2$ which carries 3 equal loads directed towards the mid-span point of its tie-rod, if 1 load is vertical and the other 2 are inclined by 45° to the right and left of it. (b) Draw the funicular shape for the same arch carrying 5 equal radial loads, evenly spaced by 30°, directed towards the mid-span point of its tie-rod. What do you conclude is the funicular shape of an arch for a uniform radial pressure directed towards a point?

6.4.7 A shallow roof is suspended from radial cables attached to a concrete circular ring of radius R. The tension in each cable is T and may be considered horizontal. The number n of cables in the roof is large enough for the cable tensions to be considered uniformly distributed radially on the ring. Determine the compression C in the ring by considering half the ring as a free body. If $R = 100$ ft, $T = 300$ k and $n = 40$, and if the weight of the ring is supported on a circular wall of radius R, what is the required section of the concrete ring for $F_c = 1.8$ ksi?

6.4.8 A circular steel pipe 4 in. in diameter must carry steam at a pressure of 200 psi. Determine its thickness for $F_t = 15$ ksi by considering as a free body a 1 in. wide ring cut out of the pipe.

6.4.9 Can you state why the circular arch used by the Romans is not the "best" shaped arch from a static viewpoint?

6.4.10 In gothic arches the rise is often larger than the span (Why?) and the thrust is not absorbed by tie-rods. Instead, heavy turrets appear over the arch supports, and widening piers carry the loads of the roof to the ground (Fig. 6.4.4). Draw qualitatively the funicular polygon for a gothic arch hinged at the crown and supporting 3 equally spaced loads, and explain the purpose of the weight of the turrets and of the widening piers.

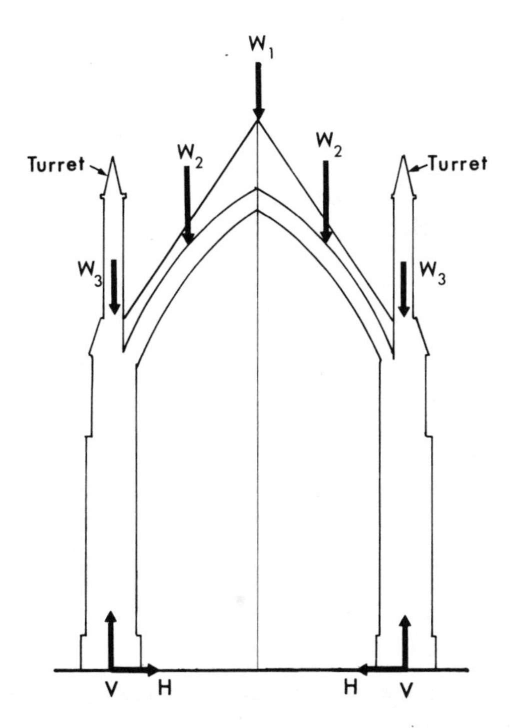

Fig. 6.4.4

6.4.11 Draw the funicular polygon for an arabic arch with a concentrated load W at the crown (Fig. 6.4.5), and explain why its shape is statically inefficient.

6.4.12 If the circular compression ring in the roof of Problem 6.4.7 were, instead, a regular hexagon, what would be the maximum bending moment in the bars of the hexagon?

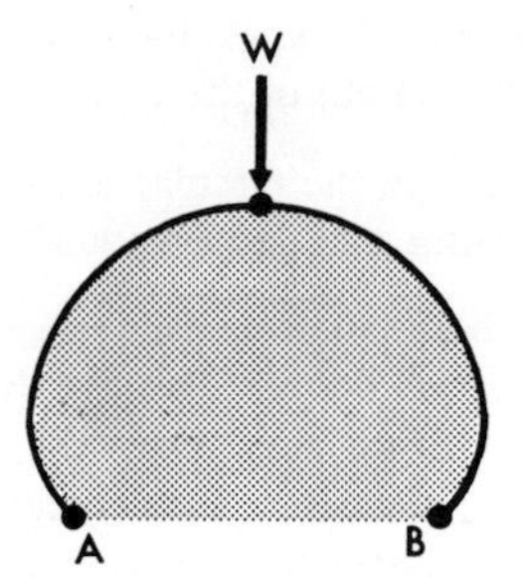

Fig. 6.4.5

6.5 Arch Design

We have seen in Section 6.1 that the cross sections of an arch are submitted to compression, bending and shear. If we assume that the extreme fiber stress in bending is smaller than the compressive stress (as is usually the case), the maximum and minimum compressive fiber stresses may be obtained by superposition of the triangular bending stress diagram and the constant compression diagram (Fig. 6.1.2a). Hence:

$$f_{c,\max} = \frac{N}{A} + \frac{M}{S}, \qquad f_{c,\min} = \frac{N}{A} - \frac{M}{S}, \tag{6.5.1}$$

where N and M are the compressive force and the bending moment, A is the area and S the section modulus of the cross section (see Section 5.8). Conservatively, one may assume that $N_{\max}$ and $M_{\max}$ occur at the same section and substitute these values for N and M in (6.5.1).

For example, consider a parabolic masonry arch spanning 100 ft, with a rise of 10 ft and a constant cross section of width $b = 1.0$ ft and depth $h = 2.5$ ft. The arch carries a uniform load $w = 2$ k/ft, representing its own dead load and the load of the roadway, and a mid-span load $W = 10$ k. We wish to compute its maximum and minimum fiber stresses.

The load w develops no moments and, by (6.2.4), a compression at most equal to:

$$N'_{\max} = \sqrt{\left(\frac{wl}{2}\right)^2 + \left(\frac{wl^2}{8f}\right)^2} = \frac{wl}{2}\sqrt{1 + \left(\frac{l}{4f}\right)^2}$$

$$= \frac{2 \times 100}{2}\sqrt{1 + \left(\frac{100}{4 \times 10}\right)^2} = 100\sqrt{1 + (2.5)^2} = 269 \text{ k}.$$

The load W applied at mid-span develops, by (6.2.4), a compression at most equal to:

$$N''_{max} = \frac{W}{2}\sqrt{1 + \left(\frac{l}{2f}\right)^2} = \frac{10}{2}\sqrt{1 + \left(\frac{100}{2 \times 10}\right)^2}$$
$$= 5\sqrt{1 + 5^2} = 25.5 \text{ k},$$

and by Table 6.2.1 a maximum moment:

$$M_{max} = -0.25\, M_{b,C} = -0.25\,\frac{Wl}{4} = -0.25\,\frac{10 \times 100}{4} = -62.5 \text{ k ft.}$$

Hence:

$$N_{max} \leq N'_{max} + N''_{max} = 269 + 25.5 = 294.5 \text{ k},$$

and with $A = 1 \times 2.5 = 2.5$ ft² and $S = 1 \times (2.5)^2/6 = 1.04$ ft³ [see equation (5.8.6)]:

$$f_{c,max} = \frac{294.5}{2.5} + \frac{62.5}{1.04} = 118 + 60 = 178 \text{ ksf} = 1{,}236 \text{ psi},$$
$$f_{c,min} = 118 - 60 = 58 \text{ ksf} = 403 \text{ psi}.$$

The allowable stress *in compression* F_c and the allowable compressive stress *in bending* F_b are usually different for the same material and the check of the *combined stress* due to compression and bending is obtained by means of the formula:

$$\frac{f_c}{F_c} + \frac{f_b}{F_b} \leq 1, \qquad (6.5.2)$$

which gives $f_c \leq F_c$ for $f_b = 0$ and $f_b \leq F_b$ for $f_c = 0$. If the arch of the preceding example were made out of a 4,000 psi concrete, for which $F_b = 1{,}800$ psi and F_c may be assumed to be 1,500 psi, equation (6.5.2) would give with $f_c = 294{,}500/(2.5 \times 144) = 818$ and $f_b = 62{,}500/(1.04 \times 144) = 417$ psi:

$$\frac{818}{1{,}500} + \frac{417}{1{,}800} = 0.55 + 0.23 = 0.78 < 1.$$

If $f_{c,min}$ is tensile, the 2 equations (6.5.1) still hold for arches made of materials with equal resistance in tension and compression, for which one only needs to check the largest of the compressive and the tensile stresses. When a reinforced concrete arch develops tensile stresses, the reinforcing steel must be capable of resisting the total tension in the section and must be located on the side of the section where tension develops. One may approximately check the steel requirements by assuming the steel to be located at the centroid of the tensile stress diagram. For example, if in the preceding example the load W were 25 k, the bending stresses would be 2.5 times higher than when $W = 10$ k. Hence, $f_b = 2.5 \times 417 = 1{,}042$ psi and:

$$f_{c,\max} = 818 + 1{,}042 = 1{,}860 \text{ psi (compressive)},$$
$$f_{\min} = 818 - 1{,}042 = -224 \text{ psi (tensile)}.$$

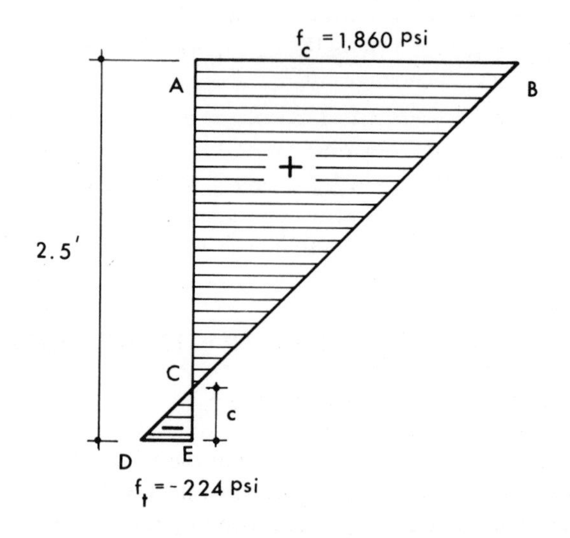

Fig. 6.5.1

The stress diagram along the depth of the section (Fig. 6.5.1) becomes negative at a distance c from the bottom of the section given by the similar triangles ABC and EDC:

$$\frac{c}{2.5 - c} = \frac{224}{1{,}860} \quad \therefore \quad 1{,}860c = 224(2.5 - c)$$

$$\therefore \quad c = \frac{560}{2{,}084} = 0.27 \text{ ft.}$$

The total tensile force, if b is the section width, is:

$$T = \tfrac{1}{2}bc \times f_t = \tfrac{1}{2}(1 \times 12)(0.27 \times 12) \times 224 = 4{,}355 \text{ lb.}$$

For $F_s = 20{,}000$ psi, the steel area is $A_s = 4{,}355/20{,}000 = 0.218$ in.^{2}. Two #3 bars, of $\frac{3}{8}$ in. diameter, with an area of 0.220 in.^{2} are sufficient to develop the required tension.

PROBLEMS

Note: All the arches in the following problems are assumed to be 3-hinge arches.

6.5.1 A brick wall 1 ft thick and 20 ft high is supported by a circular concrete arch of radius 10 ft, also 1 ft thick. Determine the depth of the arch section for a combined compressive stress not larger than 1,800 psi, and the required steel reinforcement for $f_s = 20$ ksi. Bricks weigh 140 lb/cu ft.

6.5.2 A concrete parabolic arch carries only its own dead load. What is the longest arch span l for $F_c = 1{,}800$ psi when $f/l = 0.2$ and when $f/l = 0.1$? Stone concrete weighs 150 lb/cu ft.

6.5.3 Determine the ultimate span l_u for a parabolic steel arch carrying its own dead load if the yield point of steel is $f_y = 36{,}000$ psi and $f/l = 0.2$. Steel weighs 490 lb/cu ft.

6.5.4 A concrete parabolic arch $\frac{1}{2}$ ft wide and 3 ft deep carries a total uniform load $w = 2$ k/ft on a span of 80 ft with a rise of 20 ft. Determine the value W of the largest load concentrated at mid-span that will not develop tension in the arch sections.

6.5.5 A horizontal roadway 10 ft wide, which weighs 400 psf and carries a live load of 100 psf, is supported by two circular steel arches with a radius $r = 50$ ft. Choose a WF section for the arches, for $F_s = 20$ ksi, and check whether the weight of the arches is negligible in comparison with the load they carry.

6.5.6 A pedestrian bridge consists of a parabolic steel arch and of a walkway hanging from it by means of cables. The walkway is 10 ft wide, weighs 200 psf and carries 100 psf of live load. The arch spans 50 ft and has a rise of 10 ft. Choose a WF section for the arch, assuming $F_s = 10$ ksi.

Chapter Seven

7.1 Statically Determinate Frames

In a post-and-lintel system the lintel is supported on posts fixed into a foundation but is not rigidly connected to them (Fig. 7.1.la). Under vertical loads, the lintel bends as a simply supported beam and the posts are compressed by the vertical reactions of the beam. Under a lateral load W, say a wind load, the post on the wind side acts as a cantilever, and the lintel may slide over the lee side post, which remains straight (Fig. 7.1.lb). The post-and-lintel system is statically determinate; it is not very efficient under lateral loads, since it supports the wind force on only one column by developing at its foot a maximum moment $M = Wh$ and a horizontal thrust H equal to W.

Frames

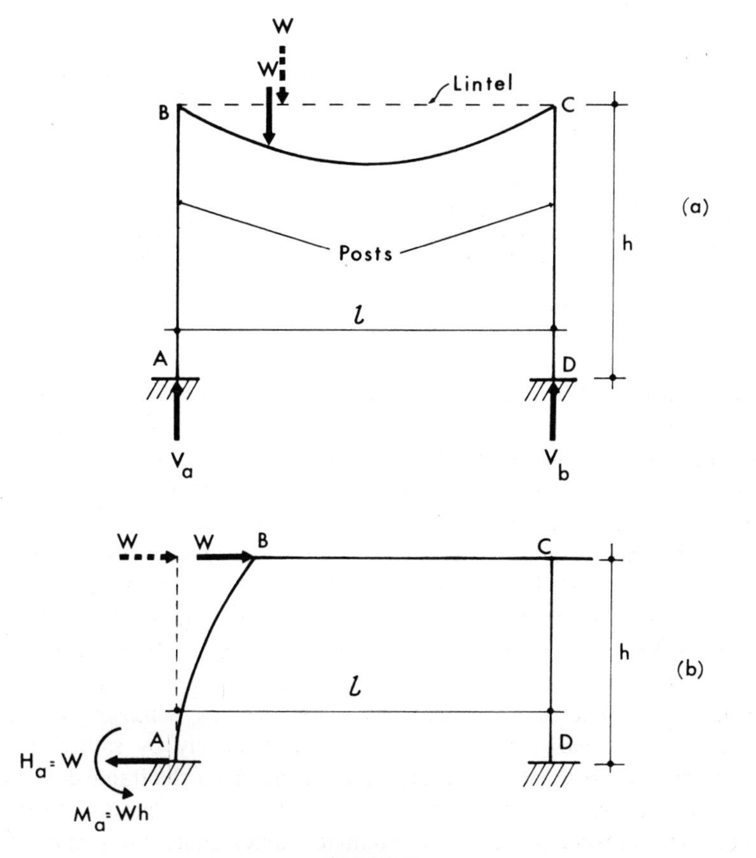

Fig. 7.1.1

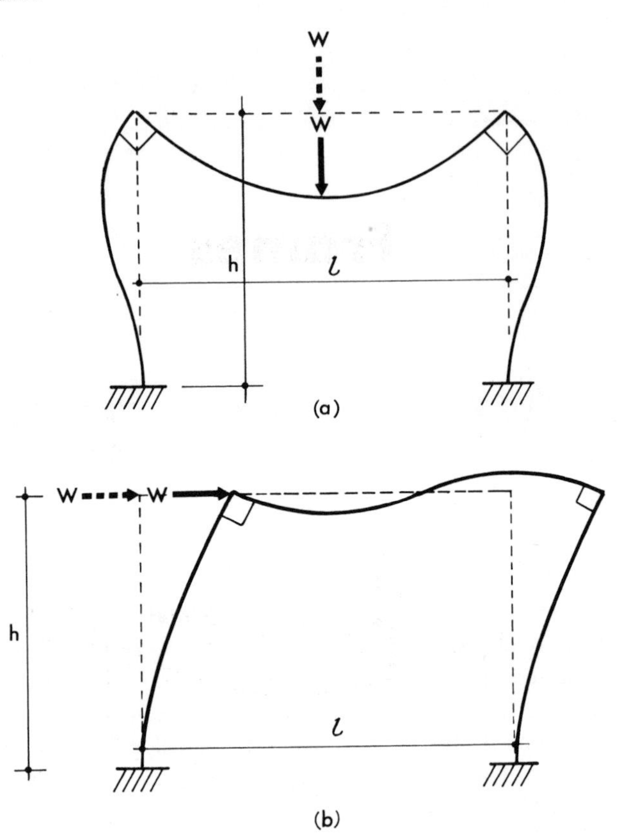

Fig. 7.1.2a–b

In most modern frames, the horizontal beam is instead rigidly connected to the columns so that the right angle between the beam and the columns is maintained during the frame deformation due to the loads (Fig. 7.1.2a, b). The rigid connections may be obtained by welding, bolting or riveting in steel frames, or through the continuity of monolithic pouring in reinforced concrete frames. It is easy to see that such a *rigid frame* is statically indeterminate by considering it as free body and introducing the reactions V_a, H_a, M_a at the foot of the left column and V_d, H_d, M_d, at the foot of the right column (Fig. 7.1.2c). Since only 3 equations of plane equilibrium can be written for the 6 unknown reactions, under a general set of loads the frame is 3 times statically indeterminate. Yet we shall see that sometimes the behavior of statically indeterminate frames may be evaluated approximately by statics, provided some additional reasonable assumptions be made about the frame deformation. To obtain a physical understanding of such deformations, let us first determine the behavior of some statically determinate frames under the action of both vertical and lateral loads.

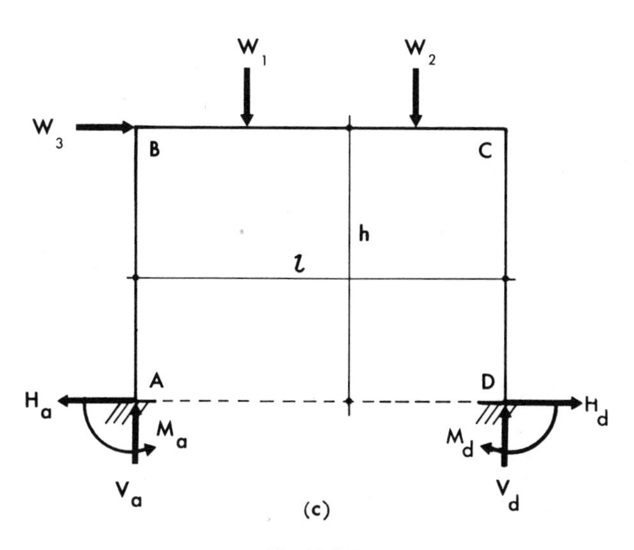

Fig. 7.1.2c

Consider, for example, the frame of Fig. 7.1.3, in which the left column is supported on a fixed hinge, the right column on a movable hinge and the beam is rigidly connected to the top of the columns. This frame is statically determinate, since the fixed hinge can only develop reactions V_a and H_a, the movable hinge only a reaction V_d and 3 equations of equilibrium can be written for these 3 unknowns. Under vertical loads (Fig. 7.1.3a), the beam deflects and both columns rotate to remain perpendicular to the curved, deflected beam; hence, the right hinge moves to the right by a small amount d. Since by horizontal equilibrium $H_a = 0$, the hinges develop only vertical reactions $V_a = W(a/l)$, $V_d = W(b/l)$ and the columns stay straight, except for the negligible amount of bending produced by the lateral frame displacement. Thus, the beam behaves essentially as if it were simply supported and, under vertical loads, the frame acts as a post-and-lintel system.

Under a lateral load W (Fig. 7.1.3b), the frame displaces to the right and the fixed hinge A resists the load with a thrust $H_a = W$, which bends the left column. The right angle at B is maintained, and the beam is bent at its left end by the moment $M_B = Wh$ at the top of the left column (the moment $V_a d$ is negligible). Since the movable hinge cannot develop a thrust, the right column remains straight and is momentless, except for the minor amount of bending due to the lateral displacement. Therefore, there is no moment applied at the right end of the beam. To evaluate the axial forces N, the shears V and the moments M in the columns and the beam, we first determine the vertical reaction V_d by taking moments about A:

$$V_d l - Wh = 0 \quad \therefore \quad V_d = W\frac{h}{l},$$

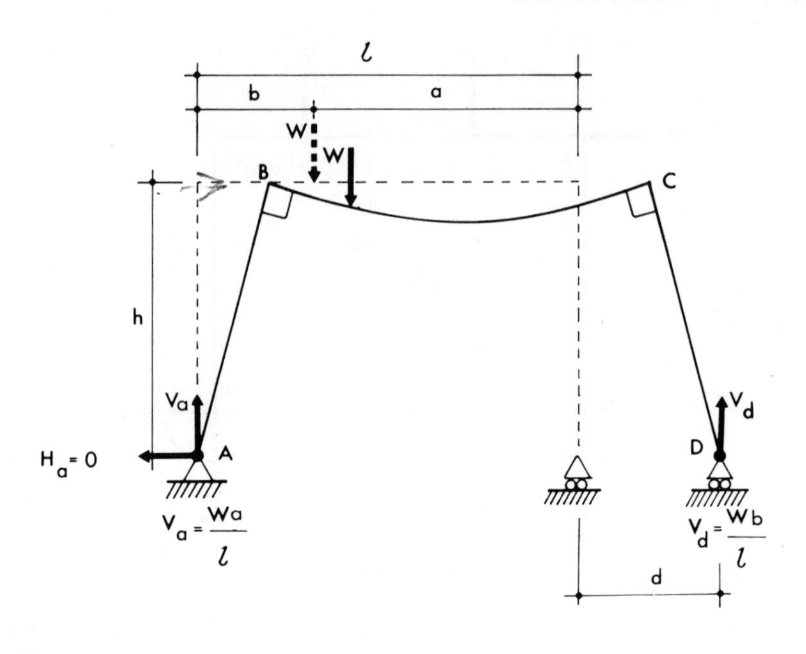
l
b
a
W
W
B
C
h
Va
Vd
Ha = 0
A
D
Va = Wa/l
Vd = Wb/l
d

(a)

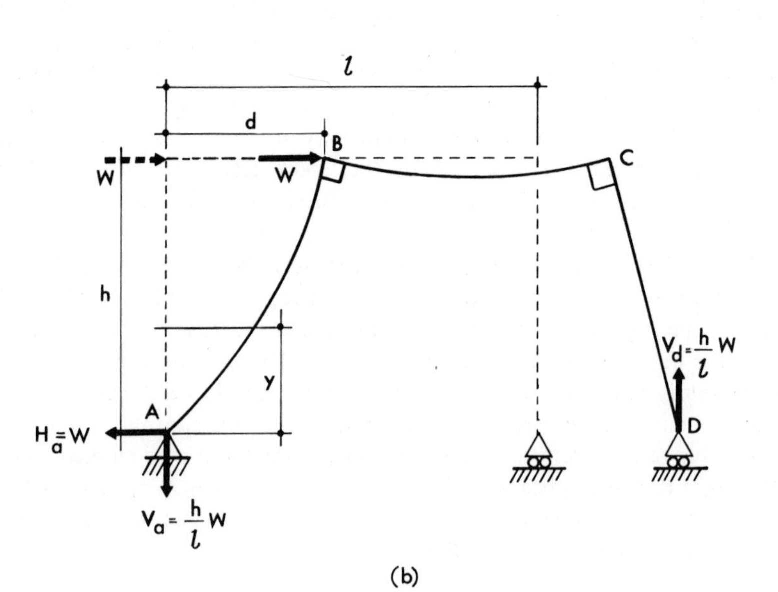
l
d
B
C
W
W
h
y
A
D
Ha = W
Va = h/l W
Vd = h/l W

(b)

Fig. 7.1.3 a–b

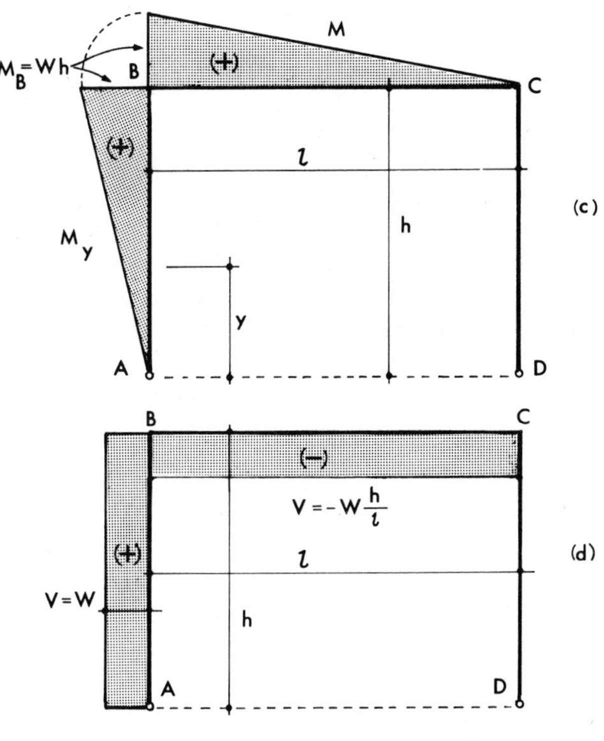

Fig. 7.1.3 c–d

and then determine the reaction V_a by vertical equilibrium:

$$V_a + V_d = 0 \quad \therefore \quad V_a = -V_d = -W\frac{h}{l}.$$

Thus, we see that the left column is acted upon by a tension:

$$T = |V_a| = W\frac{h}{l},$$

a bending moment:

$$M_y = Wy,$$

with a maximum value $M_B = Wh$ at B, and a constant shear:

$$V = H_a = W.$$

The right column develops no thrust and, hence, has $V = 0$ and $M_y = 0$. Its axial compressive force is $N = W(h/l)$.

The beam is acted upon by the moment M_B at B, has zero moment at C and, being unloaded vertically, has a linearly varying moment diagram between B and C. Its shear, which is equal to the upward axial force in the right column, $-W(h/l)$, is constant. Its axial force N is zero, since $H_d = 0$. Figure 7.1.3c gives the bending moment diagram for the frame; Fig. 7.1.3d gives its shear diagram.

Under the lateral load W (Fig. 7.1.3b), only bending and shear stresses develop in the beam; tensile as well as bending and shear stresses develop in the left column and only compressive stresses in the right column.

The frame of Fig. 7.1.4, with two fixed hinges at the foot of the columns (or legs) and one at the top of the right leg, is statically determinate because the hinge D cannot develop a thrust H_d, which would create a moment at C, where the frame has a hinge.

Under a vertical load W at $l/2$ the beam bends, the left leg rotates to

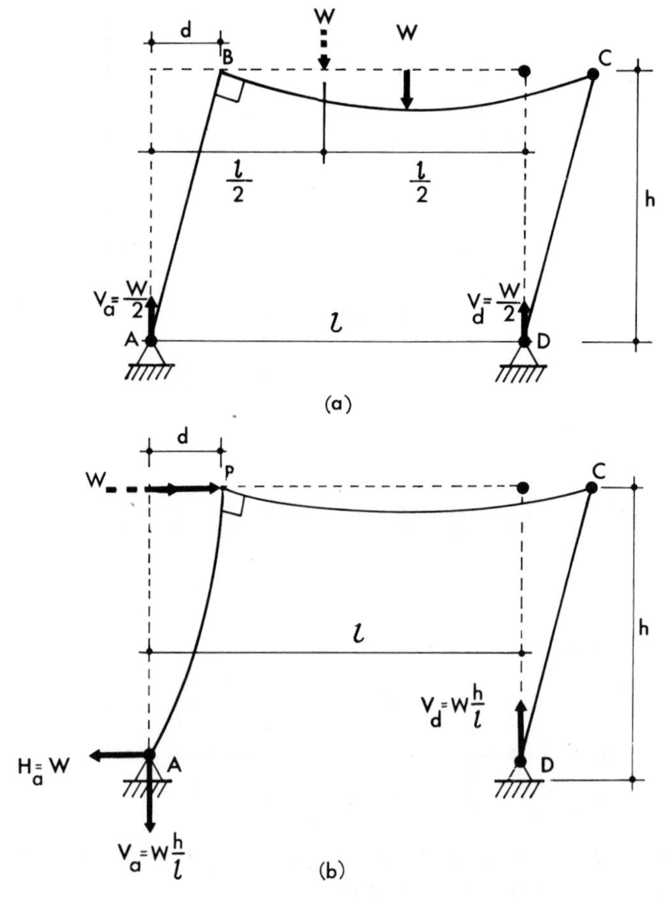

Fig. 7.1.4

maintain the right angle at B and the right leg also rotates, but the angle at C is not maintained because of the hinge. The frame, therefore, moves slightly to the right. Since the load is vertical, for horizontal equilibrium there is no thrust at A either, and both legs remain straight. They are acted upon by axial compressive forces $N_a = N_d = W/2$. The beam is simply supported, and, except for the small lateral displacement, the frame acts as a post-and-lintel system.

Under a horizontal load W (Fig. 7.1.4b), the frame displaces to the right, the angle at B is maintained but the angle at C is not because of the hinge. The right leg cannot develop a thrust because hinged at top and bottom, and remains straight. The left hinge alone equilibrates the load W by means of a thrust $H_a = W$. The left column develops tensile as well as bending and shear stresses, the right column only compressive stresses. The bending and shear diagrams for this frame are identical with those for the frame of Fig. 7.1.3, although their deformations are different.

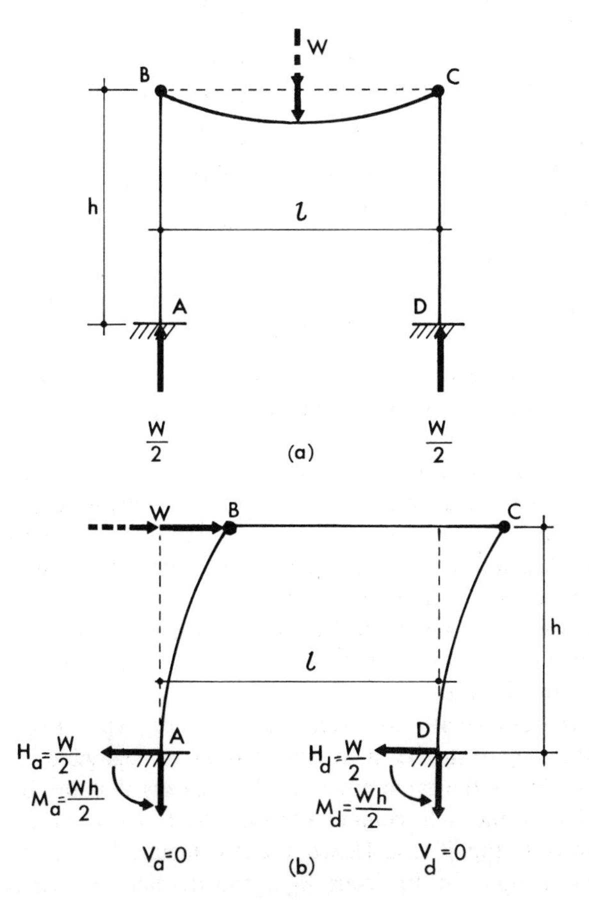

Fig. 7.1.5 a-b

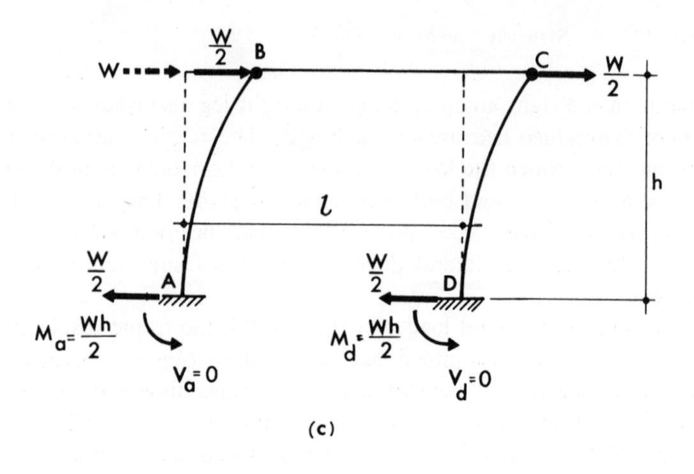

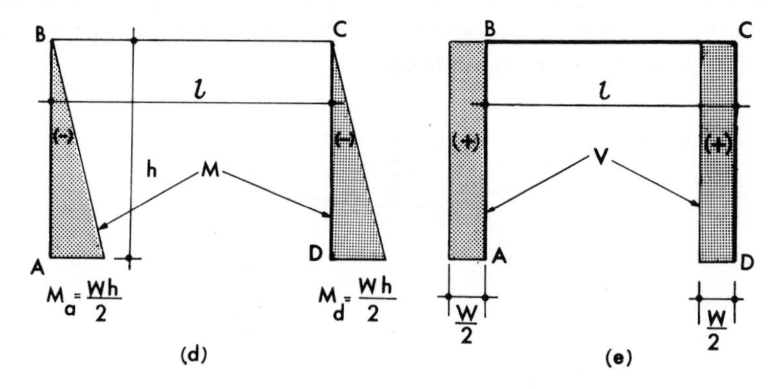

Fig. 7.1.5 c–e

Certain statically indeterminate frames may also be analyzed by statics *under particular loading conditions* which, because of symmetry, reduce the number of unknown reactions.

Consider, for example, the frame of Fig. 7.1.5, in which the beam is hinged at the top of two *identical* columns fixed into the foundations. Under a vertical load (Fig. 7.1.5a) the beam behaves as if it were simply supported, since the small relative displacement of C towards B, permitted by the movable hinge in the simply supported beam, occurs in the frame through a minor bending of the columns. Hence, under vertical loads the frame behaves essentially as a post-and-lintel system, the beam develops bending and shear stresses and the columns compressive stresses.

Under a lateral load W, however, *both* columns bend (Fig. 7.1.5b), and, since the shortening of the beam in compression is negligible, their tops are displaced laterally by the same amount. This means that the beam transfers half the load W to the right column and that the frame behaves as if it were loaded as shown in Fig. 7.1.5c. Hence, the two identical columns behave as 2 cantilevers acted upon by tip loads $W/2$ and develop at their foot identical

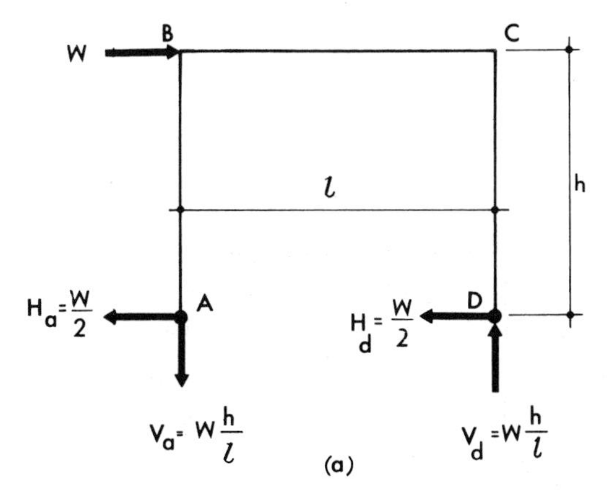
W
B
C
h
l
$H_a = \frac{W}{2}$
A
$H_d = \frac{W}{2}$
D
$V_a = W\frac{h}{l}$
$V_d = W\frac{h}{l}$
(a)

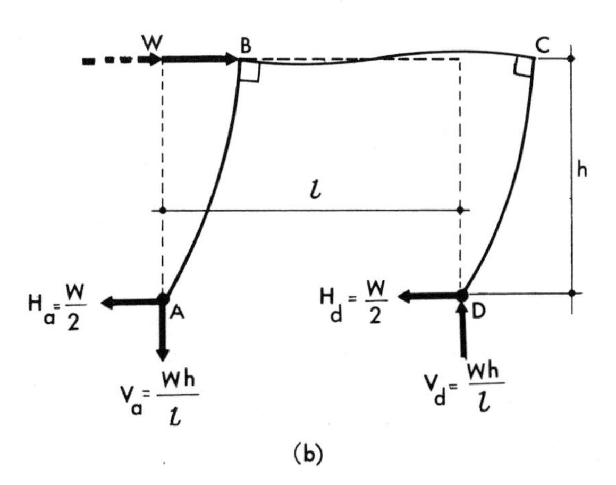
W
B
C
h
l
$H_a = \frac{W}{2}$
A
$H_d = \frac{W}{2}$
D
$V_a = \frac{Wh}{l}$
$V_d = \frac{Wh}{l}$
(b)

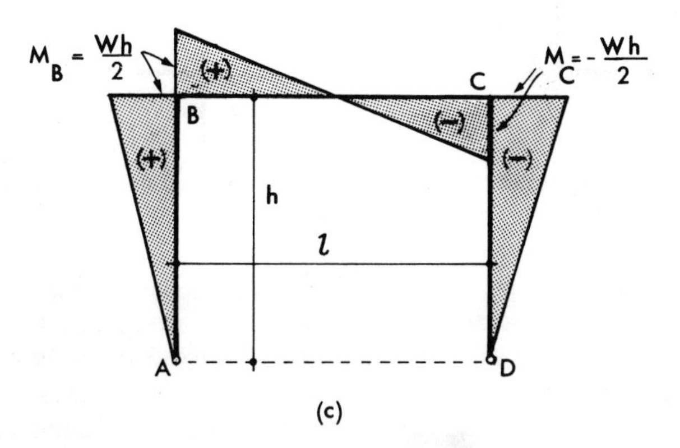
$M_B = \frac{Wh}{2}$
$M_C = -\frac{Wh}{2}$
(+)
(+)
(−)
(−)
B
C
h
l
A
D
(c)

Fig. 7.1.6 a- c

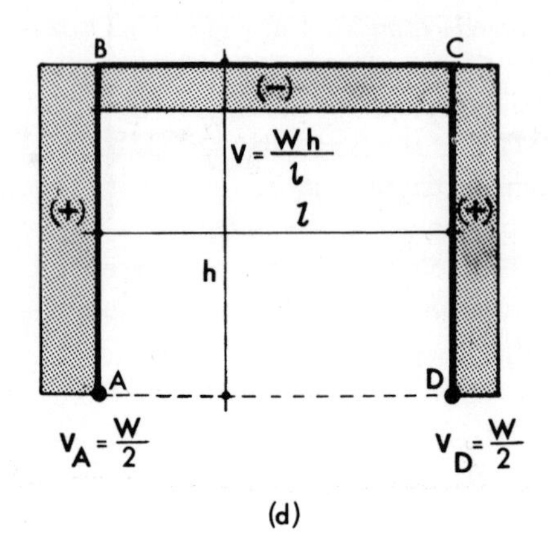
B
C
(−)
V = Wh/l
l
(+)
(+)
h
A
D
$V_A = \frac{W}{2}$
$V_D = \frac{W}{2}$

(d)

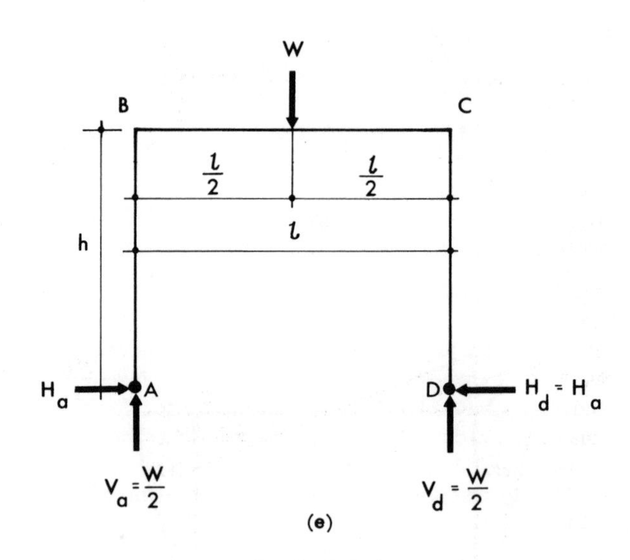
W
B
C
l/2
l/2
l
h
H_a
A
D
$H_d = H_a$
$V_a = \frac{W}{2}$
$V_d = \frac{W}{2}$

(e)

Fig. 7.1.6 d– e

thrusts $H_a = H_d = W/2$, while the beam is unloaded. (Notice that this would not be true if the columns were not identical.) Figures 7.1.5d and e give the bending moment and shear diagrams of the frame.

Similarly, if the *hinged frame* of Fig. 7.1.6a has equal columns, $H_a = H_d = W/2$ by symmetry; the moments at the top of the columns are $M_B = M_C = (W/2)\,h$. By rotational equilibrium about A, $V_d = W(h/l)$; by vertical equilibrium, $V_a = -V_d$ and the frame deforms as in Fig. 7.1.6b. Figure 7.1.6c gives the bending moment diagram of the frame with negative moments developing tension in the upper beam fibers and in the outer column fibers. The moment diagram in the unloaded beam varies linearly from $+Wh/2$ at B to $-Wh/2$ at C with zero moment at mid-span. Figure 7.1.6d gives the shear diagram for the frame.

It is easy to see, instead, that even under *symmetrical vertical* loads the frame of Fig. 7.1.6 cannot be solved by statics, since (Fig. 7.1.6e) with $V_a = V_d = W/2$, by symmetry, the other 2 equations of plane equilibrium give:

$$\sum F_x = 0: \quad H_a - H_d = 0 \quad \therefore \quad H_d = H_a,$$

$$\sum M_A = 0: \quad \frac{W}{2}l - \frac{W}{2}l = 0,$$

and do not allow the evaluation of H_a.

PROBLEMS

7.1.1 The steel frame of Fig. 7.1.3 has $l=30$ ft, $h=15$ ft and carries on its beam a uniform load $w = 2$ k/ft. (a) Determine its moment and shear diagrams; (b) choose a WF section for the beam for $F_b = 15$ ksi.

7.1.2 The steel frame of Fig. 7.1.3 has $l = 30$ ft, $h = 15$ ft and carries a horizontal wind load $W = 5$ k at its top. Its beam is a 14WF74. (a) Determine its moment and shear diagrams; (b) determine the maximum bending stress in the beam due to the wind load alone and the combined stress due to the wind load and a uniform load of 2 k/ft at mid-span (which to all practical purposes is the maximum bending stress); (c) check whether the combined maximum stress is within 1.33% of the stress due to the vertical load. (*Note:* Most codes allow a 33% increase in allowable stresses when wind stresses are added to vertical load stresses.)

7.1.3 The frame of Fig. 7.1.4 has the same dimensions and load as those of the frame in Problem. 7.1.1. Answer questions (a) and (b) of Problem. 7.1.1. for this frame.

7.1.4 The frame of Fig. 7.1.4 has the same dimensions and wind load as the frame in Problem. 7.1.2. Answer for this frame questions (a), (b), and (c) of Problem 7.1.2.

7.1.5 The frame of Fig. 7.1.5 carries a uniform load $w = 10$ k/ft on its beam and a wind load $W = 5$ k at its top. Its dimensions are $l = 30$ ft and $h = 15$ ft. (a) Choose a WF section for its beam if $F_b = 20$ ksi; (b) choose, on the basis of axial stresses only, a WF section for its columns if $F_c = 12$ ksi, and check whether the maximum stress due to bending and axial force is less than 1.33 $\times$ 20 ksi.

7.1.6 The frame of Fig. 7.1.7 carries a load W at the tip of its cantilevered beam. Determine its reactions at A and D, draw its bending moment diagram and sketch its deformation. Is $H_A = H_B = 0$? Why?

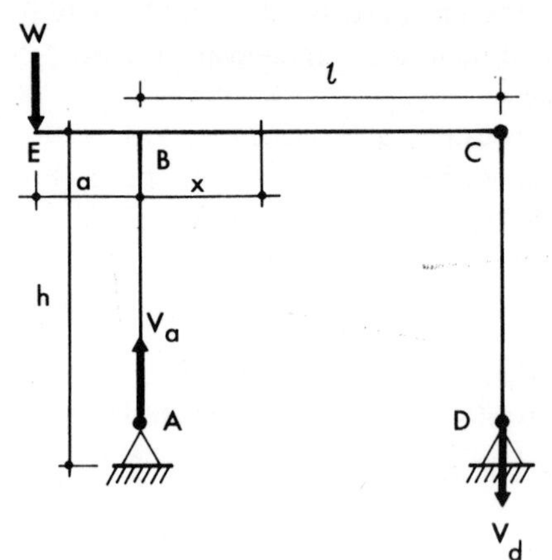

Fig. 7.1.7

7.1.7 Determine the reactions, draw the bending moment diagram and sketch the deformation of the frame of Fig. 7.1.8.

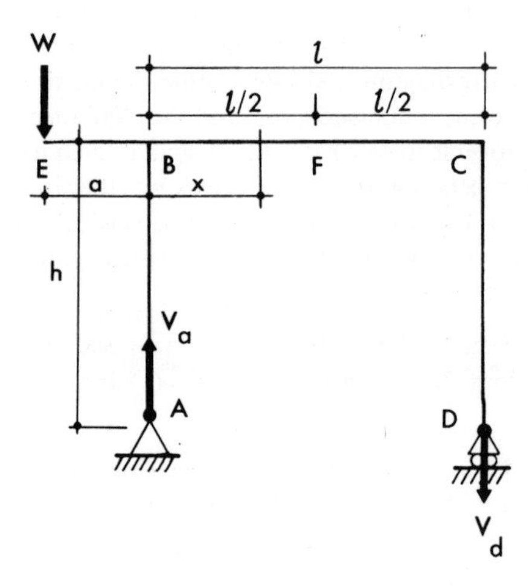

Fig. 7.1.8

7.1.8 The frame of Fig. 7.1.7 carries a load $w = 2$ k/ft over the entire length of its beam. Its dimensions are $a = 15$ ft and $l = 30$ ft. Determine its bending moment diagram and choose WF sections for its beam and legs if $F_b = 22$ ksi and $F_c = F_t = 15$ ksi.

7.1.9 Plot a graph of the reaction V_d at D in the frame of Fig. 7.1.7 as a load W travels from E to C.

7.1.10 Plot a graph of the reaction V_d at D and of the bending moment under the load in the frame of Fig. 7.1.8 as a load W travels from E to C.

7.2 Approximate Solution of Statically Indeterminate Frames

Although most frames used in modern construction are statically indeterminate, some of them may be analyzed approximately by making use of reasonable simplifying assumptions.

Consider, for example, the symmetrical rigid frame of Fig. 7.2.1, which is fixed at the foot of its identical columns and acted on by a horizontal force W at B. The frame is statically indeterminate since, *even taking symmetry into account*, the 3 equations of plane equilibrium give, for example:

$$\sum F_x = 0: \quad W - 2H = 0 \quad \therefore \quad H = W/2,$$
$$\sum F_y = 0: \quad V_a + V_d = 0 \quad \therefore \quad V_a = -V_d,$$
$$\sum M_A = 0: \quad -Wh + 2M - V_d l = 0 \quad \therefore \quad M = \tfrac{1}{2}(Wh + V_d l).$$

These equations, while determining H, do not allow the evaluation of the 3 other unknowns, V_a, V_d and M.

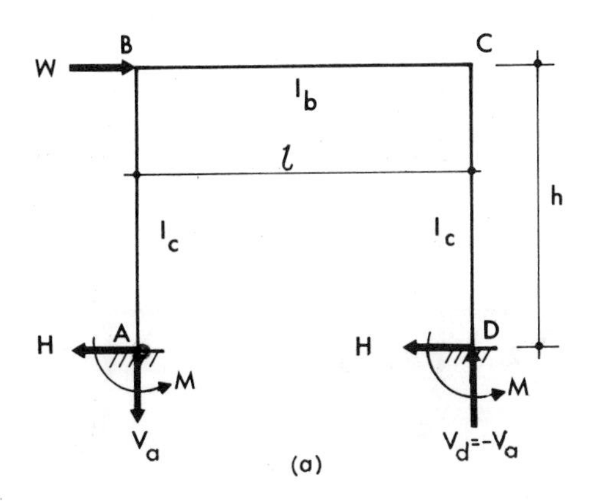

Fig. 7.2.1a

But in solving those design problems of the preceding section which dealt with statically determinate frames under vertical loads, you may have noticed that beam sections are usually much stiffer in bending than column sections, i.e., that the moment of inertia I_b of the beam divided by l is much larger than the moment of inertia I_c of the columns divided by h. If, in the limit, we make the *simplifying assumption that I_b is infinitely large in comparison with I_c*, the infinitely stiff beam will not bend, but will remain straight and horizontal, sliding rigidly to the right under the action of the horizontal load W. The frame deformation will be that shown in Fig. 7.2.1b, with the top of the columns displaced to the right by d but fixed into the infinitely rigid beam, just as

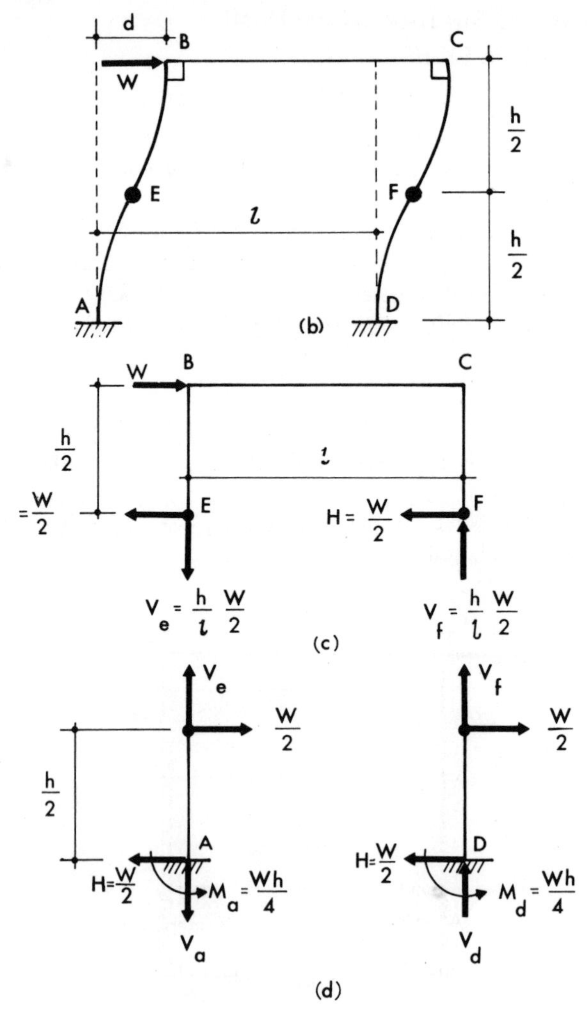

Fig. 7.2.1b–d

their foot is fixed into the foundations. The lower half of the columns is bent to the right and develops tensile stresses in the left fibers and compressive stresses in the right fibers, while the upper half is bent to the left and develops tensile stresses on the right and compressive stresses on the left fibers. The points E and F at column mid-height are *inflection points*, where the columns have no curvature and *develop no bending stresses*. Hence, under the assumption of an infinitely rigid beam, the frame behaves as if E and F were hinges, and the upper part of the frame acts like a symmetrical frame of height $h/2$, hinged at the foot of the columns (Fig. 7.2.1c). For this frame:

$$H = \frac{W}{2} \text{ (by symmetry)},$$

$$V_e = -V_f = \frac{W}{2}\left(\frac{h}{l}\right) \text{ (by moments about } E \text{ and } F\text{)},$$

and hence:

$$M_b = -M_c = H\frac{h}{2} = \frac{Wh}{4}.$$

Considering the lower half of the columns as free bodies (Fig. 7.2.1d), we finally obtain:

$$M_a = -M_d = \frac{Wh}{4}.$$

The bending moments in the columns, calling positive moments which develop tension on the inside fibers, are shown in Fig. 7.2.1e; they vary linearly since the columns carry no lateral loads.

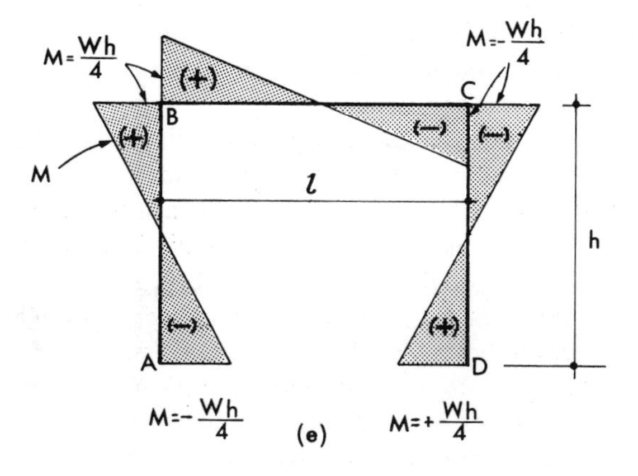

Fig. 7.2.1e

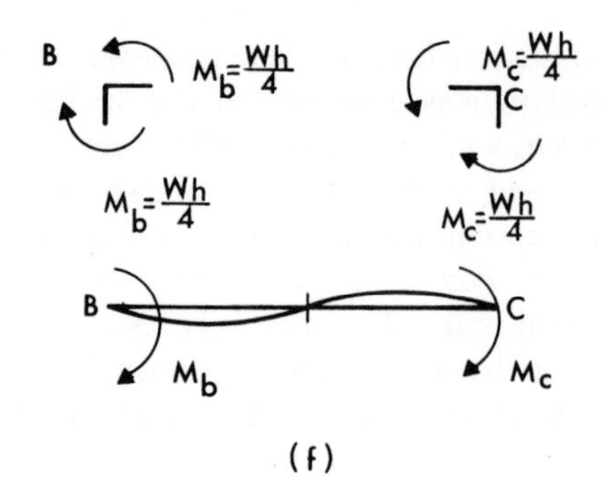

(f)

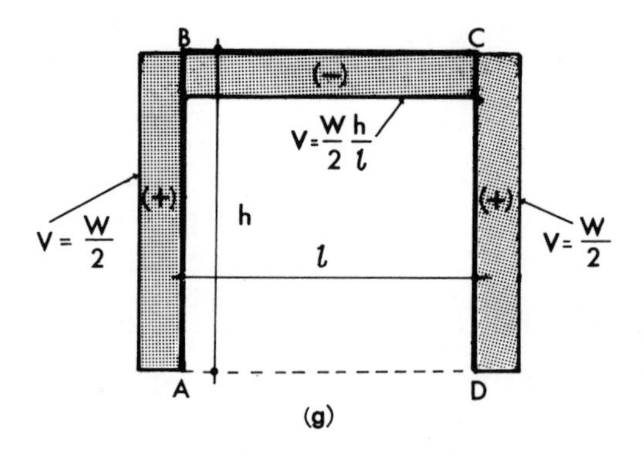

(g)

Fig. 7.2.1f–g

Using the joints B and C as free bodies (Fig. 7.2.1f), we see that the moments M_b and M_c exerted by the beam on the joints are counterclockwise and equal to $Wh/4$. Hence, the moments exerted by the joints on the beam ends are both clockwise and equal to $Wh/4$, and the beam, which actually is not infinitely rigid, deflects as shown in Fig. 7.2.1f, developing an inflection point at mid-span. Its bending moment diagram is also shown in Fig. 7.2.1e, while Fig. 7.2.1g gives the frame's shear diagram.

Thus, by assuming that the beam is infinitely rigid, we have reduced the frame to be statically determinate for horizontal loads.

It is important to notice that, if the simplifying assumption of an infinitely rigid beam ($I_b = \infty$) were made for the frame of Fig 7.2.1 under symmetrical vertical loads, its columns would still act as if built-in at top and bottom, and since they do not carry lateral loads, they would remain straight and be momentless. Therefore, the beam would have no end moments and behave as if it were simply supported. Since for a given set of vertical loads, the positive moments in a beam are greatest when the beam is simply supported, the assumption $I_b = \infty$, which gives maximum positive moments and no negative moments in the beam, is safe, for example, for the beam of a steel frame. But it is certainly unsafe for its columns which, having a small I_c, may not be capable of resisting even the relatively small bending moments due to the actual deformation shown in Fig. 7.2.2.

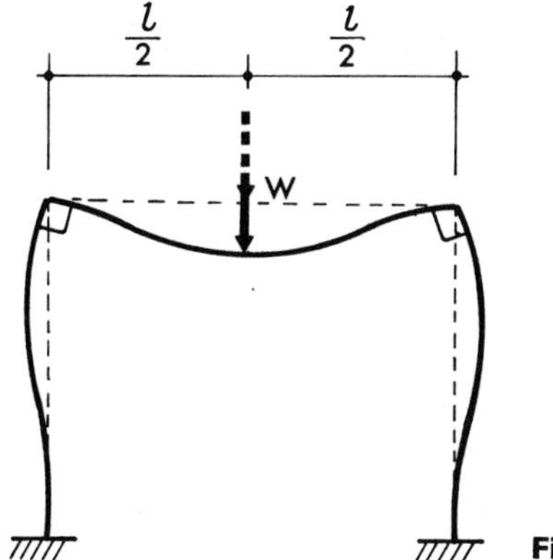

Fig. 7.2.2

An accurate analysis of the frame under vertical loads cannot be easily obtained by simplifying assumptions and statics, because the location of inflection points in the columns and the beam is very sensitive to the rigidity ratio $(I_b/l)/(I_c/h)$. Yet, for purposes of preliminary design, when a rigid frame is hinged at the foot of the columns, one may assume the beam to develop, under a uniform load w, inflection points (i.e., hinges) at a distance $l/10$ from its ends, so that the maximum positive moment in the beam of the frame is (Fig. 7.2.3b):

$$M_e = \tfrac{1}{8}w(0.8l)^2 = 0.08\, wl^2,$$

and the maximum negative moment is (Fig. 7.2.3b):

$$M_b = 0.4\, wl(0.1\, l) + \tfrac{1}{2}(0.1\, wl)(0.1\, l) = 0.045\, wl^2.$$

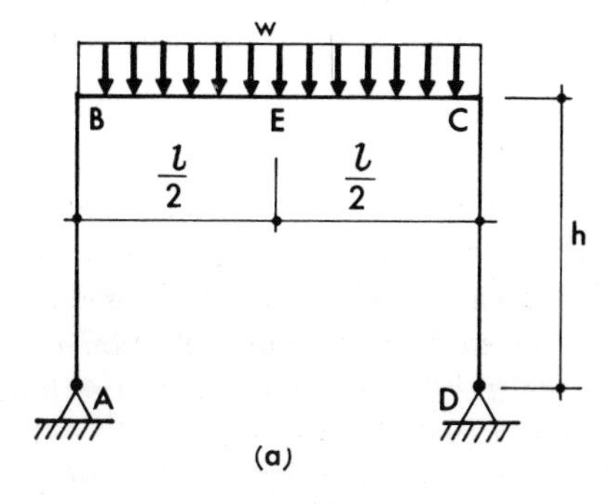

Fig. 7.2.3a

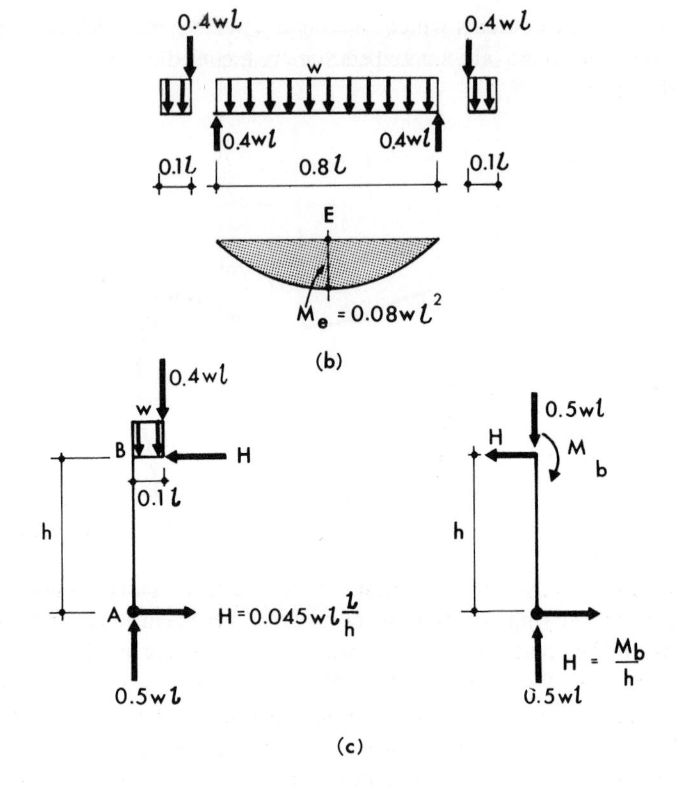

Fig. 7.2.3b-c

By rotational equilibrium of the column about B (Fig. 7.2.3c):

$$Hh - M_b = 0 \quad \therefore \quad H = 0.045\, wl\left(\frac{l}{h}\right).$$

H is also the compression in the beam as shown by the free body diagrams of Fig. 7.2.3c. By vertical equilibrium, the column reactions equal half the load:

$$V_a = V_d = 0.5\, wl.$$

For frames like that in Fig. 7.2.4a, with columns fixed at their foot, experience shows that the inflection points in the beam may also be assumed to develop at a distance $l/10$ from its ends, and that M_e and M_b have approximately the same values as in hinged frames. The inflection points in the columns, which may be said to be at their hinged foot in the hinged frame, may be proved to develop in all cases at a height $h/3$ (Fig. 7.2.4b), so that:

$$H(\tfrac{2}{3}h) - M_b = 0 \quad \therefore \quad H = 0.0675\, wl\left(\frac{l}{h}\right),$$

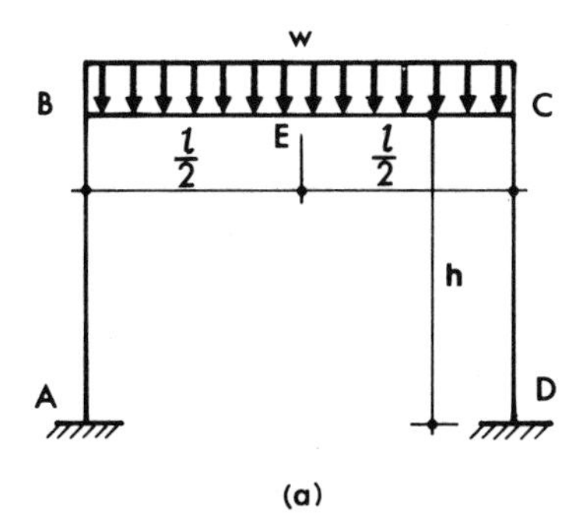

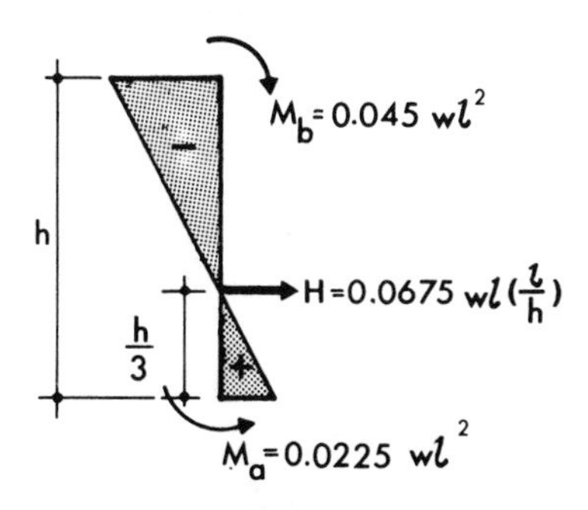

Fig. 7.2.4

and

$$M_a = H\left(\frac{h}{3}\right) = \frac{M_b}{2} = 0.0225\ wl^2.$$

For a hinged multi-bay, single story frame under lateral loads (Fig. 7.2.5a), the approximate *portal method* assumes that the total lateral load is shared by each bay as if the frame consisted of a series of single-bay frames (Fig. 7.2.5b), each one of which absorbs a fraction of the total lateral load W proportional to the moment of inertia of its columns. For equal columns this assumption implies that in a frame with m bays, the shear in the outer columns is $W/(2m)$

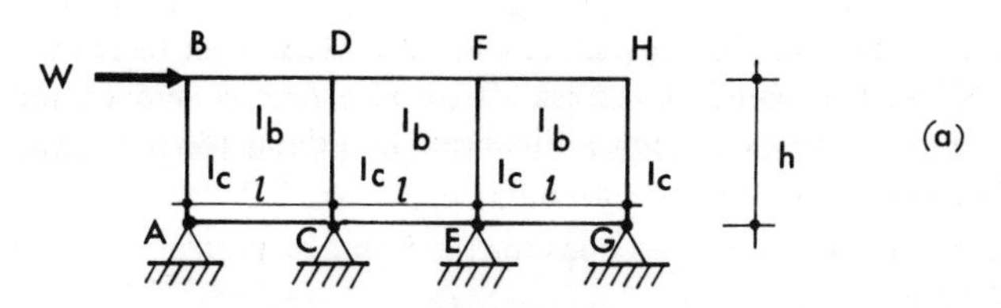

Fig. 7.2.5a

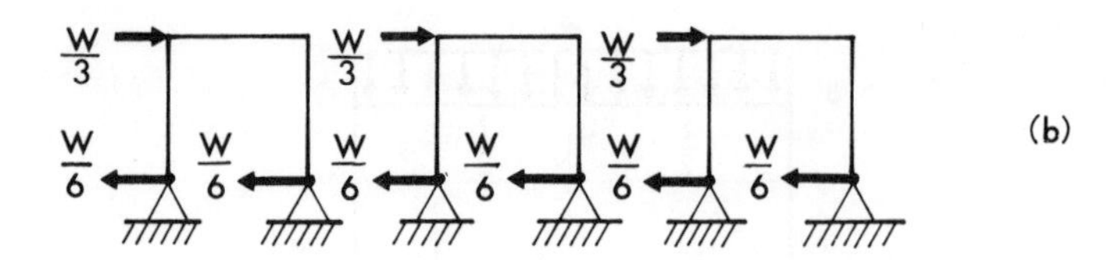

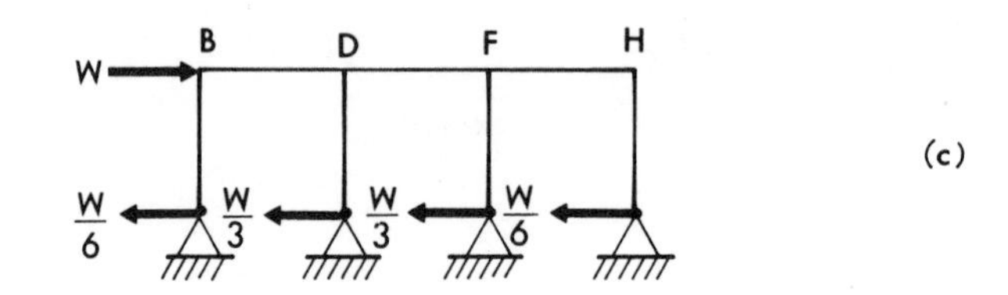

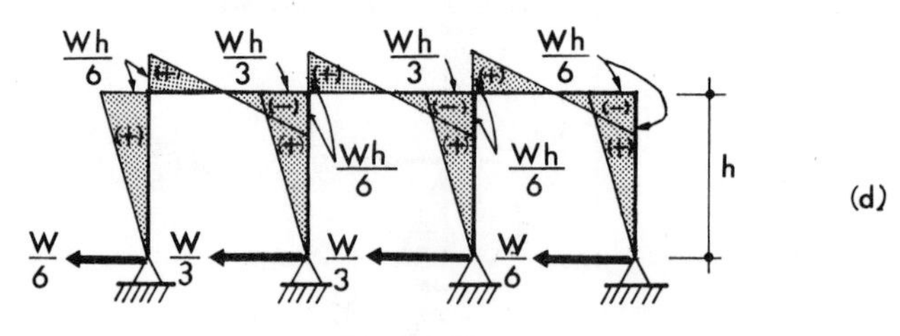

Fig. 7.2.5b–d

and in the inner columns W/m (Fig. 7.2.5c). The moments at the top of the outer columns are $Wh/(2m)$ and at the top of the inner columns Wh/m. The moments in the beam at the outer supports are $Wh/(2m)$. The moments Wh/m at the top of the inner columns, by symmetry, are balanced by 2 equal moments $Wh/(2m)$ at the ends of the beams meeting at that column. Hence, the moments at the end of each beam are all equal to $Wh/(2m)$, and the beams develop an inflection point at mid-span. Figure 7.2.5d gives the bending moment diagram for a three-bay frame.

PROBLEMS

7.2.1 A fixed frame with $h = 15$ ft and $l = 20$ ft carries a uniform load $w = 10$ k/ft over its beam. Determine suitable WF sections for its beam and columns for $F_b = 20$ ksi and $F_c = 15$ ksi, after evaluating the compression H and the maximum bending moment in the beam and the maximum compression and bending moment in the columns.

7.2.2 Determine suitable WF sections for the frame of Problem 7.2.1 if the frame is hinged.

7.2.3 A fixed steel frame with $h = 12$ ft and $l = 30$ ft resists a lateral wind force $W = 5$ k at its top. Determine suitable WF sections for its beam and its columns for $F_s = 6$ ksi.

7.2.4 Design the frame of Problem 7.2.3 if the frame is hinged.

7.2.5 A two-story fixed frame has $l = 30$ ft and a story height $h = 12$ ft. It carries uniform loads $w_2 = 1$ k/ft and $w_1 = 3$ k/ft on the upper and lower beams, respectively (Fig. 7.2.6). Design the frame with WF sections considering only bending in the beams and $F_s = 18$ ksi, and compression and bending in the columns and $F_s = 22$ ksi.

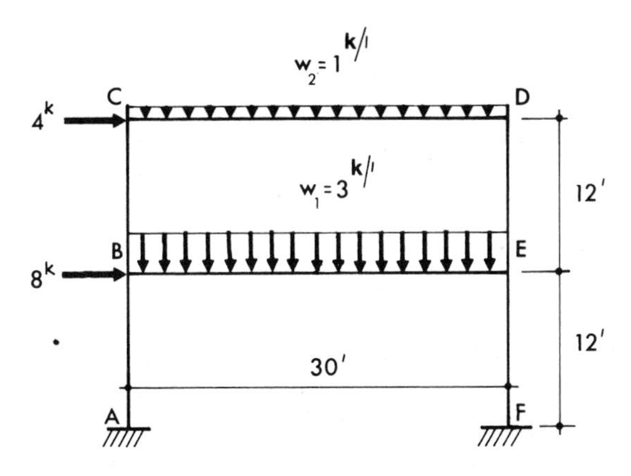

Fig. 7.2.6

7.2.6 The frame of Problem 7.2.5 resists wind loads $W_2 = 4$ k and $W_1 = 8$ k at its upper and lower beams (Fig. 7.2.6). Obtain the maximum moments in the beams and maximum moments and compression in the columns and check whether the stresses are below $F_s = 6$ ksi.

7.2.7 A 4,000 psi concrete fixed frame with $h = 12$ ft and $l = 24$ ft carries a load $w = 3$ k/ft on its beam. Determine the cross section of its beam at mid-span by considering bending only (see Section 5.9) and the cross section of its columns by considering compression only, assuming $b = 8$ in. for both. Determine the areas of steel in compression and tension required to resist the bending moments at the top and at the bottom of the columns, ignoring concrete resistance. Assume $F_s = 22$ ksi and, for the columns only, $F_c = 1{,}000$ ksi. Neglect the dead load of the frame.

7.2.8 The frame of Problem 7.2.7 resists a wind force $W = 3$ k at the beam level. Evaluate the additional steel areas in tension and compression required to resist the wind moments.

7.2.9 A one-story steel frame with three 10 ft bays has identical columns 10 ft high hinged at their foot and carries a horizontal load of 12 k at the beam level. Determine WF sections for its columns and beams for $F_s = 6$ ksi.

7.2.10 A one-story, reinforced concrete frame has two 18 ft wide bays and identical columns 12 ft high fixed at their foot. Determine the bending moment diagram for the frame due to a horizontal load of 20 k applied at the beam level, assuming the beam to be much stiffer than the columns.

7.3 The Cantilever Method

As a final example of the reduction of a statically indeterminate frame to a statically determinate one by means of simplifying assumptions, consider the frame of Fig. 7.3.1a acted upon by lateral loads. The assumption (made in Section 7.2 for one-bay, one-story frames) that under the action of lateral loads, inflection points develop at mid-span in the beams and at mid-height in the columns (Fig. 7.3.1b), does not reduce this frame to be statically determinate. This may be easily checked by noticing, for example, that the 3 unknown vertical reactions in the columns at A, B and C cannot be determined by statics alone as was the case for the simple frame, since only 2 independent equations may be written among them. Hence, one additional simplifying assumption is needed to determine the axial forces in the columns.

The additional assumption made in the so-called *cantilever method* is that (as shown in Fig. 7.3.1a) the axial load in a column at the level of each set of column hinges is proportional to the column area A and to its distance d from the centroid of the column areas (see Appendix A.1).

The cantilever method assumption is equivalent to stating that under the action of the external loads the frame behaves as a cantilever beam and develops bending stresses, which vary linearly through the depth of the beam, i.e., through the width of the frame. The axial forces in the columns are then the product of these stresses times the column areas.

The distance $\bar{x}$ of the centroid 0 of the column areas from the point A in the frame of Fig. 7.3.1a is located by equating the sum of the moments of the areas about A to the sum of the areas times $\bar{x}$ (see Appendix A.1):

$$2 \times 0 + 2 \times 20 + 1 \times 30 = (2 + 2 + 1)\bar{x} \quad \therefore \quad \bar{x} = 14 \text{ ft}.$$

The linear stress variation goes through the centroid 0, and indicating by R_1, R_2, R_3 the axial forces at any hinge level in the columns of column lines 1,2,3, the cantilever method assumption gives:

$$\frac{R_2}{R_3} = \left(\frac{A_2}{A_3}\right)\left(\frac{d_2}{d_3}\right) = \left(\frac{2}{1}\right)\frac{6}{16} \quad \therefore \quad R_2 = \frac{3}{4}R_3, \tag{a}$$

$$\frac{R_1}{R_3} = \left(\frac{A_1}{A_3}\right)\left(\frac{d_1}{d_3}\right) = \left(\frac{2}{1}\right)\frac{-14}{16} \quad \therefore \quad R_1 = -\frac{7}{4}R_3, \tag{b}$$

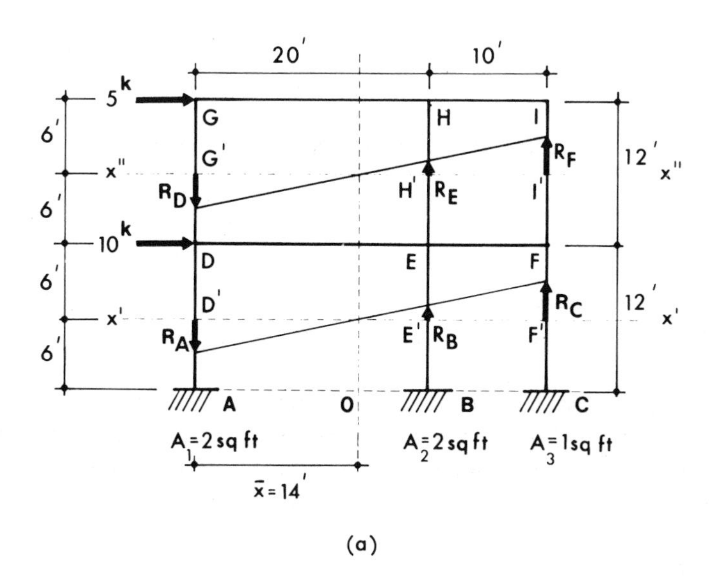

(a)

(b)

Fig. 7.3.1

where the minus sign of R_1 indicates that, if R_3 is compressive, R_1 is tensile and vice versa. If we cut a free-body diagram by means of a horizontal section at the first hinge line $x' - x'$, we obtain for rotational equilibrium about D':

$$R_C \times 30 + R_B \times 20 - 5 \times 18 - 10 \times 6 = 0,$$

or, by (a) and (b):

$$R_C \times 30 + \tfrac{3}{4} R_C \times 20 - 150 = 0 \quad \therefore \quad R_C = \tfrac{150}{45} = 3.33\text{ k},$$
$$R_B = \tfrac{3}{4} R_C = 2.50\text{ k}, \qquad R_A = -\tfrac{7}{4} R_C = -5.83\text{ k}.$$

Similarly, a section at the second hinge line $x'' - x''$ gives:

$$R_F \times 30 + R_E \times 20 - 5 \times 6 = 0,$$

or, by (a) and (b):

$$R_F \times 30 + \tfrac{3}{4} R_F \times 20 - 5 \times 6 = 0 \quad \therefore \quad R_F = \tfrac{30}{45} = 0.67\text{ k},$$
$$R_E = \tfrac{3}{4} R_F = 0.5\text{ k}, \qquad R_D = -\tfrac{7}{4} R_F = -1.17\text{ k}.$$

Once the axial forces in the columns are obtained, the shears, bending moments and axial forces in the beams are computed by the equilibrium of free body diagrams starting from the top of the building and working down.

With reference to Fig. 7.3.1c, one obtains:

(G)

$$\sum F_z = 0: \quad -1.17 + V_1 = 0 \quad \therefore \quad V_1 = 1.17\text{ k},$$
$$\sum M_{G'} = 0: \quad 1.17 \times 10 + H_1 \times 6 - 5 \times 6 = 0 \quad \therefore \quad H_1 = 3.06\text{ k},$$
$$\sum F_x = 0: \quad 5 - 3.06 - H_1' = 0 \quad \therefore \quad H_1' = 1.94\text{ k}.$$

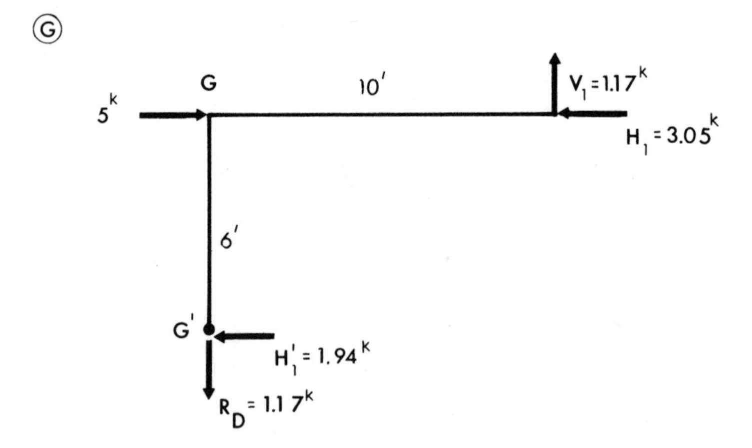

(H)

$$\sum F_z = 0: \quad -1.17 + 0.5 + V_2 = 0 \quad \therefore \quad V_2 = 0.67\text{ k},$$
$$\sum M_{H'} = 0: \quad +H_2 \times 6 + 0.67 \times 5 + 1.17 \times 10 - 3.06 \times 6 = 0$$
$$\therefore \quad H_2 = 0.56\text{ k},$$
$$\sum F_x = 0: \quad 3.06 - 0.56 - H_2' = 0, \qquad H_2' = 2.50\text{ k}.$$

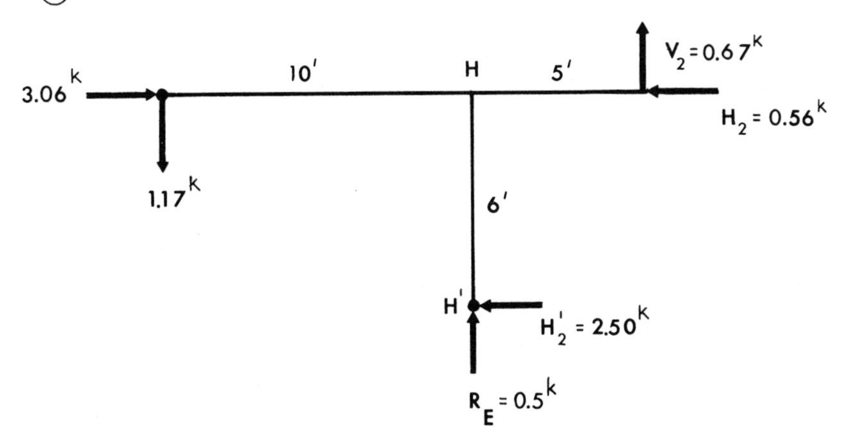

(I)

$$\sum F_x = 0: \quad +0.56 - H_3' = 0 \quad \therefore \quad H_3' = 0.56 \text{ k},$$

and as a check:

$$\sum F_z = 0: \quad -V_2 + R_F = -0.67 + 0.67 = 0,$$

$$\sum M_{I'} = 0: \quad 0.67 \times 5 - 0.56 \times 6 = 0,$$

$$\sum F_x = 0 \text{ for frame above upper hinges:}$$

$$5.0 - 1.94 - 2.50 - 0.50 - 0.56 = 0.$$

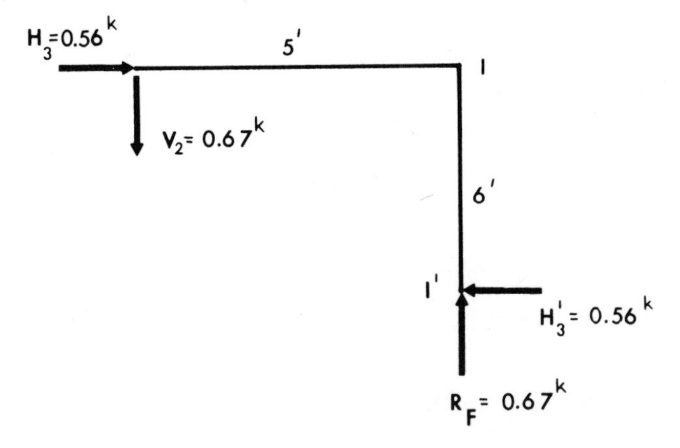

(D)

$$\sum F_z = 0: \quad V_1' + 1.17 - 5.83 = 0 \quad \therefore \quad V_1' = 4.67\text{ k},$$
$$\sum M_{D'} = 0: \quad -1.94 \times 12 - 10 \times 6 + 4.67 \times 10 + H_1'' \times 6 = 0$$
$$\therefore \quad H_1'' = 6.11\text{ k},$$
$$\sum F_x = 0: \quad 10 + 1.94 - 6.11 - H_1''' = 0 \quad \therefore \quad H_1''' = 5.83\text{ k}.$$

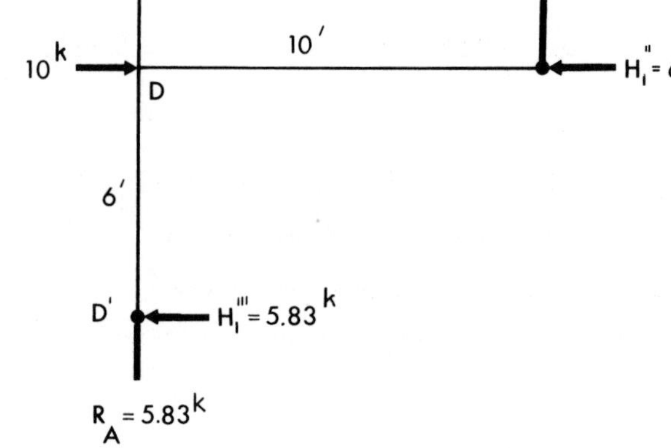

(E)

$$\sum F_z = 0: \quad -4.67 + 2.5 - 0.5 + V_2' = 0 \quad \therefore \quad V_2' = 2.67\text{ k},$$
$$\sum M_{E'} = 0: \quad 4.67 \times 10 - 2.50 \times 12 - 6.11 \times 6$$
$$+ 2.67 \times 5 + H_2'' \times 6 = 0 \quad \therefore \quad H_2'' = 1.11\text{ k},$$
$$\sum F_x = 0: \quad -1.11 + 6.11 + 2.50 - H_2''' = 0 \quad \therefore \quad H_2''' = 7.50\text{ k}.$$

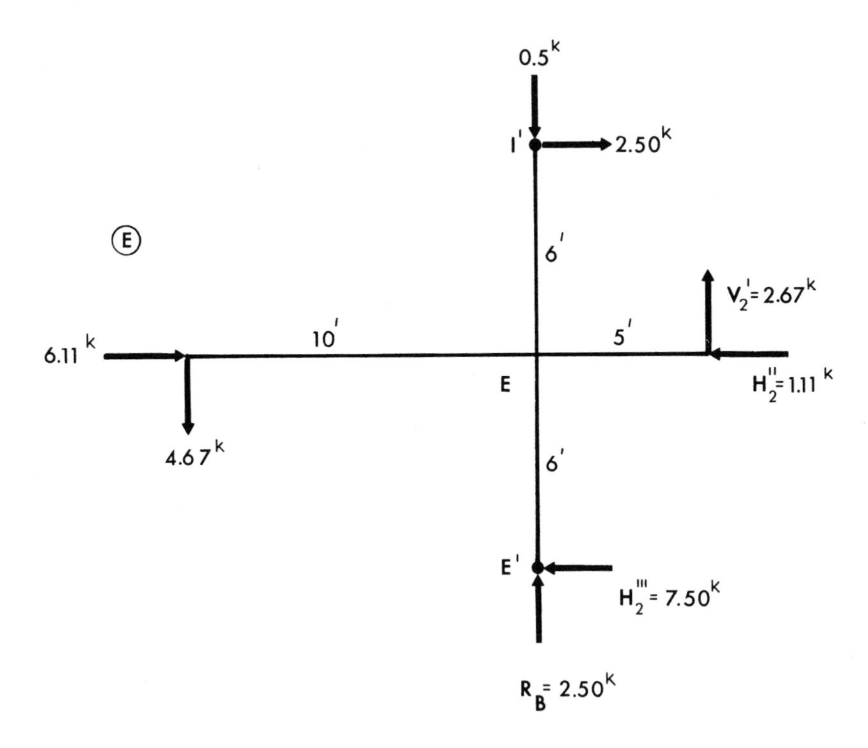

(F)

$$\sum F_x = 0: \quad 0.56 + 1.11 - H_3''' = 0 \quad \therefore \quad H_3''' = 1.67\text{ k},$$

and as a check:

$$\sum F_z = 0: \quad 3.33 - 2.67 - 0.67 = 0,$$

$$\sum M_F = 0: \quad 0.56 \times 6 + 1.67 \times 6 - 2.67 \times 5 = 0,$$

$$\sum F_x = 0 \text{ above lower hinge line:}$$

$$15.00 - 5.83 - 7.50 - 1.67 = 0.$$

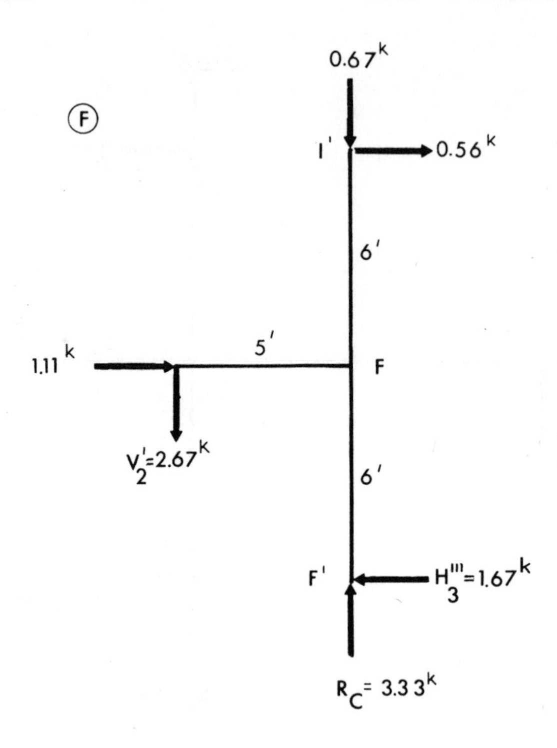

The bending moments at the ends of the bars and beams are:

$M_{GH} = M_{GD} = 1.94 \times 6 = 1.17 \times 10 = 11.67$ k ft,

$M_{HG} = 1.17 \times 10 = 11.67$ k ft, $\quad M_{HI} = 0.67 \times 5 = 3.33$ k ft,

$M_{HE} = 2.50 \times 6 = 15.00$ k ft,

$M_{IH} = M_{IF} = 0.67 \times 5 = 0.56 \times 6 = 3.33$ k ft,

$M_{DG} = 1.94 \times 6 = 11.67$ k ft, $\quad M_{DE} = 4.67 \times 10 = 46.67$ k ft,

$M_{DA} = 5.83 \times 6 = 35.00$ k ft,

$M_{ED} = 4.67 \times 10 = 46.67$ k ft, $\quad M_{EH} = 2.50 \times 6 = 15.00$ k ft,

$M_{EF} = 2.67 \times 5 = 13.33$ k ft, $\quad M_{EB} = 7.50 \times 6 = 45.00$ k ft,

$M_{FE} = 2.67 \times 5 = 13.33$ k ft, $\quad M_{FI} = 0.56 \times 6 = 3.33$ k ft,

$M_{FC} = 1.67 \times 6 = 10.00$ k ft,

$M_A = 1.67 \times 6 = 10.00$ k ft, $\quad M_B = 2.50 \times 6 = 15.00$ k ft,

$M_C = 1.67 \times 6 = 10.00$ k ft.

PROBLEMS

7.3.1 Analyze the symmetrical frame in Fig. 7.3.2 by the cantilever method.

7.3.2 Evaluate the moment at A in the frame in Fig. 7.3.3 by the cantilever method.

7.3.3 Evaluate the moment at C in the frame in Fig. 7.3.3 by the cantilever method if all columns have the same area.

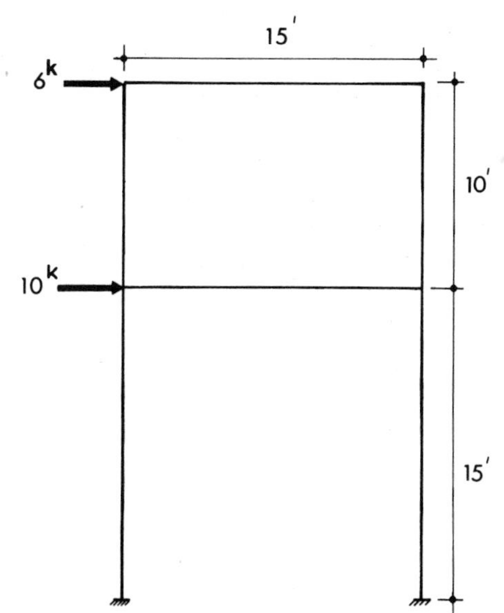

Fig. 7.3.2

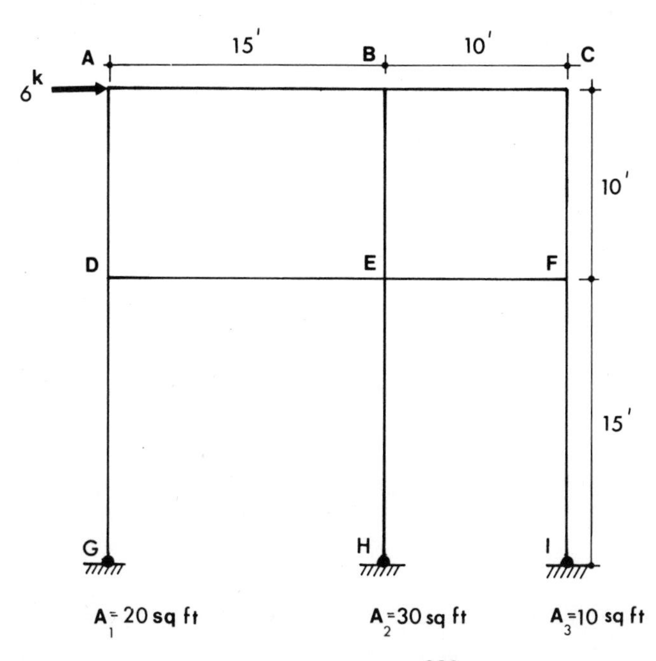

Fig. 7.3.3

7.3.4 Evaluate the moment at E in the column EA of the frame in Fig. 7.3.4, in which all columns have the same area, using the cantilever method.

7.3.5 Evaluate by the cantilever method the moment at E in the beam EF of the frame in Fig. 7.3.4, in which all the columns have the same area.

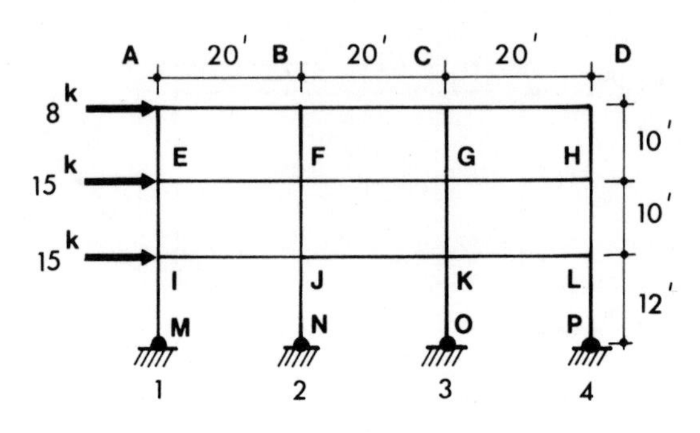

Fig. 7.3.4

Chapter Eight

8.1 Three-Dimensional Structures

The statically determinate plane structures considered in the preceding chapters were loaded in their plane, developed reactions lying in this plane and were analyzed by means of the 3 equations of plane equlibrium, $\sum F_x = 0$, $\sum F_z = 0$, $\sum M_y = 0$. Many three-dimensional structures may be reduced to combinations of plane structures, either statically determinate or indeterminate. For example, for many loading conditions the framework of a high-rise building may be analyzed as a set of parallel plane frames, each loaded in its plane and connected by the floors of the building. But some structures exhibit a truly three-dimensional behavior which is not analyzable by plane statics. Such are space trusses and frames, ribbed domes, pneumatic roofs, cable suspended structures and thin shells.

Many three-dimensional structures are statically determinate and may be analyzed by the 6 equations of space equilibrium (see Sections 1.3 and 1.4):

$$\sum F_x = 0, \qquad \sum F_y = 0, \qquad \sum F_z = 0, \tag{8.1.1}$$

$$\sum M_x = 0, \qquad \sum M_y = 0, \qquad \sum M_z = 0, \tag{8.1.2}$$

Space Structures

of which the equations of plane equilibrium are a special case. Moreover, the behavior of statically indeterminate, three-dimensional structures may be often approximated, at least in preliminary design, by that of judiciously chosen, similar statically determinate structures.

We shall first consider the three-dimensional behavior of statically determinate structures capable of developing bending stresses (such as combinations of beams in space), but we will then limit our analysis to space trusses, ribbed domes, membranes and thin shells, so loaded and supported as to develop negligible bending stresses. The analysis of the first type of structures requires the use of all 6 equations of equilibrium, while the second (which, being momentless, might be called *funicular in space*) is analyzed by means of equations (8.1.1) only.

8.2 Three-Dimensional Beam Behavior

Consider the post of Fig. 8.2.1, which carries a rectangular sign of weight W connected to the points A and B of the cantilevered beam by two short rigid bars, and assume the weights of the beam and of the post to be negligible. Under the action of the vertical force W, this structure behaves as a plane structure, and its bending moments, shears and axial forces may be obtained by plane statics. Referring the post and beam to an x-axis parallel to the beam, a z-axis parallel to the post and a y-axis positive into the plane of the structure (Fig. 8.2.1a), let us label the reactions R, the shears V and the normal forces N with subscripts indicating their line of action, and the bending moments M with subscripts indicating their rotational axis. Thus (Fig. 8.2.1b), the shears, moments and axial forces in the beam and post are, with the usual sign convention:

$$\text{(A–B)} \quad V_z = \frac{W}{2}, \qquad M_y = -\frac{1}{2}Wx, \qquad N_x = 0;$$

$$\text{(B–C)} \quad V_z = W, \qquad M_y = -\frac{1}{2}Wx - \frac{1}{2}W(x-a) = -W\left(x - \frac{a}{2}\right),$$

$$N_x = 0;$$

$$\text{(C–D)} \quad V_x = 0, \qquad M_y = -W\left(\frac{a}{2} + c\right), \qquad N_z = -W.$$

Figure 8.2.1b shows that the post reactions at D are an upward vertical force $R_z = -W$ and a counterclockwise moment $-W(a/2 + c)$. Figure 8.2.1c gives the bending moment diagram for the beam and post.

On the other hand, if a lateral wind exerts on the sign a pressure p per unit area, a horizontal force $P = pad$ is applied to the structure and its behavior becomes three-dimensional since P does not act in the plane of the structure. The force P bends the beam in the horizontal x, y-plane, but also twists the beam around its axis x because of the lever arm $d/2$.

To analyze the beam under the action of the wind force P only, we consider it as a free body cut out from the vertical post and refer it to the x-, y-, z-axes of Fig. 8.2.2a. In this three-dimensional loading condition, it is more convenient to consider the forces and moments, respectively, as positive when acting in the direction of the positive axes and rotating in accordance with the right-hand screw convention of sign, in which $+M_x$ rotates $+y$ towards $+z$, $+M_y$ rotates $+z$ towards $+x$ and $+M_z$ rotates $+x$ towards $+y$.

The 3 reactions R_x, R_y, R_z and 3 *reactive* moments $M_{C,x}$, $M_{C,y}$, $M_{C,z}$ at the support section C are determined by applying equations (8.1.1) and (8.1.2) to the beam "free body." Taking the moment equations about axes parallel to x, y, z through C, we obtain:

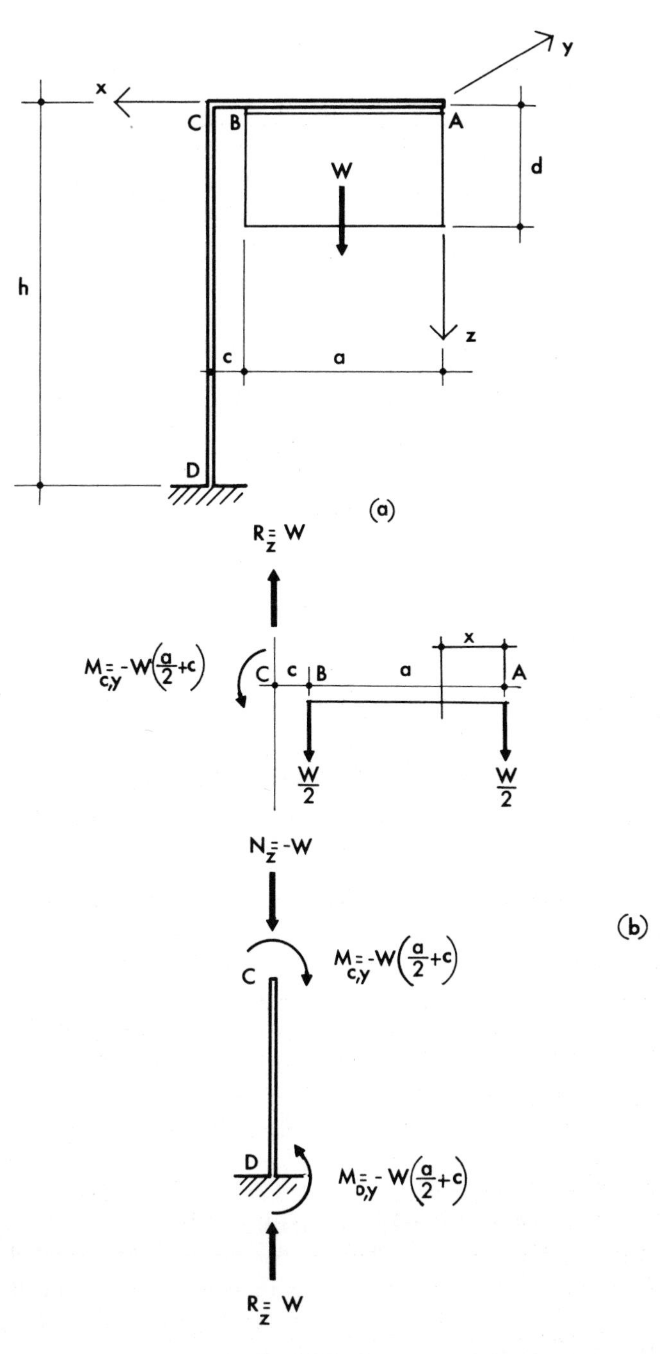

x
y
C
B
A
W
d
h
z
c
a
D
(a)
$R_z = W$
$M_{c,y} = -W\left(\frac{a}{2}+c\right)$
x
C
c
B
a
A
$\frac{W}{2}$
$\frac{W}{2}$
$N_z = -W$
(b)
C
$M_{c,y} = -W\left(\frac{a}{2}+c\right)$
D
$M_{D,y} = -W\left(\frac{a}{2}+c\right)$
$R_z = W$

Fig. 8.2.1a–b

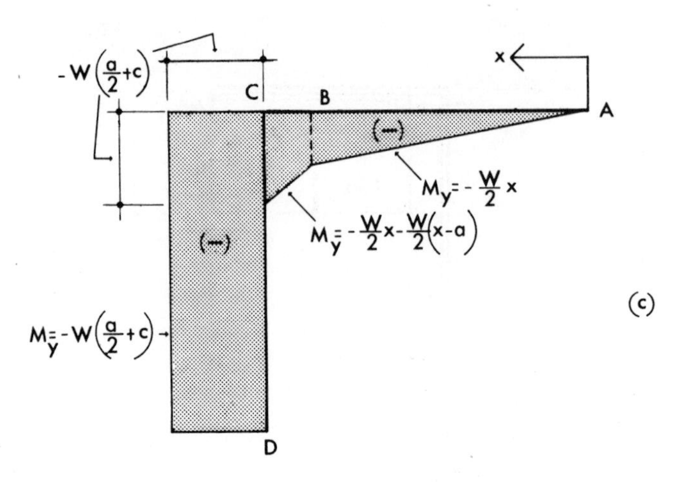

Fig. 8.2.1c

$$\sum F_x = 0: \quad R_x + 0 = 0 \quad \therefore \quad R_x = 0;$$
$$\sum F_y = 0: \quad R_y + P = 0 \quad \therefore \quad R_y = -P;$$
$$\sum F_z = 0: \quad R_z + 0 = 0 \quad \therefore \quad R_z = 0;$$
$$\sum M_{x,C} = 0: \quad -P\frac{d}{2} + M_{C,x} = 0 \quad \therefore \quad M_{C,x} = +P\frac{d}{2};$$
$$\sum M_{y,C} = 0: \quad M_{C,y} + 0 = 0 \quad \therefore \quad M_{C,y} = 0;$$
$$\sum M_{z,C} = 0: \quad M_{C,z} - P\left(\frac{a}{2} + c\right) = 0 \quad \therefore \quad M_{C,z} = P\left(\frac{a}{2} + c\right).$$

To evaluate the horizontal shear and bending moment due to P at a section x of the beam, P is first split into two forces $P/2$ applied at E and F; these are then lifted to the points A and B on the beam axis by adding at A and B two moments $M_x = -(P/2)(d/2) = -Pd/4$ (see Section 2.3). The cantilever beam thus develops in the horizontal x, y-plane the shears V_y and the bending moments M_z shown in Fig. 8.2.2b and c, in which the signs of V_y and M_z are chosen according to the usual beam sign convention.

The moments $M_x = -Pd/4$ at A and B are *twisting moments.* The twisting moment at any section x of the beam is the algebraic sum of all the twisting moments applied to the beam from its free end A up to the section x. The *twisting moment diagram* for the beam appears in Fig. 8.2.2d* and is considered positive when acting as a $+M_x$ moment on the face of the section facing in the $+x$-direction.

*We shall investigate in Section 8.3 the internal torsional stresses which must be developed by the beam to equilibrate these external twisting moments.

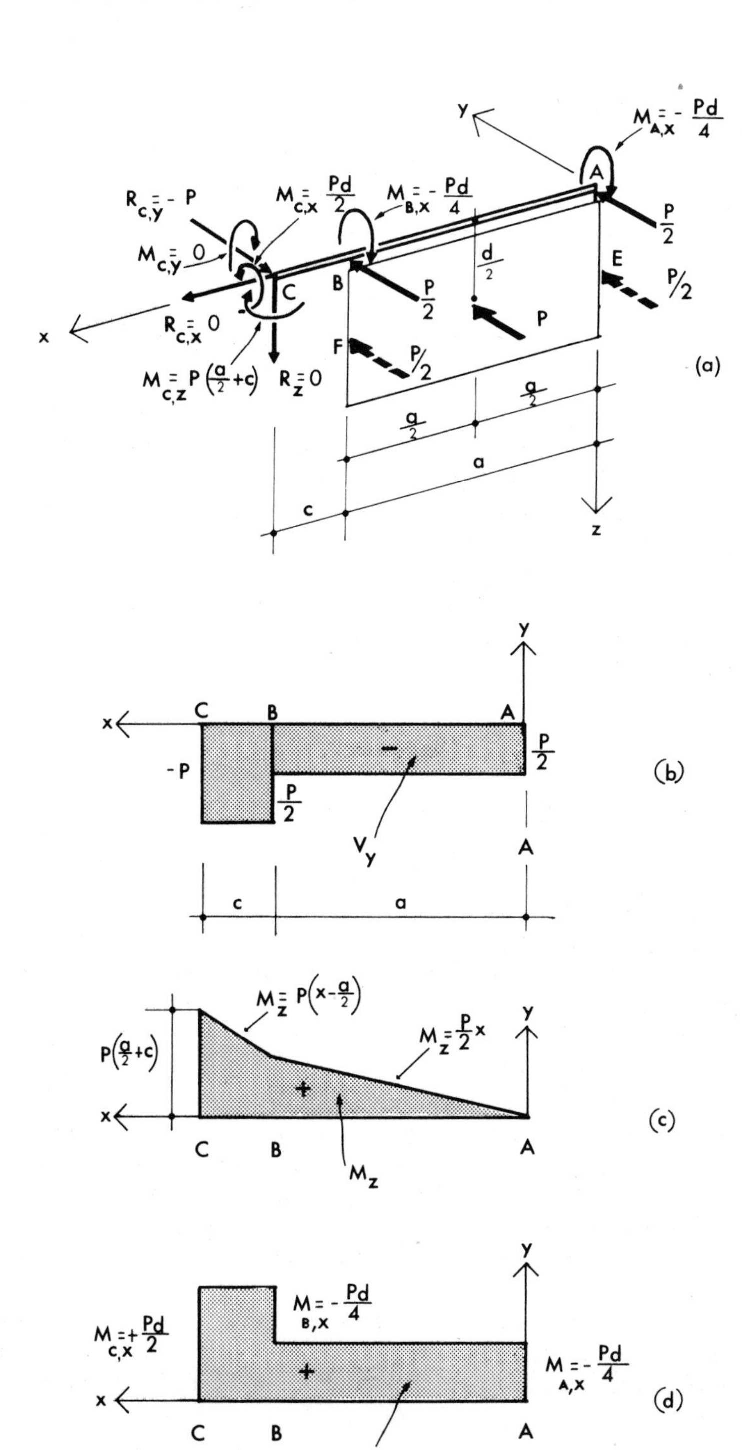
y
$M_{A,x} = -\frac{Pd}{4}$
A
$R_{C,y} = -P$
$M_{C,x} = \frac{Pd}{2}$
$M_{B,x} = -\frac{Pd}{4}$
$\frac{P}{2}$
$M_{C,y} = 0$
$\frac{d}{2}$
E
$P/2$
B
C
$\frac{P}{2}$
x
$R_{C,x} = 0$
P
F
$P/2$
(a)
$M_{C,z} = P\left(\frac{a}{2}+c\right)$
$R_z = 0$
$\frac{a}{2}$
$\frac{a}{2}$
a
c
z
y
x
C
B
A
-P
$\frac{P}{2}$
$\frac{P}{2}$
V_y
A
(b)
c
a
$M_z = P\left(x-\frac{a}{2}\right)$
y
$M_z = \frac{P}{2}x$
$P\left(\frac{a}{2}+c\right)$
+
x
C
B
A
(c)
M_z
y
$M_{B,x} = -\frac{Pd}{4}$
$M_{C,x} = +\frac{Pd}{2}$
+
$M_{A,x} = -\frac{Pd}{4}$
x
(d)
C
B
A
M_x

Fig. 8.2.2

The forces and moments exerted by the beam on the post at C are equal and opposite to the beam reactions $R_{C,y}$, $M_{C,z}$ and $M_{C,x}$. Hence, the reactions on the post at D must equilibrate the force $-R_{C,y} = P$ and the moments $-M_{C,z} = -P(a/2 + c)$, $-M_{C,x} = -Pd/2$ at C (Fig. 8.2.3a):

$$R_{D,y} = -P, \qquad M_{D,x} = -P\left(H - \frac{d}{2}\right), \qquad M_{D,z} = P\left(\frac{a}{2} + c\right).$$

It is seen from Fig. 8.2.3 that the beam bending moment at C, $M_{C,z} = P(a/2 + c)$, is the twisting moment in the post, and that the beam twisting moment, $M_{C,x} = Pd/2$, contributes to the bending moment in the post. Figures 8.2.3b, c and d give the shear, bending moment and twisting moment diagrams for the post. The shear diagram V_y is constant and equal to P. Indicating as positive moments which develop tension in the post's front fibers (the fibers with negative y), we see that the bending moment diagram is the sum of the constant diagram $-Pd/2$ due to the end moment $M_{C,x} = -Pd/2$ and the linear diagram Pz due to the force P; hence:

$$M_x = P\left(z - \frac{d}{2}\right).$$

The twisting moment diagram is constant and equal to:

$$M_{C,z} = P\left(\frac{a}{2} + c\right).$$

The shears, axial forces, bending moments and twisting moments due to the *combined* action of the vertical load W and the horizontal load P are obtained by superposition (see Section 2.5). Thus the beam develops: (a) bending moments in the vertical plane with $M_{y,\max} = -W(a/2 + c)$, (b) bending moments in the horizontal plane with $M_{z,\max} = P(a/2 + c)$, (c) twisting moments with $M_{x,\max} = P(d/2)$, (d) shears in the vertical plane with $V_{z,\max} = -W$ and (e) shears in the horizontal plane with $V_{y,\max} = -P$. Under the combined action of W and P, the post develops: (a) bending moments in the y, z-plane with $M_{x,\max} = -P(H - d/2)$, (b) bending moments in the x, z-plane with $M_{y,\max} = -W(a/2 + c)$, (c) a constant twisting moment $M_z = P(a/2 + c)$, (d) a constant horizontal shear $V_y = P$ and (e) a constant axial compressive force $N_z = W$.

The normal stresses in a beam due to axial forces and to bending moments acting in two perpendicular planes are obtained by superposition, i.e., by adding the stresses due to each action separately. For example, if the post of Fig. 8.2.1

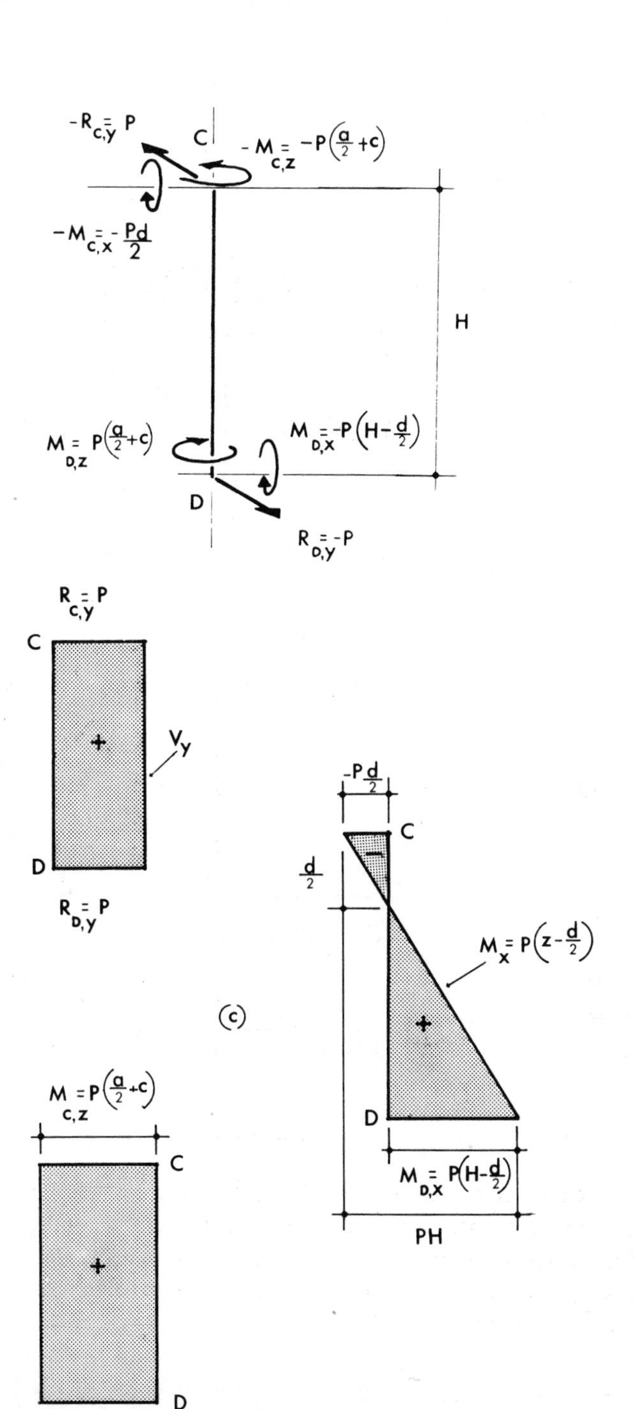

-R C,y = P
C
- M C,z = -P(a/2 + c)
-M C,x = - Pd/2
H
M D,z = P(a/2 + c)
M D,x = -P(H - d/2)
D
R D,y = -P
R C,y = P
C
(b)
+
V y
D
R D,y = P
-P d/2
C
d/2
M x = P(z - d/2)
−
+
(c)
D
M D,x = P(H - d/2)
PH
M C,z = P(a/2 + c)
C
(d)
+
D
M D,z = P(a/2 + c)

Fig. 8.2.3

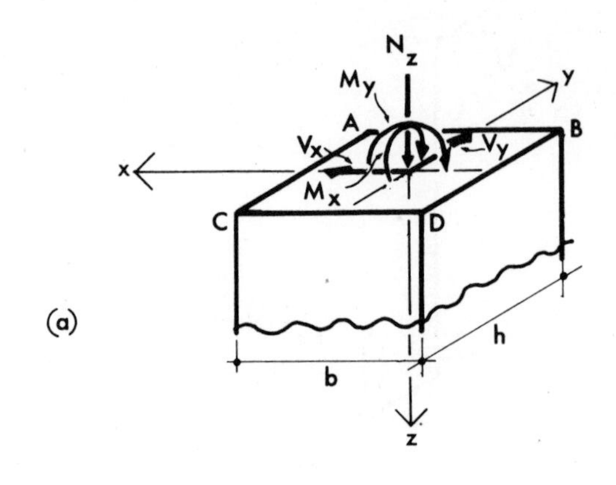

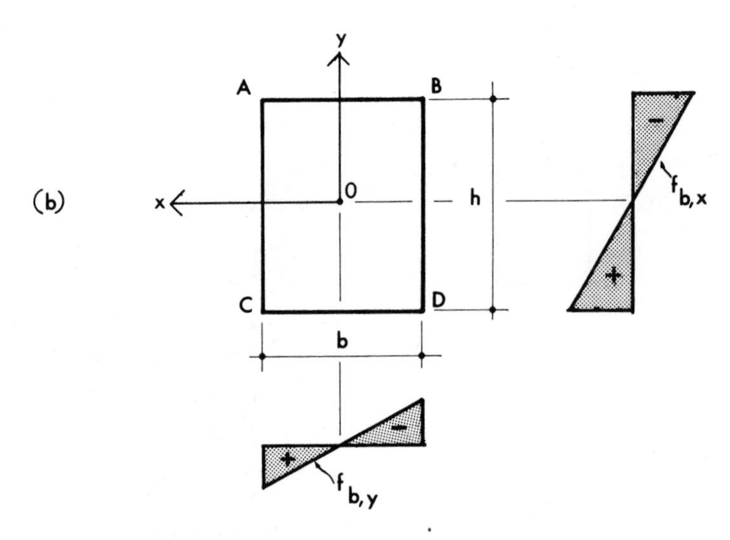

Fig. 8.2.4

has the rectangular cross section of Fig. 8.2.4a and is acted upon at a section z by a compressive axial load N_z, a bending moment M_x in the y, z-plane and a bending moment M_y in the x, z-plane (as shown in the figure), then the corresponding stresses $f_c, f_{b,x}$ and $f_{b,y}$, considered positive when tensile, are (see Sections 3.4, 5.8 and Fig. 8.2.4b):

$$f_c = -\frac{N_z}{bh}, \qquad f_{b,x} = -\frac{M_x y}{bh^3/12}, \qquad f_{b,y} = \frac{M_y x}{hb^3/12}.$$

Notice that $f_{b,x}$ is tensile (i.e., positive) for negative values of y and that the moments of inertia are $I_x = bh^3/12$ for $f_{b,x}$ and $I_y = hb^3/12$ for $f_{b,y}$, since the roles of h and b are interchanged in evaluating $f_{b,x}$ and $f_{b,y}$. Hence, the maximum compressive stress will occur at B, where:

$$f_B = -\frac{N_z}{bh} - \frac{M_x h/2}{bh^3/12} + \frac{M_y(-b/2)}{hb^3/12} = -\frac{1}{bh}\left(N_z + \frac{6M_x}{h} + \frac{6M_y}{b}\right), \quad (8.2.1)$$

and the maximum tensile (or minimum compressive) stress occurs at C, where:

$$f_C = -\frac{1}{bh}\left(N_z - \frac{6M_x}{h} - \frac{6M_y}{b}\right). \quad (8.2.2)$$

Thus, f_C is compressive or tensile depending on the values of N_z, M_x and M_y.

If the shears in the section are V_x and V_y ($V_x = 0$ and $V_y = P$ in the post of Section 8.2) the maximum shear stresses are (see Section 5.7):

$$v_x = \frac{3}{2}\left(\frac{V_x}{bh}\right), \qquad v_y = \frac{3}{2}\left(\frac{V_y}{bh}\right), \quad (8.2.3)$$

and occur along the x-, y-axes through the center 0 of the section. Since v_x and v_y are at right angles to each other, the maximum shear stress at 0 is given by:

$$v_{\max} = \frac{3}{2bh}\sqrt{v_x^2 + v_y^2}. \quad (8.2.4)$$

For example, for:

$$a = 10 \text{ ft}, \quad d = 5 \text{ ft}, \quad c = 2 \text{ ft}, \quad H = 30 \text{ ft}, \quad p = 30 \text{ psf},$$
$$W = 4{,}000 \text{ lb}, \quad b = 1 \text{ ft}, \quad h = 2 \text{ ft},$$

we obtain:

$$N_z = 4{,}000 \text{ lb}, \quad P = 30 \times 10 \times 5 = 1{,}500 \text{ lb} = V_y,$$

$$M_{x,\max} = P\left(H - \frac{d}{2}\right) = 1{,}500(30 - 2.5) = 41{,}250 \text{ ft lb},$$

$$M_{y,\max} = W\left(\frac{a}{2} + c\right) = 4{,}000(5 + 2) = 28{,}000 \text{ ft lb},$$

$$f_B = -\frac{1}{1 \times 2}\left(4{,}000 + \frac{6 \times 41{,}250}{2} + \frac{6 \times 28{,}000}{1}\right)$$
$$= -2{,}000 - 61{,}875 - 84{,}000 = -147{,}875 \text{ psf} = -1{,}027 \text{ psi},$$

$$f_C = -2{,}000 + 61{,}875 + 84{,}000 = +143{,}875 \text{ psf} = +999 \text{ psi},$$

$$v_y = \frac{3}{2}\left(\frac{1{,}500}{1 \times 2}\right) = 1{,}125 \text{ psf} = 7.81 \text{ psi}, \qquad v_x = 0.$$

PROBLEMS

8.2.1 Determine the shear, bending and twisting moment diagrams in the cantilevered beam of Fig. 8.2.5.

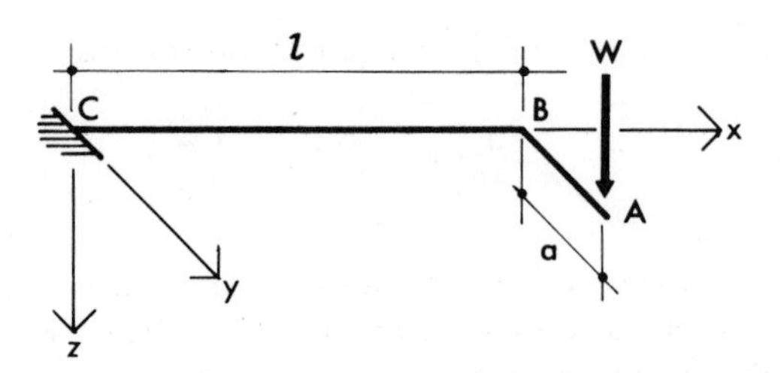

Fig. 8.2.5

8.2.2 Determine the shear, bending and twisting moment diagrams of the cantilever system of Fig. 8.2.6.

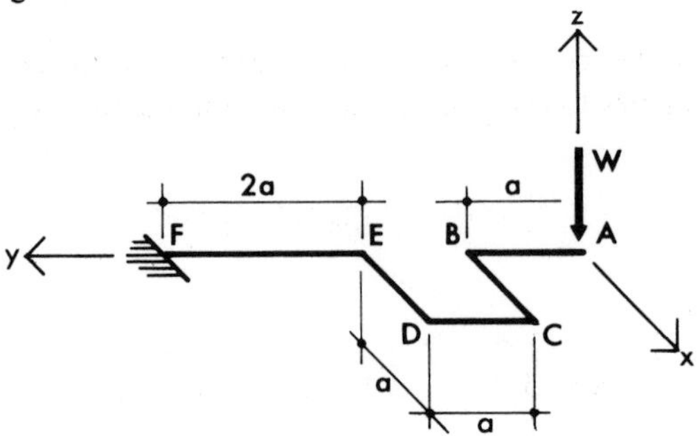

Fig. 8.2.6

8.2.3 Determine the shear, bending and twisting moment diagrams for the symmetrical beam system of Fig. 8.2.7, in which the bar CD is simply supported but prevented from rotating around the x-axis at C and D.

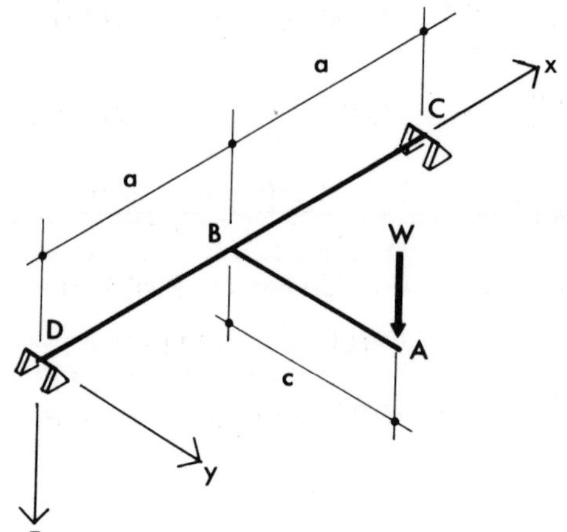

Fig. 8.2.7

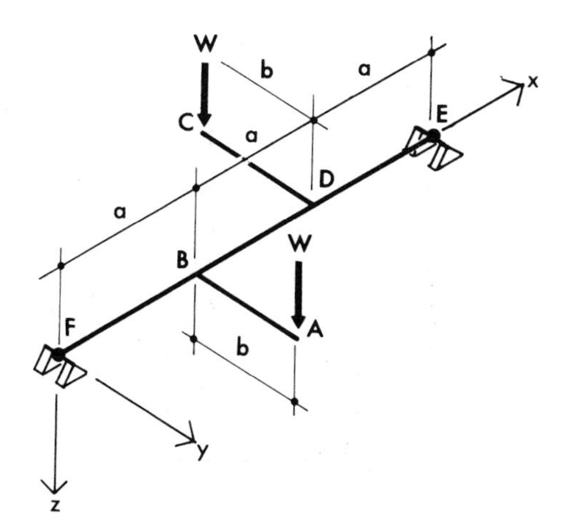

Fig. 8.2.8

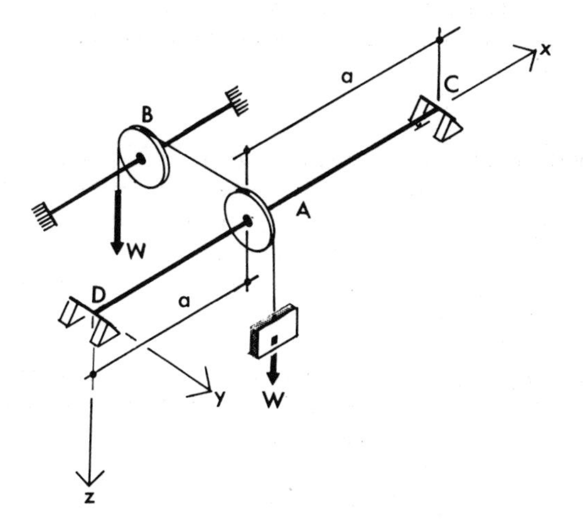

Fig. 8.2.9

8.2.4 Determine the shear, bending and twisting moment diagrams for the beam system of Fig. 8.2.8, in which the bar EF is simply supported and not prevented from rotating around the x-axis at E and F.

8.2.5 A weight W is lifted by means of a rope passing over a pulley A at mid-span of the beam of Fig. 8.2.9 and over a second pulley B at the level of the beam. Determine the shear and bending moment diagrams for this beam.

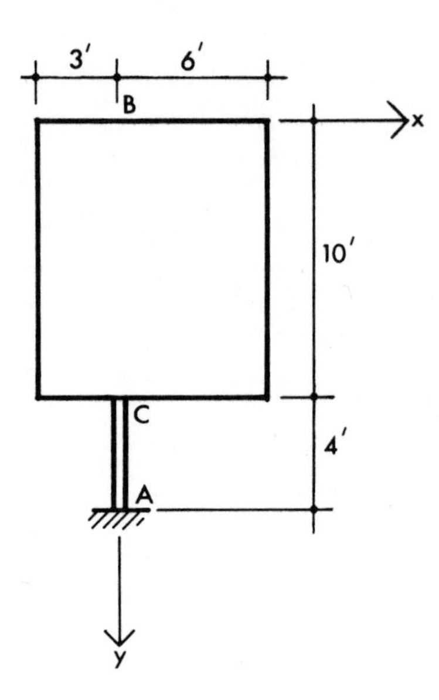

Fig. 8.2.10

8.2.6 The post of Fig. 8.2.10 carries an unsymmetrical vertical sign which is under a wind pressure of 20 psf. Determine the shear, bending and twisting moment diagrams for the post AB.

8.2.7 Determine the thickness of two steel pipes of radius 10 in. and 5 in. used, respectively, as post and beam in the illustrative problem of Section 8.2 (Fig. 8.2.1), if $H = 15$ ft, $c = 2$ ft, $a = 10$ ft, $d = 5$ ft, $W = 6{,}000$ lb and $p = 30$ psf. Use $F_b = 20$ ksi and neglect torsional stresses. Use the formulas of Section 8.2 to evaluate maximum moments and axial and shear forces.

8.2.8 A rectangular column of cross section $b \times h$ supports a compressive load W with an eccentricity e parallel to the side h of its cross section (Fig. 8.2.11). For what value of e/h is the compressive stress zero at the extreme fiber AB? (*Note:* Shift the load W to the center 0 of the section by adding an appropriate moment M_y in the vertical plane through 0.)

8.2.9 A rectangular cross section column of sides b and $h = 3b$ supports a load W with an eccentricity e parallel to b and $2e$ parallel to h. For what value of e/b is the stress at one of the corners of the section equal to zero? What is the maximum stress in the column for this value of e/b? (*Note:* Shift the load W to the center of the section by adding appropriate moments M_x and M_y in the vertical plane through 0.)

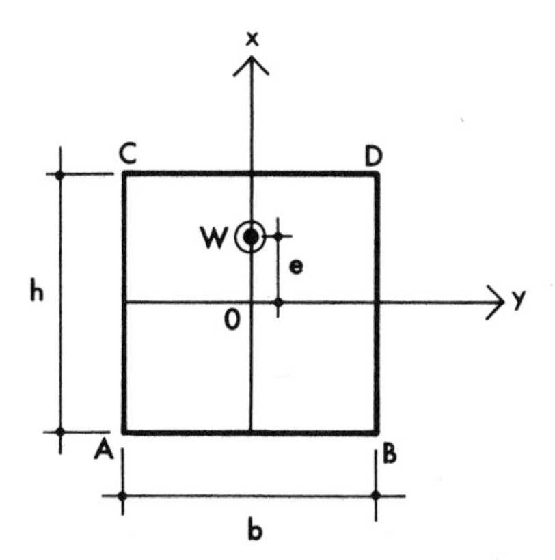

Fig. 8.2.11

8.2.10 A masonry column is designed to carry a centered load of 576 k on its 2 ft × 2 ft cross section. It is found that the actual load is displaced 5.65 in. from the center of the section in a direction at 45° to its sides. By how much is the maximum compressive stress increased in the column? What is the maximum tensile stress developed in the column section?

8.3 Torsional Stresses in Beams

We wish to investigate what kind of internal stresses must be developed by a beam of *symmetrical cross section* in order to equilibrate an external twisting moment $M_x = M_t$ applied at its end $x = 0$. From Fig. 8.3.1a it is seen that for equilibrium in rotation about the beam axis of a free body cut by a section at x, these so-called *torsional stresses* must lie in the plane of the section (i.e., must be shear stresses v_t) and have a resultant moment about the x-axis equal

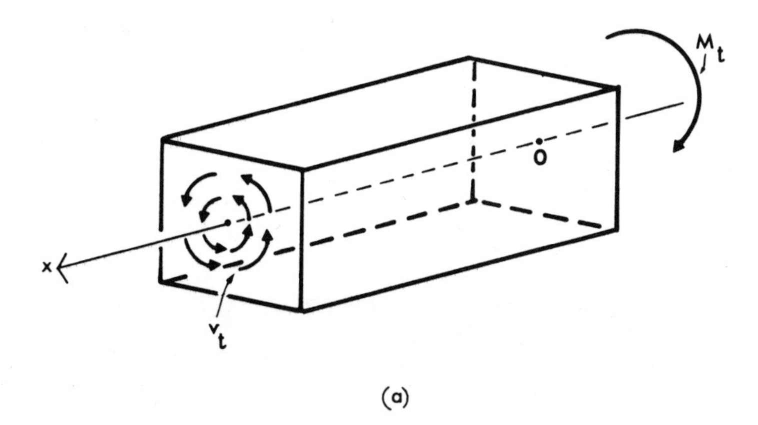

Fig. 8.3.1a

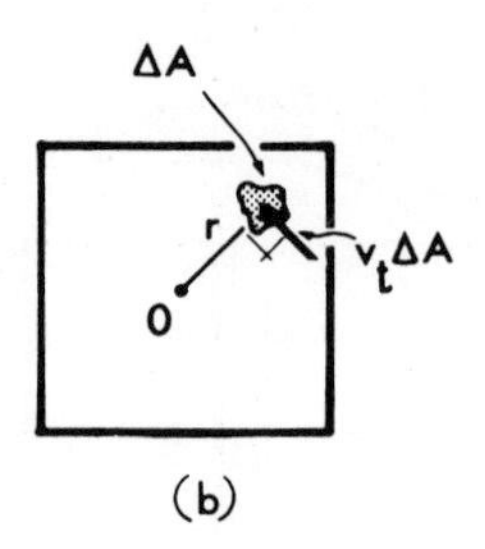

Fig. 8.3.1b

and opposite to M_t. This means that (Fig. 8.3.1b) the sum of the products of the stresses v_t times the elementary areas ΔA times their lever arm r about 0 must be equal to M_t:

$$\sum (v_t \, \Delta A)r = M_t.$$

The only cross section for which it is easy to add up the $(v_t \, \Delta A)r$ terms is the circular cross section, either hollow or full. In a hollow circular section of radius R and small thickness t (Fig. 8.3.2), the torsional shear stress v_t is practically constant, and since the lever arms r of the areas $\Delta A = t\Delta s$ are all equal to R, the moment of the $v_t \, \Delta A$ forces about 0 is:

$$M_t = v_t R \sum t\Delta s = v_t Rt \sum \Delta s = v_t Rt(2\pi R) = 2\pi R^2 t v_t,$$

so that:

$$v_t = \frac{M_t}{2\pi R^2 t}. \tag{8.3.1}$$

For a full circular section (Fig. 8.3.3), experiments show that the torsional shears vary linearly from zero at 0 to a maximum v_t at the section boundary. Adding up the moments of the torsional shears on each ring of small thickness $t = \Delta r$, and radius r varying from zero to R, we obtain:

$$M_t = \frac{\pi}{2} R^3 v_t,*$$

*At a distance r from 0, the value of the torsional stress is $v_t(r/R)$ and the contribution to the torsional moment of the shear stresses on a ring of radius r and thickness $t = dr$ is $(v_t r/R)(2\pi r dr) \times r$. Hence, the total torsional moment is:

$$\begin{aligned} M_t &= \int_0^R \left(v_t \frac{r}{R}\right)(2\pi r dr)r \\ &= \frac{2\pi v_t}{R} \int_0^R r^3 \, dr \\ &= \frac{2\pi v_t}{R} \frac{R^4}{4} \\ &= \frac{\pi}{2} R^3 v_t. \end{aligned}$$

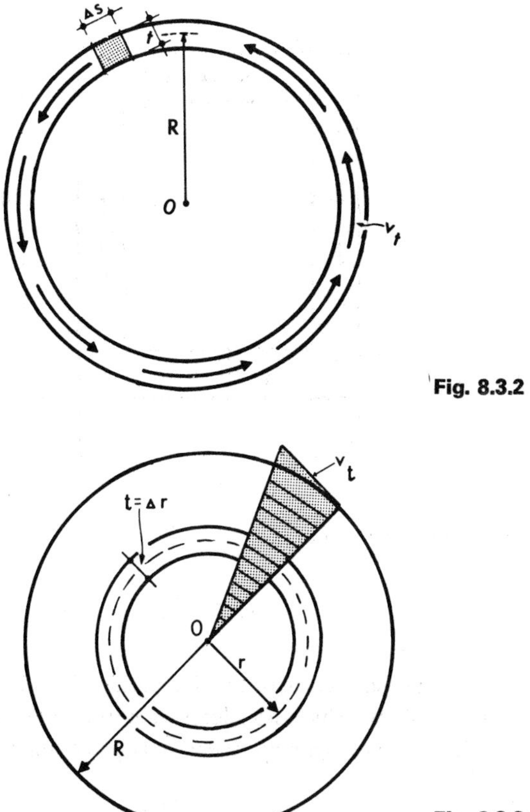

Fig. 8.3.2

Fig. 8.3.3

so that:

$$v_t = \frac{2}{\pi}\left(\frac{M_t}{R^3}\right). \tag{8.3.2}$$

For a rectangular cross section $b \times h$ with $b \leq h$, it may be shown that the maximum torsional stress occurs at the middle of the *longer* sides and is given with good approximation by:

$$v_t = \left(3 + 1.8\,\frac{b}{h}\right)\frac{M_t}{hb^2} \quad (\text{for } b < h). \tag{8.3.3}$$

For a box section with thin walls (Fig. 8.3.4), again, v_t is practically constant and:

$$M_t = v_t \times 2(bt) \times \frac{h}{2} + v_t \times 2(ht) \times \frac{b}{2} = 2bhtv_t = 2Atv_t,$$

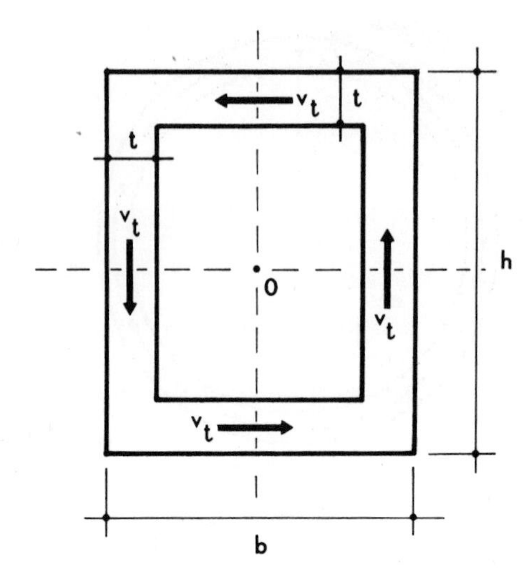

Fig. 8.3.4

where A is the area of the *full* section. Thus:

$$v_t = \frac{M_t}{2At}, \tag{8.3.4}$$

a formula which can be used with good accuracy for all hollow, thin sections.

It may also be shown (by a nonelementary theory) that for I, C and L thin sections (i.e., for so-called *open sections*), v_t is given approximately by:

$$v_t = \frac{3M_t}{2\sum bt^2} \tag{8.3.5}$$

where b and t are the length and thickness of each side of the section.

For example, in the rectangular post of the structure of Fig. 8.2.1, the twisting moment $M_t = M_z = P(a/2 + c) = 1{,}500(10/2 + 2) = 10{,}500$ ft lb (see p. 238) develops maximum torsional shear stresses given by (8.3.3):

$$v_t = \left(3 + 1.8\,\frac{1}{2}\right)\frac{10{,}500}{2 \times (1)^2} = 20{,}475 \text{ psf} = 142 \text{ psi.}$$

The torsional shear stress v_t must be added to the maximum shear stress $v_y = 7.81$ psi due to v_y, which also occurs at the middle of the longer sides h, so that the maximum total shear stress is:

$$v_{max} = 142 + 7.81 \doteq 150 \text{ psi.}$$

PROBLEMS

8.3.1 A rectangular, hollow steel section has $b = 1$ ft, $h = 2$ ft and $t = 1$ in. Determine its twisting moment capacity for an allowable shear stress $F_s = 10$ ksi.

8.3.2 A circular pipe is used as the cross section of the post in Problem 8.2.6 (Fig. 8.2.10). The pipe diameter is 8 in. and its thickness is $\frac{3}{8}$ in. Determine its maximum torsional shear stress.

8.3.3 Wood 2 × 4's ($1\frac{5}{8}$ in. × $3\frac{5}{8}$ in.) are used to build the structure of Fig. 8.2.7, where $a = 5$ ft, $c = 3$ ft and $W = 100$ lb. Determine the maximum bending stress and the maximum shear stress in the two beams of the structure.

8.3.4 A hollow beam of thickness t must develop a twisting moment M_t with an allowable torsional shear stress F_s. If the torsional stress governs the beam design, would the beam be deeper for a circular section of diameter D or a square section of side a? Which beam is heavier?

8.4 The Tripod

The *tripod* is the most elementary space truss. It consists of 3 inclined bars AD, BD, CD hinged at a point D and of 3 horizontal hinged bars connecting the ends of A, B, and C of the first 3 bars (Fig. 8.4.1). The tripod is a *hinged tetrahedron.*

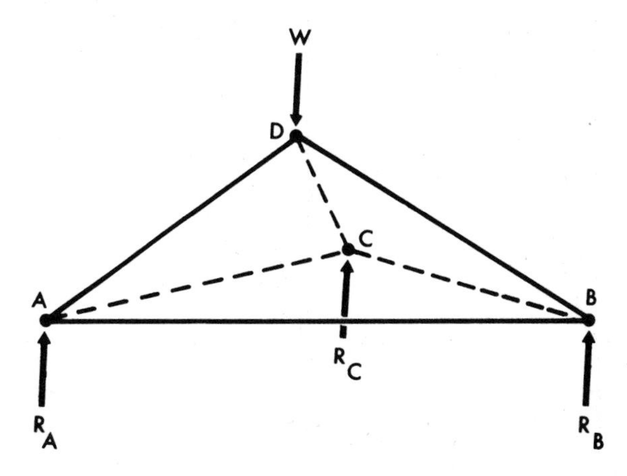

Fig. 8.4.1

Let us assume that a vertical load W, perpendicular to the horizontal plane of the 3 support points A, B, C, is applied at the *vertex* D, so that the reactions at A, B and C are also vertical. The value of these reactions is easily obtained by rotational equilibrium about the 3 lines AB, BC, CA or by rotational equilibrium about 2 of these lines and by vertical equilibrium. For example, the reactions of the tripod of Fig. 8.4.2 are given by:

$$R_C(3a) - Wa = 0 \qquad \therefore \quad R_C = \frac{W}{3},$$

$$R_A(4a) - Wa = 0 \qquad \therefore \quad R_A = \frac{W}{4},$$

$$R_A + R_B + R_C = W \quad \therefore \quad R_B = W - \frac{W}{3} - \frac{W}{4} = \frac{5W}{12}.$$

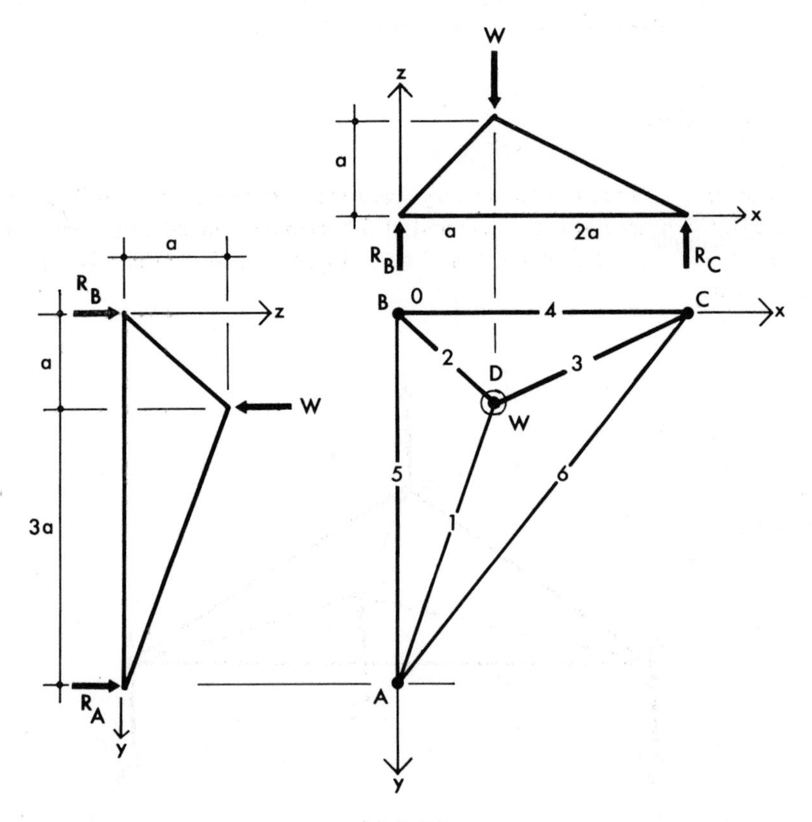

Fig. 8.4.2

Once the reactions are known, the forces in the bars are obtained by the method of *space joint equilibrium*. For this purpose, we refer the tripod to the x-, y-, z-axes of Fig. 8.4.2 and compute a table of: (1) the projections X, Y, Z of the bar lengths along the 3 axes, (2) the bar lengths $L = \sqrt{X^2 + Y^2 + Z^2}$ and (3) the ratios X/L, Y/L, Z/L (Table 8.4.1).

Table 8.4.1

Bar	X/a	Y/a	Z/a	L/a	X/L	Y/L	Z/L
1	1	3	1	$\sqrt{11}$	$1/\sqrt{11}$	$3/\sqrt{11}$	$1/\sqrt{11}$
2	1	1	1	$\sqrt{3}$	$1/\sqrt{3}$	$1/\sqrt{3}$	$1/\sqrt{3}$
3	2	1	1	$\sqrt{6}$	$2/\sqrt{6}$	$1/\sqrt{6}$	$1/\sqrt{6}$
4	3	0	0	3	1	0	0
5	0	4	0	4	0	1	0
6	3	4	0	5	3/5	4/5	0

For example:

$$L_1 = \sqrt{a^2 + (3a)^2 + a^2} = a\sqrt{11}, \quad \frac{Y_1}{L_1} = \frac{3}{\sqrt{11}}$$

$$L_3 = \sqrt{(2a)^2 + a^2 + a^2} = a\sqrt{6}, \quad \frac{X_3}{L_3} = \frac{2}{\sqrt{6}}.$$

The equilibrium of the joints A, B and C in, say, the vertical z-direction allows the direct evaluation of the forces F in the bars 1, 2 and 3 since the vertical component F_z of a bar force F is:

$$F_z = \frac{Z}{L} F. \tag{a}$$

Assuming all bar forces to be compressive, we obtain:

$$(A) \qquad R_A - F_{1z} = 0, \qquad \frac{W}{4} - \frac{1}{\sqrt{11}} F_1 = 0 \quad \therefore \quad F_1 = \frac{\sqrt{11}}{4} W,$$

$$(B) \qquad R_B - F_{2z} = 0, \qquad \frac{5W}{12} - \frac{1}{\sqrt{3}} F_2 = 0 \quad \therefore \quad F_2 = \frac{5}{4\sqrt{3}} W,$$

$$(C) \qquad R_C - F_{3z} = 0, \qquad \frac{W}{3} - \frac{1}{\sqrt{6}} F_3 = 0 \qquad \therefore \quad F_3 = \sqrt{\frac{2}{3}}\, W.^*$$

The positive sign of F_1, F_2 and F_3 shows that these forces are compressive, as assumed. (A negative value of a bar force would indicate that the direction of the force was incorrectly assumed.) The forces in the bars 4, 5 and 6 are obtained by considering the equilibrium in the x- and/or y-directions of joints A and B. Assuming all unknown forces to be tensile, we obtain:

$$(A) \qquad -F_{1x} + F_{5x} + F_{6x} = 0; \qquad -\frac{1}{\sqrt{11}}\left(\frac{\sqrt{11}}{4} W\right) + 0 + \frac{3}{5} F_6 = 0$$

$$\therefore \quad F_6 = \frac{5}{12} W,$$

$$(A) \qquad F_{1y} - F_{5y} - F_{6y} = 0; \qquad +\frac{3}{\sqrt{11}}\left(\frac{\sqrt{11}}{4} W\right) - F_5 - \frac{4}{5}\left(\frac{5}{12} W\right) = 0$$

$$\therefore \quad F_5 = \frac{5}{12} W,$$

$$(B) \qquad -F_{2x} + F_{4x} + F_{5x} = 0; \qquad -\frac{1}{\sqrt{3}}\left(\frac{5}{4\sqrt{3}} W\right) + F_4 + 0 = 0$$

$$\therefore \quad F_4 = \frac{5}{12} W.$$

*The forces F_1, F_2 and F_3 could also have been obtained from the equilibrium of joint D by solving the system of 3 simultaneous equations:

$$\sum F_z = 0: \qquad W - F_{1z} - F_{2z} - F_{3z} = 0$$

$$\therefore \quad \frac{1}{\sqrt{11}} F_1 + \frac{1}{\sqrt{3}} F_2 + \frac{1}{\sqrt{6}} F_3 = W, \tag{a}$$

$$\sum F_x = 0: \qquad F_{1x} + F_{2x} - F_{3x} = 0$$

$$\therefore \quad \frac{1}{\sqrt{11}} F_1 + \frac{1}{\sqrt{3}} F_2 - \frac{2}{\sqrt{6}} F_3 = 0, \tag{b}$$

$$\sum F_y = 0: \qquad -F_{1y} + F_{2y} + F_{3y} = 0$$

$$\therefore \quad -\frac{3}{\sqrt{11}} F_1 + \frac{1}{\sqrt{3}} F_2 + \frac{1}{\sqrt{6}} F_3 = 0, \tag{c}$$

where all forces are assumed to be compressive. Subtracting (c) from (a):

$$\frac{1-(-3)}{\sqrt{11}} F_1 = W \qquad \therefore \quad F_1 = \frac{\sqrt{11}}{4} W,$$

subtracting (c) from (b):

$$\frac{4}{\sqrt{11}} F_1 - \frac{3}{\sqrt{6}} F_3 = 0 \qquad \therefore \quad F_3 = \frac{4\sqrt{6}}{3\sqrt{11}} F_1 = \frac{4\sqrt{6}}{3\sqrt{11}}\left(\frac{\sqrt{11}}{4}\right) W$$

$$= \frac{\sqrt{6}}{3} W = \sqrt{\frac{2}{3}}\, W;$$

and by (c):

$$F_2 = \sqrt{3}\left(\frac{3}{\sqrt{11}} F_1 - \frac{1}{\sqrt{6}} F_3\right) = \sqrt{3}\left(\frac{3}{\sqrt{11}}\frac{\sqrt{11}}{4} - \frac{1}{\sqrt{6}}\frac{\sqrt{6}}{3}\right) W = \frac{5}{4\sqrt{3}} W.$$

The positive sign of F_4, F_5 and F_6 shows that these forces are tensile, as assumed.

When the load at D has a horizontal component, the reactions at A, B and C must not only satisfy vertical equilibrium and rotational equilibrium about the lines AB, BC and CA, but must also satisfy equilibrium in the x- and y-directions and rotational equilibrium about the z-axis. This is equivalent to saying that the reactions must also guarantee plane equilibrium in the x, y-plane. Hence, one of the 3 supports could be a fixed hinge reacting in the x- *and* y-directions, while another could be a movable hinge reacting only in the x- *or* y-direction and the third a purely vertical support (Fig. 8.4.3a). Three movable hinge supports, developing horizontal reactions in any 3 directions, provided these do not meet at one point (Fig. 8.4.3b), will also guarantee horizontal equilibrium. (If the 3 horizontal reactions meet at a point 0 (Fig.

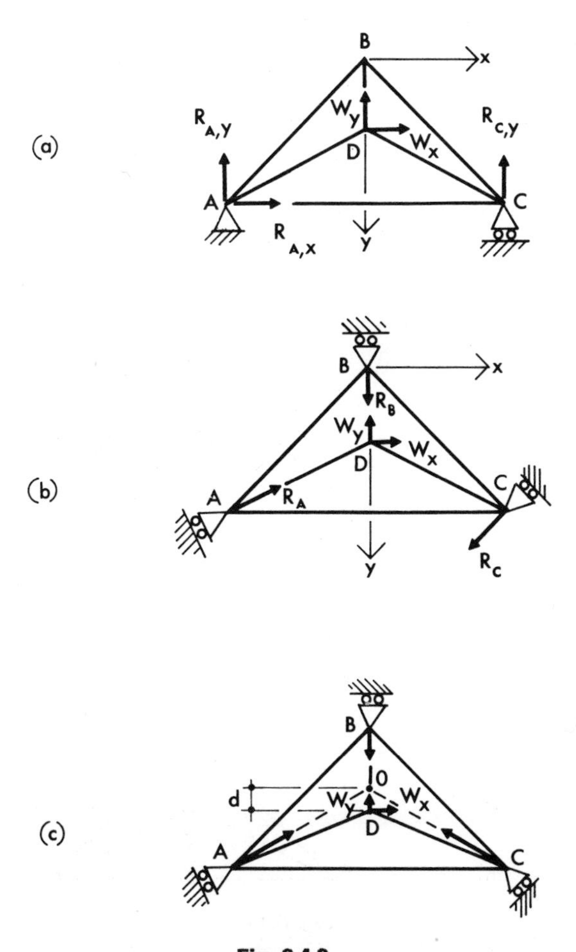

Fig. 8.4.3

8.4.3c), the tripod cannot be in equilibrium about a z-axis through 0, since the moment M_z of W about z, say $W_x d$, cannot be balanced by the moment of the horizontal reactions if all 3 reactions go through 0.) Once the horizontal components of the reactions are evaluated, the forces in the bars are obtained by joint equilibrium, as was done for a vertical force W.

The evaluation of bar forces in tripods is a basic task because many space trusses are assembled by using tetrahedral elements as building blocks.

PROBLEMS

8.4.1 Evaluate the forces in the bars of the tripod of Fig. 8.4.2 due to a horizontal load W parallel to $+x$ applied at D. Assume A to be a fixed hinge, B to react in the x- and z-directions and C only in the z-direction.

8.4.2 Solve Problem 8.4.1 assuming that A and C react in the x- and z-directions and B in the y- and z-directions.

8.4.3 The base ABC of a tripod has 3 equal sides of length a. The vertex D is at a height $h = a/3$ over the center 0 of the base. Determine the forces in the bars due to: (a) a vertical load W at D and (b) a horizontal force H at D acting in the plane OAD, assuming B and C to react in the y- and z-directions and A in the x- and z-directions (Fig. 8.4.4).

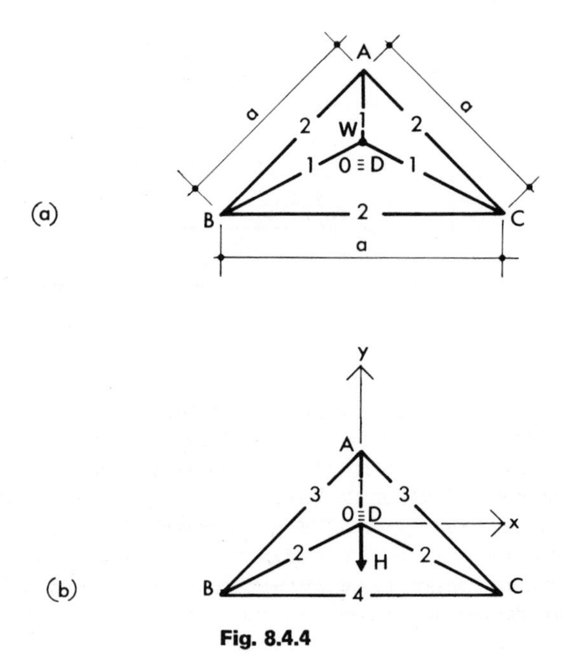

Fig. 8.4.4

8.4.4 A sculpture of weight W hangs from 3 equal wires of length l, meeting at a point D and attached to the corners A, B, C of a horizontal equilateral triangle of sides $a = (3/2)l$ and center 0. Determine the minimum value of a horizontal force H acting at D in the plane OAD which makes the wire AD slack.

8.4.5 Determine the forces in the bars of the tripod of Fig. 8.4.5 when a vertical load $W = 50$ lb is applied at D.

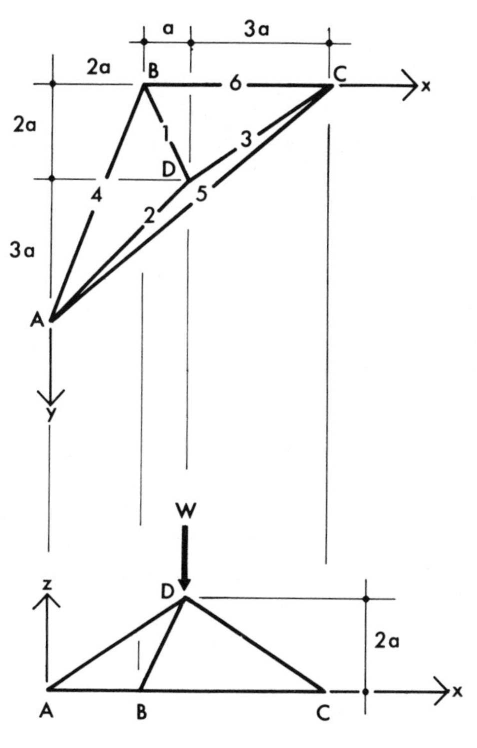

Fig. 8.4.5

8.4.6 A TV tower 300 ft high is hinged at its base and guyed by 3 wires attached at a height of 150 ft. The wires are anchored at 3 points evenly spaced on a circle a distance of 150 ft from the foot of the tower. A wind exerting a pressure of 40 psf acts on the lateral surface of the tower, which is equivalent to 3 sq ft per foot of tower. Each guy wire is initially pre-stressed by a tensile force $T = 150$ k. Determine the maximum tension in the windward wire and the minimum tension in the lee wires if the wind blows horizontally in the direction defined by the tower and one of the guy wires. Determine the diameter of the guy wires for $F_s = 50$ ksi.

8.5 A Statically Determinate Space Truss

A large variety of space trusses with horizontal upper and lower chords (which facilitate roofing and ceiling problems) may be obtained by combining tetrahedral elements. Most of these (Fig. 8.5.1) are statically indeterminate. In

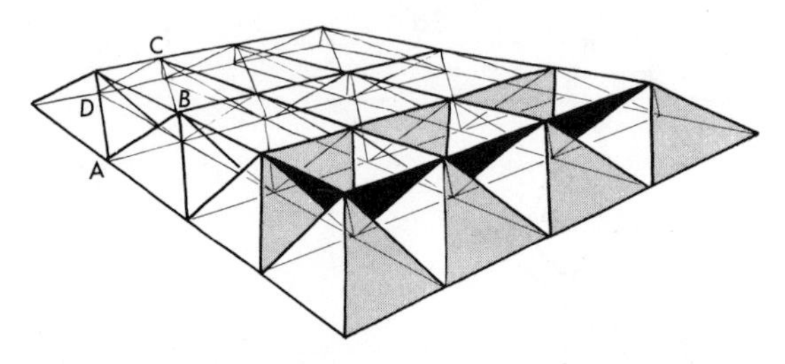

Fig. 8.5.1

order to check the determinacy of such space trusses, we notice that any 3 initial joints are rigidly connected by 3 bars and that 3 additional bars are needed to rigidly connect a new joint to the previously connected joints. Hence, calling j the number of joints, the number N_b of bars is:

$$N_b = 3 + 3(j - 3) = 3j - 6. \tag{8.5.1}$$

Equation (8.5.1) holds provided the 3 bars connecting the new joint to the previous joints do not lie in the same plane, since only 2 bars are needed to rigidly connect a new joint to previously connected joints which lie in the same plane. Hence, calling j the number of joints rigidly connected to previously connected joints by 3 bars not lying in the same plane, and calling p the number of joints rigidly connected to previously connected joints by 2 bars lying in the plane of the previous joints, we find that the number of bars N_b in a statically determinate space truss is:

$$N_b = 3j + 2p - 6. \tag{8.5.2}$$

We will now analyze a space truss with horizontal upper and lower chords, the *Takenaka truss*, which is statically determinate when "simply supported" on the perimeter of a rectangular area and loaded "uniformly," i.e., by equal loads applied to its upper or lower chord joints.

The Takenaka truss (Fig. 8.5.2a) is an assemblage of inverted tetrahedra with square bases of side a on the upper chord points U and vertices on the lower chord points V a distance h below their base, which are connected by lower chord bars V–V of length $\sqrt{2}\,a$. When the loads are applied to the upper chord points, the upper bars U–U and B–U (shown in solid lines) are in compression; the internal diagonals U–V (shown in dotted lines) are also in compression; the external diagonals B–V and the lower chord bars V–V (shown in dot-dash lines) are in tension. The evaluation of bar forces is obtained by space equilibrium of the truss joints.

Let us consider, for simplicity of solution, the symmetrical truss of Fig. 8.5.2 with a depth $h = a/\sqrt{2}$ and, hence, diagonals inclined at 45°, loaded by 4 equal loads W at the upper chord points U and supported at 8 boundary points B by 8 equal reactions $W/2$.

Assuming all bar forces to be positive when tensile, we obtain by vertical equilibrium of the bars at a support point B_1 and with $\cos 45° = 1/\sqrt{2}$:

$$-\frac{W}{2} + \frac{F_2}{\sqrt{2}} = 0 \quad \therefore \quad F_2 = \frac{W}{\sqrt{2}};$$

by horizontal equilibrium in the x- and y-directions at B_1:

$$\sum F_x = \frac{F_1}{\sqrt{2}} - \frac{F_1'}{\sqrt{2}} = 0 \quad \therefore \quad F_1 = F_1',$$

$$\sum F_y = +\frac{F_1'}{\sqrt{2}} + \frac{F_1}{\sqrt{2}} + \frac{F_2}{\sqrt{2}} = 0 \quad \therefore \quad F_1 = F_1' = -\frac{F_2}{2} = -\frac{W}{2\sqrt{2}};$$

by vertical equilibrium at U, with equal forces F_3 in the diagonals U–V and U–V' because of symmetry:

$$W + \frac{2F_3}{\sqrt{2}} = 0 \quad \therefore \quad F_3 = -\frac{W}{\sqrt{2}};$$

and by equilibrium in the x-direction at V':

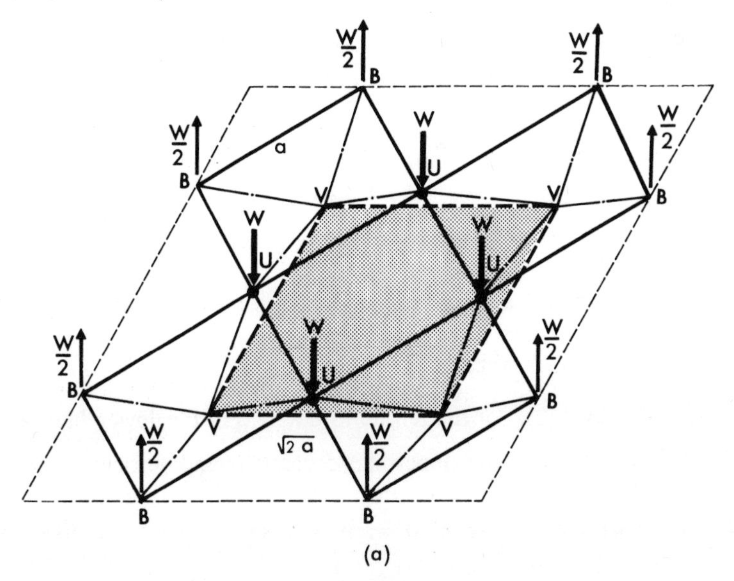

Fig. 8.5.2a

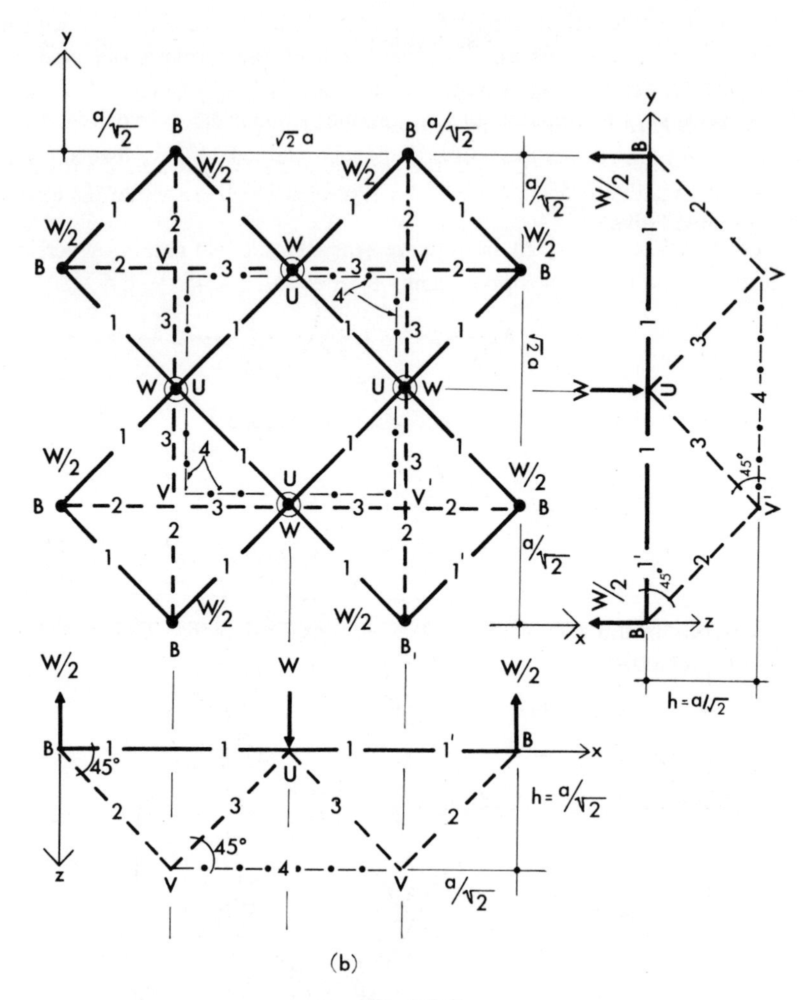

(b)

Fig. 8.5.2b

$$+\frac{F_2}{\sqrt{2}} - \frac{F_3}{\sqrt{2}} - F_4 = 0 \quad \therefore \quad F_4 = \frac{W/\sqrt{2}}{\sqrt{2}} - \frac{-W/\sqrt{2}}{\sqrt{2}} = W.$$

This last result may be checked by cutting a vertical section parallel to y through the median line U–U and taking moments of the reactions at 4 points B, of one of the loads and of the tensile forces in 2 of the lower bars 4 about the line U–U:

$$2\frac{W}{2}(\sqrt{2}\,a) + 2\frac{W}{2}\frac{a}{\sqrt{2}} - W\frac{a}{\sqrt{2}} - 2F_4\frac{a}{\sqrt{2}} = 0 \quad \therefore \quad F_4 = W.$$

PROBLEMS

8.5.1 Determine the forces in the bars of the Takenaka truss of Fig. 8.5.2 when the loads W are applied at the vertices V.

8.5.2 Prove that the bars labeled with the same numbers in the Takenaka truss of Fig. 8.5.3 develop the same forces, and determine which are tensile and which are compressive.

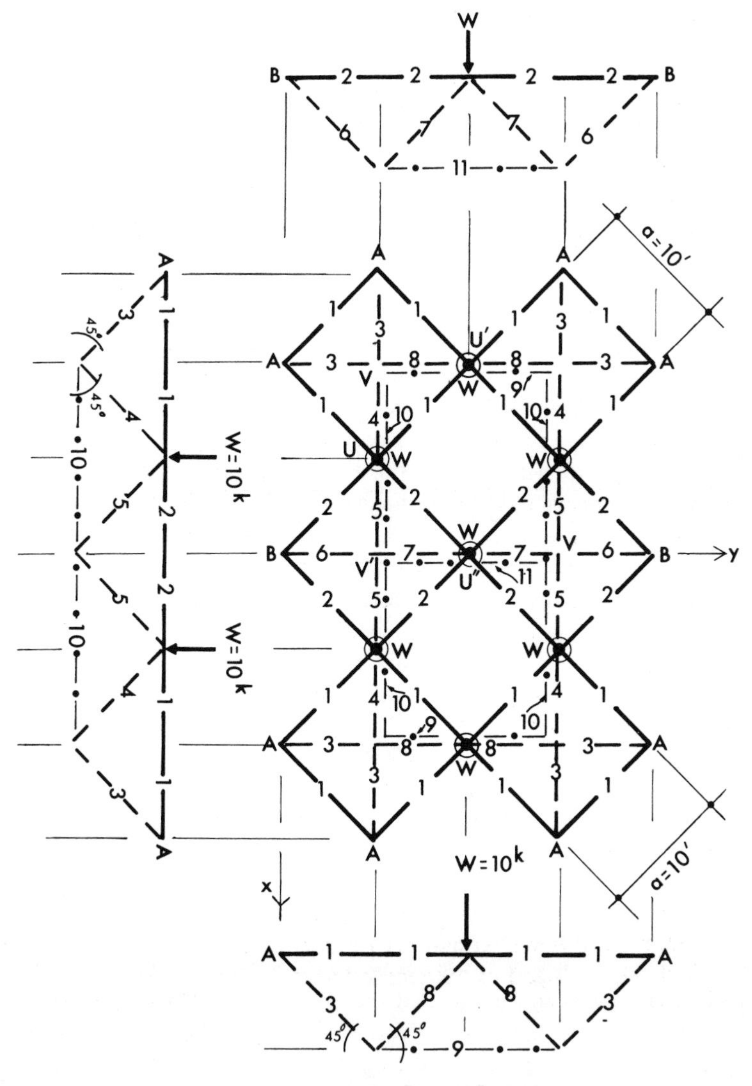

Fig. 8.5.3

8.5.3 Determine the equations for the bar forces in the Takenaka truss of Fig. 8.5.3 by joint equilibrium without prior evaluation of the reactions and check that they are satisfied by the values given in the list of answers.

8.5.4 The Takenaka truss of Problem 8.5.1 (Fig. 8.5.2) carries loads $W = 10$ k. Its bars are steel pipes 2 in. in diameter. Evaluate the pipe thicknesses t for $F_t = 20$ ksi, $F_c = 6$ ksi.

8.5.5 The Takenaka truss of Fig. 8.5.3 carries loads $W = 10$ k applied at the upper joints. Its bars are steel pipes 2 in. in diameter. Evaluate the maximum pipe thickness t of its steel pipes for $F_t = 20$ ksi and $F_c = 6$ ksi.

8.5.6 The Takenaka truss of Problem 8.5.3 has loads $W = 10$ k hanging from its vertices V. Determine the forces in the bars and the maximum thickness t of its steel pipes for $F_t = 20$ ksi and $F_c = 6$ ksi.

8.6 The Schwedler Dome

The Schwedler "dome" is a statically determinate, space truss which may be used to build domes and towers. As shown in Fig. 8.6.1, a Schwedler dome consists of polygonal horizontal rings (e.g., A', B', C', D', E', F'), whose joints are connected by meridional bars (as $A'A''$) as well as diagonal bars (as $A'B''$), these last all inclined in the same direction. The supports at A, B, C, D, E, F are assumed capable of reacting in the x-, y- and z-directions.

In order to understand the mechanism by which a Schwedler dome carries loads to the ground, consider the square, truncated pyramidal element of Fig. 8.6.2 (a "square dome" may be built by superimposing a series of such elements), loaded by a single vertical load W at A. It is easy to prove that all the bars indicated by thin lines in Fig. 8.6.2 are unstressed.

To this purpose, consider the bars meeting at A and lying in the plane of the dome face $AEFB$, i.e., the bars AB, 2 and 3. The forces in these 3 bars lie in the plane of the face $AEFB$, and, hence, have no components in the direction n perpendicular to the face. Therefore, for equilibrium of joint A in the n-direction, the component F_{1n} of F_1 in the n- direction must be equal and opposite to the component W_n of W in the n-direction:

$$F_{1n} - W_n = 0. \tag{a}$$

Equation (a) shows that if there is no load at a joint like A, $F_{1n} = 0$, and, hence, F_1 is zero. Applying this result to the unloaded joint B, considered as part of the face $AEFB$, we find that the force in the bar BD is zero. Similarly, considering the unloaded joints B and D as part of the face $BDGF$, we find that the forces in the bars AB and CD are also zero. Since the joints B and D are unloaded, the bars BF, BG and the bars DG, DH are also unstressed, as

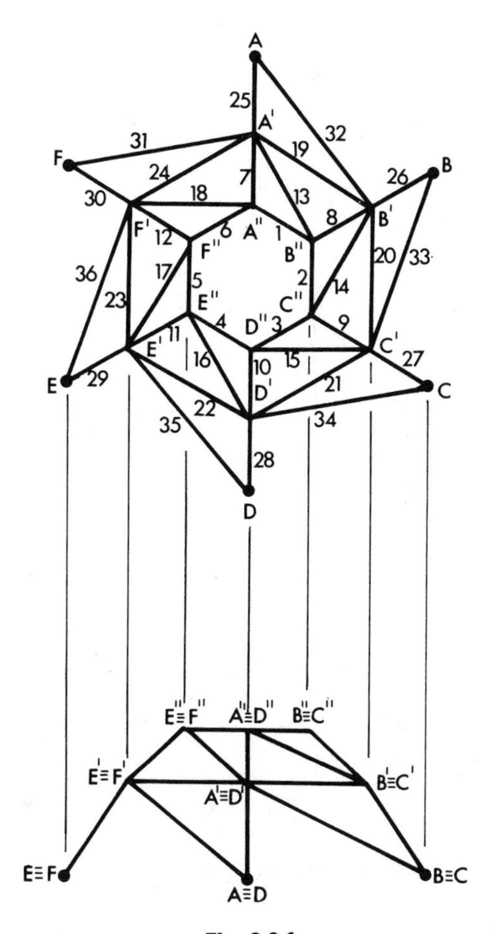

Fig. 8.6.1

shown by the equilibrium equations for B and D in the $BDGF$ and $DCHG$ planes, respectively. Thus, our initial statement is proved.

The forces in the stressed bars 1 to 5 may be found by the space joint method, referring the bars to the x-, y-, z-axes of Fig. 8.6.2 after computing the bar lengths L and their projections X, Y, Z along the axes, which appear in Table 8.6.1.

The vertical reactions at F, H and E are computed first by taking moments of the load and the vertical reactions about the lines EH and EF:

$$R_{F,z} \times 3a - Wa = 0 \quad \therefore \quad R_{F,z} = \frac{W}{3},$$

$$R_{H,z} \times 3a - Wa = 0 \quad \therefore \quad R_{H,z} = \frac{W}{3},$$

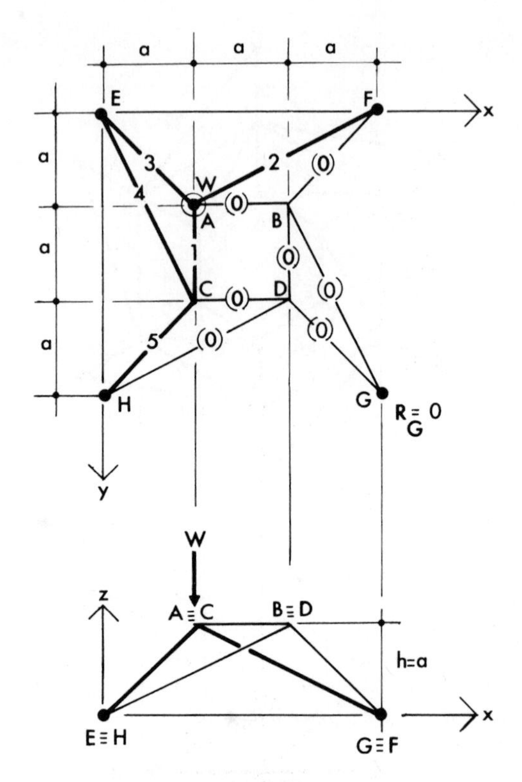

Fig. 8.6.2

Table 8.6.1

Bars	1	2	3	4	5
L/a	1	$\sqrt{6}$	$\sqrt{3}$	$\sqrt{6}$	$\sqrt{3}$
X/L	0	$2/\sqrt{6}$	$1/\sqrt{3}$	$1/\sqrt{6}$	$1/\sqrt{3}$
Y/L	1	$1/\sqrt{6}$	$1/\sqrt{3}$	$2/\sqrt{6}$	$1/\sqrt{3}$
Z/L	0	$1/\sqrt{6}$	$1/\sqrt{3}$	$1/\sqrt{6}$	$1/\sqrt{3}$

and by vertical equilibrium:

$$R_{E,z} + R_{F,z} + R_{H,z} - W = 0 \quad \therefore \quad R_{E,z} = W - \frac{W}{3} - \frac{W}{3} = \frac{W}{3}.$$

Assuming the bar forces F_1 to F_5 to be tensile, we then obtain by joint equilibrium:

$$\sum F_z = 0 \text{ at } F: \quad -\frac{W}{3} - \frac{1}{\sqrt{6}} F_2 = 0 \quad \therefore \quad F_2 = -\frac{\sqrt{6}}{3} W,$$

$$\sum F_z = 0 \text{ at } H: \quad -\frac{W}{3} - \frac{1}{\sqrt{3}} F_5 = 0 \quad \therefore \quad F_5 = -\frac{\sqrt{3}}{3} W,$$

$$\sum F_x = 0 \text{ at } A: \quad +\frac{2}{\sqrt{6}} F_2 - \frac{1}{\sqrt{3}} F_3 = 0$$

$$\therefore \quad F_3 = \frac{2\sqrt{3}}{\sqrt{6}} F_2 = -\frac{2\sqrt{3}}{3} W,$$

$$\sum F_x = 0 \text{ at } C: \quad -\frac{1}{\sqrt{6}} F_4 - \frac{1}{\sqrt{3}} F_5 = 0$$

$$\therefore \quad F_4 = -\frac{\sqrt{6}}{\sqrt{3}} F_5 = \frac{\sqrt{6}}{3} W,$$

$$\sum F_y = 0 \text{ at } A: \quad F_1 - \frac{1}{\sqrt{3}} F_3 - \frac{1}{\sqrt{6}} F_2 = 0$$

$$\therefore \quad F_1 = \frac{1}{\sqrt{3}}\left(-\frac{2\sqrt{3}}{3} W\right) + \frac{1}{\sqrt{6}}\left(-\frac{\sqrt{6}}{3} W\right) = -W.$$

From the values of the bar forces we may compute the components of the reactions at F, H and E in the x- and y-directions by equilibrium of these joints. Assuming the reaction components positive when acting in the $+x$- and $+y$-directions, we obtain:

at F:

$$R_{F,x} - \frac{2}{\sqrt{6}} F_2 = 0 \quad \therefore \quad R_{F,x} = \frac{2}{\sqrt{6}} F_2 = \frac{-2W}{3},$$

$$R_{F,y} + \frac{1}{\sqrt{6}} F_2 = 0 \quad \therefore \quad R_{F,y} = -\frac{1}{\sqrt{6}} F_2 = \frac{W}{3};$$

at H:

$$R_{H,x} + \frac{1}{\sqrt{3}} F_5 = 0 \quad \therefore \quad R_{H,x} = -\frac{1}{\sqrt{3}} F_5 = \frac{W}{3},$$

$$R_{H,y} - \frac{1}{\sqrt{3}} F_5 = 0 \quad \therefore \quad R_{H,y} = \frac{1}{\sqrt{3}} F_5 = \frac{-W}{3};$$

at E:

$$R_{E,x} + \frac{1}{\sqrt{3}} F_3 + \frac{1}{\sqrt{6}} F_4 = 0 \quad \therefore \quad R_{E,x} = -\frac{1}{\sqrt{3}} F_3 - \frac{1}{\sqrt{6}} F_4$$

$$= \frac{2W}{3} - \frac{W}{3} = \frac{W}{3},$$

$$R_{E,y} + \frac{1}{\sqrt{3}} F_3 + \frac{2}{\sqrt{6}} F_4 = 0 \quad \therefore \quad R_{E,y} = -\frac{1}{\sqrt{3}} F_3 - \frac{2}{\sqrt{6}} F_4$$

$$= \frac{2W}{3} - \frac{2W}{3} = 0;$$

at G:

$$R_{G,z} = R_{G,x} = R_{G,y} = 0.$$

If the truncated pyramidal element of Fig. 8.6.2 is superimposed on a similar element, the bar forces in the lower element are computed by applying to its upper joints the reactions of the upper element.

PROBLEMS

8.6.1 Indicate which bars are stressed if a vertical load W is applied to the joint A'' of the Schwedler truss of Fig. 8.6.1

8.6.2 Compute the bar forces in the Schwedler truss of Fig. 8.6.2 when 4 vertical loads W are applied to the joints A, B, C and D. Determine the reactions at E, F, G and H.

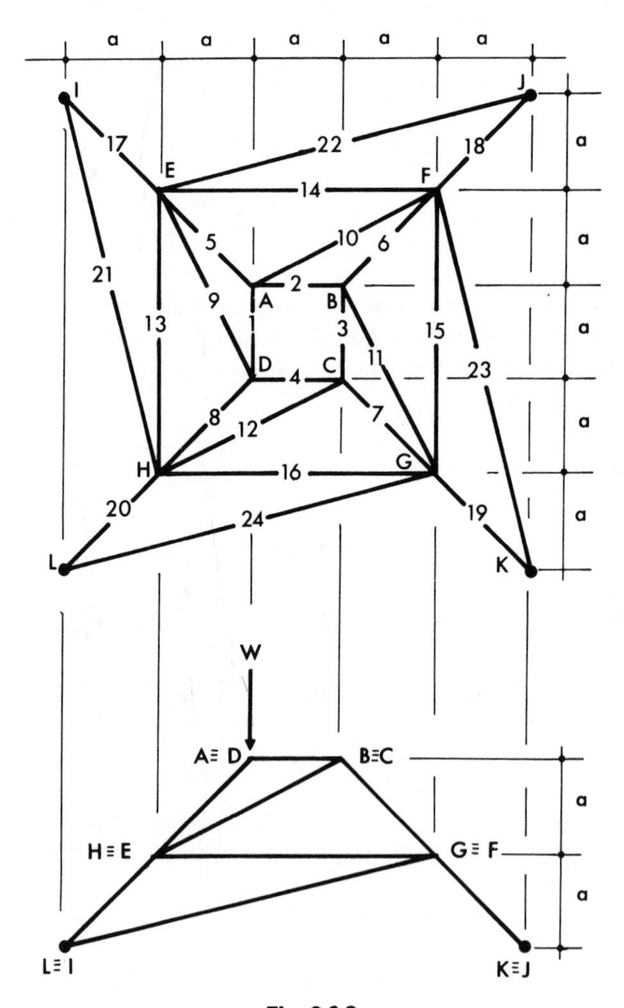

Fig. 8.6.3

8.6.3 The Schwedler dome of Fig. 8.6.3 is loaded by a vertical load W at the joint A. (a) Determine the stressed bars of the dome. (b) Evaluate the forces in the bars of the dome when 4 equal loads W are applied at A, B, C, and D.

8.6.4 Determine the stressed bars in the space truss of Fig. 8.6.4 loaded by a vertical load W at A, and evaluate the forces in these bars.

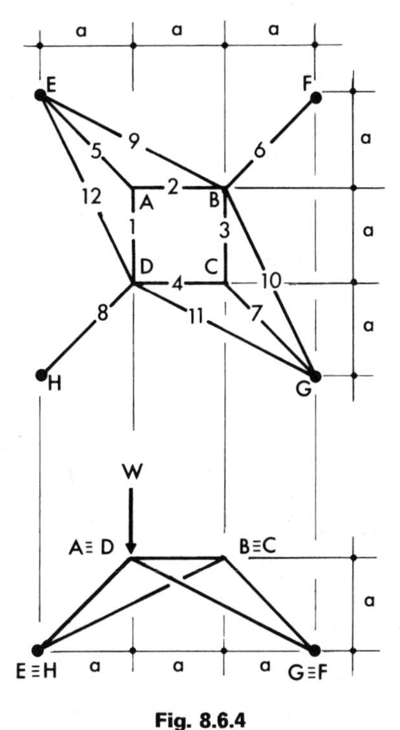

Fig. 8.6.4

8.6.5 Determine the forces in the bars of the truss of Fig. 8.6.4 due to 4 vertical loads W at A, B, C and D.

8.7 Axisymmetric Ribbed Domes

If the Schwedler dome of Fig. 8.6.2 is loaded symmetrically with 4 vertical loads W at A, B, C and D, the forces in its bars are obtained by superposition as shown in Fig. 8.7.1. Noticing that $F_3 = -(2\sqrt{3}/3)W$ and $F_5 = -(\sqrt{3}/3)W$, while F_2 and F_4 are equal and opposite $[F_2 = -F_4 = (-\sqrt{6}/3)W]$, we see that all the meridional bars develop the same compressive force $F_m = F_3 + F_5 = -\sqrt{3}\,W$ and all the parallel bars the same compressive force $F_p = F_1 = -W$, while all the diagonals are unstressed. Therefore, the forces in a ribbed,

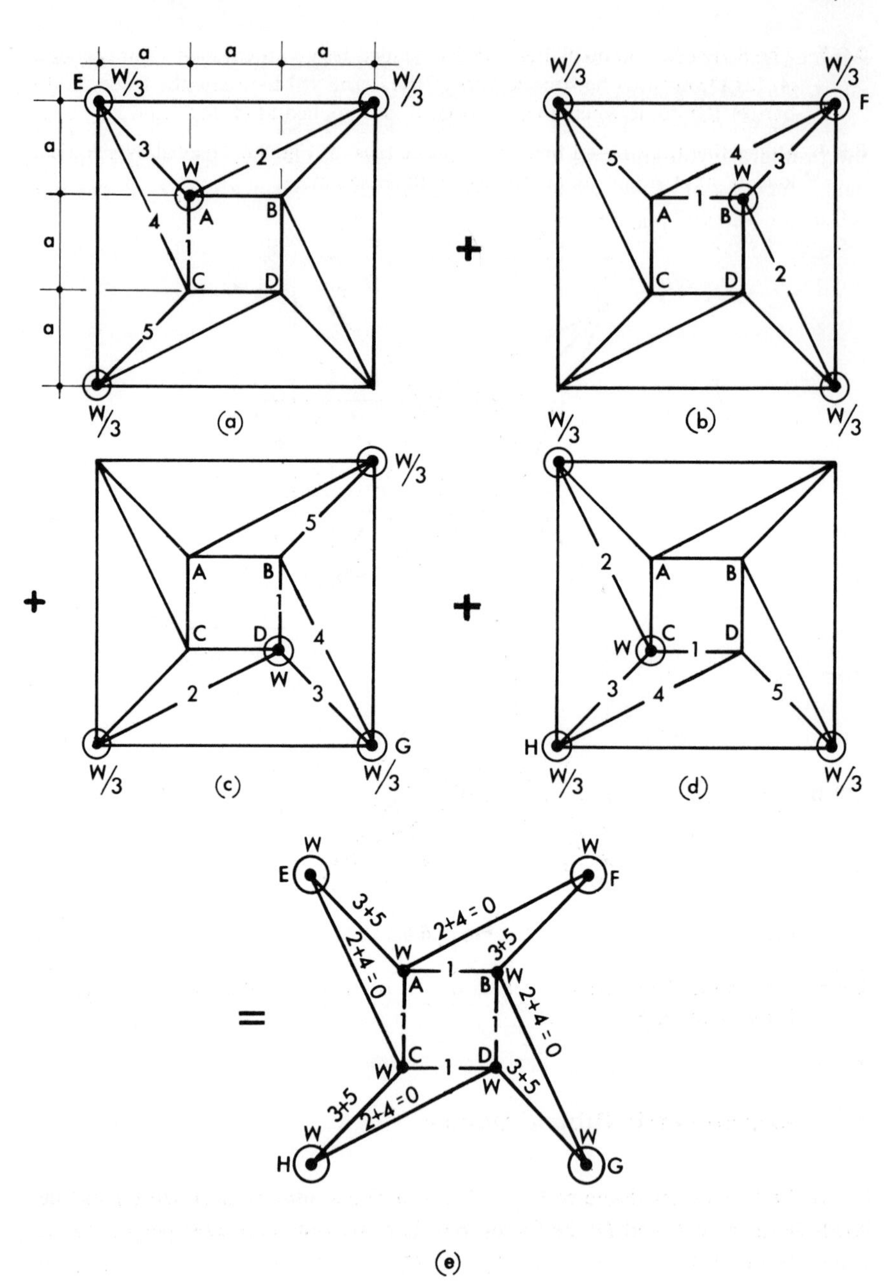

Fig. 8.7.1

symmetrical dome symmetrically loaded and supported, a so-called *axisymmetric dome*, may be evaluated by ignoring the diagonals.

Using the dome of Fig. 8.7.1 as an example and indicating by $H = \sqrt{2}\, F_1$ the resultant in the diagonal direction AD of the two horizontal forces F_1 in the bars 1 meeting at A, we obtain by rotational equilibrium about E of the bar AE in the vertical plane through AE (Fig. 8.7.2):

$$Ha + W(\sqrt{2}\, a) = 0 \quad \therefore \quad H = -\sqrt{2}\, W,$$

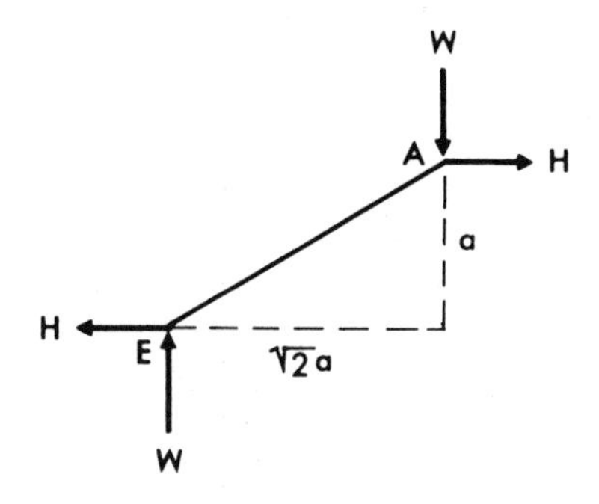

Fig. 8.7.2

from which:

$$H = \sqrt{2}\, F_1 = -\sqrt{2}\, W \quad \therefore \quad F_1 = -W,$$

and by vertical equilibrium:

$$-W - \frac{1}{\sqrt{3}} F_{AE} = 0 \quad \therefore \quad F_{AE} = -\sqrt{3}\, W.$$

Consider now the meridian of an axisymmetric dome, whose shape is defined in Fig. 8.7.3a, and assume that the dome has n such meridians ($n = 8$ in Fig. 8.7.3b), so that the horizontal angle between the meridional planes is $\alpha = 2\pi/n$. As the sum of the angles of a triangle equals $180^\circ = \pi$, the horizontal angle β between the parallels and the meridional planes is given by:

$$2\beta + \alpha = \pi \quad \therefore \quad \beta = \frac{\pi - \alpha}{2} = \frac{\pi}{2} - \frac{\pi}{n}.$$

Hence, the *thrust* H (i.e., the resultant in the radial horizontal direction of the two equal, parallel forces F_p meeting at a joint on the meridian) is:

$$H = 2F_p \cos\beta = 2F_p \cos\left(\frac{\pi}{2} - \frac{\pi}{n}\right) = 2F_p \sin\frac{\pi}{n}. \tag{a}$$

Let us indicate by H_1, H_2, H_3 and H_4 the values of the thrust H at the parallel levels A, B, C and D, assumed to be positive when acting inward, i.e., when

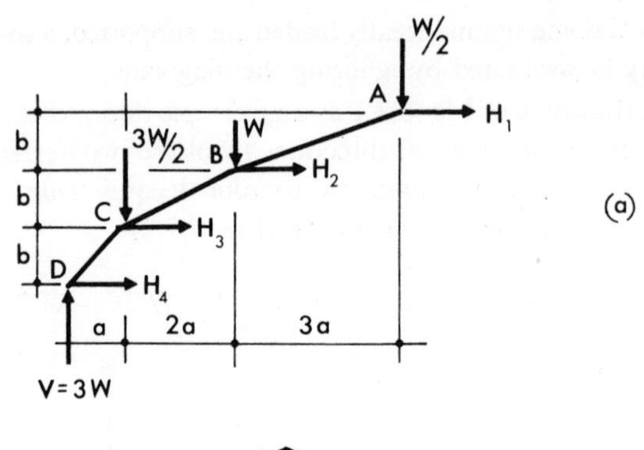

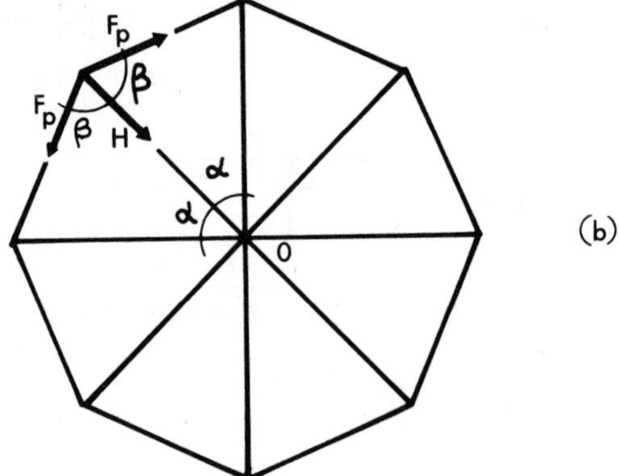

Fig. 8.7.3

the parallels are in tension. For the loads of Fig. 8.7.3, moment equations about B, C and D and a horizontal equilibrium equation give:

$$H_1 b + \frac{W}{2}(3a) = 0 \quad \therefore \quad H_1 = -\frac{3}{2}\left(\frac{a}{b}\right) W,$$

$$H_1(2b) + H_2(b) + \frac{W}{2}(5a) + W(2a) = 0 \quad \therefore \quad H_2 = -\frac{3}{2}\left(\frac{a}{b}\right) W,$$

$$H_1(3b) + H_2(2b) + H_3(b) + \frac{W}{2}(6a) + W(2a) + \frac{3W}{2}(a) = 0$$

$$\therefore \quad H_3 = +\left(\frac{a}{b}\right) W,$$

$$H_1 + H_2 + H_3 + H_4 = 0 \quad \therefore \quad H_4 = +2\left(\frac{a}{b}\right) W.$$

H_1 and H_2 are negative while H_3 and H_4 are positive, indicating that *the parallels are in compression at A and B and in tension at C and D.*

To obtain the parallel bar forces, we make use of equation (a), which for $n = 8$ gives:

$$F_p = \frac{H}{2 \sin \pi/8} = \frac{H}{2 \times 0.38} = 1.32\, H,$$

from which:

$$F_{p1} = 1.32 \left[-1.5 \left(\frac{a}{b}\right) W \right] = -1.98 \left(\frac{a}{b}\right) W,$$

$$F_{p2} = 1.32 \left[-1.5 \left(\frac{a}{b}\right) W \right] = -1.98 \left(\frac{a}{b}\right) W,$$

$$F_{p3} = 1.32 \left(\frac{a}{b}\right) W = +1.32 \left(\frac{a}{b}\right) W,$$

$$F_{p4} = 13.2 \left[2\left(\frac{a}{b}\right) W \right] = 2.64 \left(\frac{a}{b}\right) W.$$

The forces N in the meridional bars are the resultants of the sum of the thrusts H and of the sum of the vertical reactions V:

$$[\sum H]_1 = H_1 = -\frac{3}{2}\left(\frac{a}{b}\right) W, \qquad [\sum H]_2 = H_1 + H_2 = -3\left(\frac{a}{b}\right) W,$$

$$[\sum H]_3 = H_1 + H_2 + H_3 = -2\left(\frac{a}{b}\right) W;$$

$$[\sum V]_1 = V_1 = \frac{W}{2}, \qquad [\sum V]_2 = \frac{W}{2} + W = \frac{3W}{2},$$

$$[\sum V]_3 = \frac{W}{2} + W + \frac{3W}{2} = 3W,$$

and are all compressive:

$$N_1 = -\sqrt{\left(\frac{W}{2}\right)^2 + \left(\frac{3}{2}\right)^2 \left(\frac{a}{b}\right)^2 W^2} = -\frac{W}{2}\sqrt{1 + 9\left(\frac{a}{b}\right)^2},$$

$$N_2 = -\sqrt{\left(\frac{3W}{2}\right)^2 + 3^2 \left(\frac{a}{b}\right)^2 W^2} = -\frac{3}{2} W \sqrt{1 + 4\left(\frac{a}{b}\right)^2},$$

$$N_3 = -\sqrt{(3W)^2 + 2^2 \left(\frac{a}{b}\right)^2 W^2} = -3W\sqrt{1 + \frac{4}{9}\left(\frac{a}{b}\right)^2}.$$

PROBLEMS

8.7.1 The axisymmetric conical space truss of Fig. 8.7.4 carries on each meridian the loads shown. Evaluate the forces in its meridional and parallel bars.

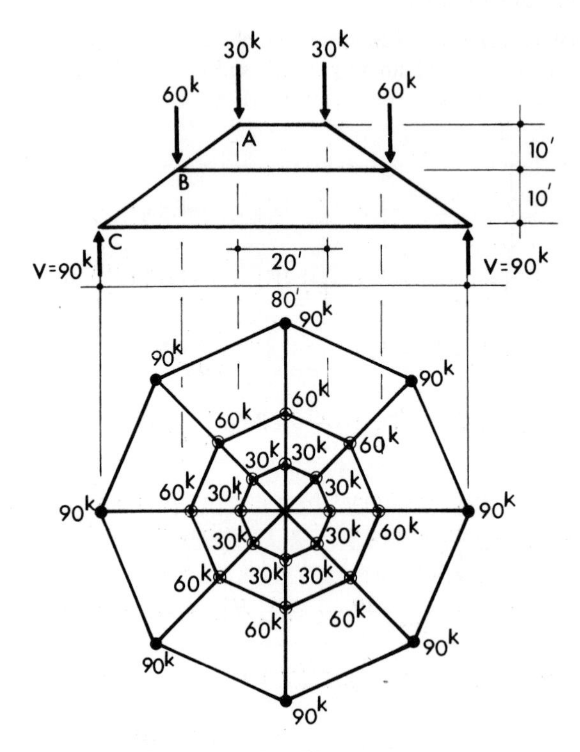

Fig. 8.7.4

8.7.2 A spherical space truss of radius 100 ft has 16 meridians and 4 parallels spaced as shown in Fig. 8.7.5 and is loaded symmetrically as indicated in the figure. Evaluate the forces in its parallel and meridional bars.

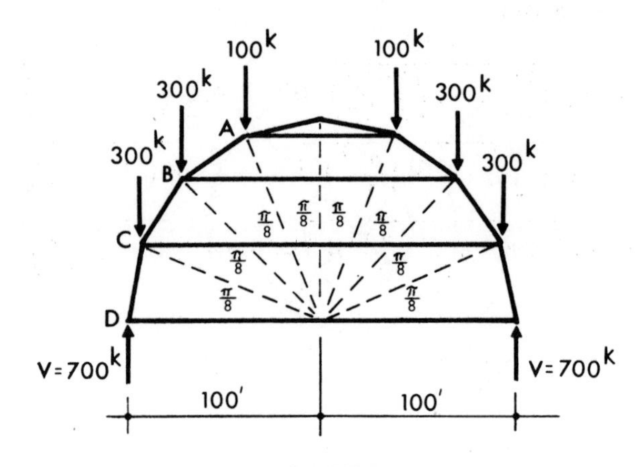

Fig. 8.7.5

8.7.3 The spherical space truss of Problem 8.7.2 carries a lantern, which adds 500 k loads at the joints A of the top parallel. Evaluate the added forces in the bars due to the lantern loads.

8.7.4 A suspended spherical swimming pool of radius 20 ft is supported by a space truss with 16 meridians and 4 parallels spaced by $\pi/8$ (Fig. 8.7.6). The hydraulic pressure loads of the water are directed radially and have values $P =$

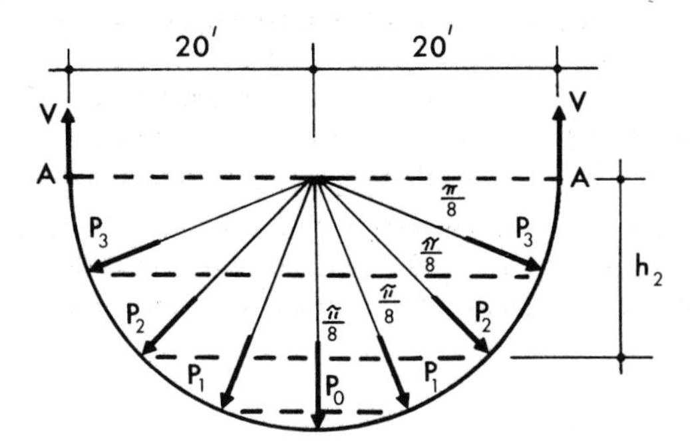

Fig. 8.7.6

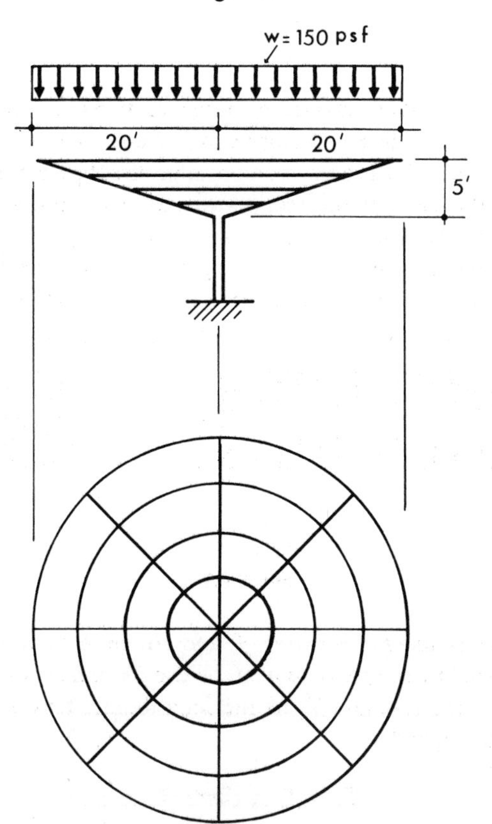

Fig. 8.7.7

pA, where p is the pressure and A the area contributory to the joint. The pressure p in psf, proportional to the depth h of water in feet, is given by $p = 62\,h$, and $A_0 = 48$ sq ft, $A_1 = 24$ sq ft, $A_2 = 44$ sq ft, $A_3 = 57$ sq ft. Evaluate the forces in the parallel and meridional bars of the truss. (*Note:* Divide the load P_0 equally between the 16 meridians.)

8.7.5 An inverted conical space truss (Fig. 8.7.7) is used as an umbrella roof. Its rise is 5 ft, its diameter 40 ft. It has 8 meridians and 4 evenly spaced parallels. Because of the roof's small slope, its dead and live loads may be added and considered to be a uniform load in horizontal projection of 150 psf. Determine the contributory loads at each joint, the reaction at the vertex support, and the forces in the lowest meridional and the upper parallel bars.

8.7.6 A circular steel dome with 8 meridians and 4 parallels has a radius of 50 ft and carries a dead load of 100 psf and a snow load of 30 psf. Determine the compressive force in the lowest meridional bars and the cross section of these bars for $F_s = 20$ ksi.

8.8 Membranes

Membranes are two-dimensional resisting structures so thin that they cannot develop appreciable bending or compressive stresses, and hence, react only in tension. A membrane, like a cable, is an unstable structure which changes shape to adapt itself to the loads. In this section we shall only consider the equilibrium of cylindrical and spherical membranes under internal pressure.

A cylindrical membrane of radius r, length l and thickness t is closed by two rigid diaphragms and is acted upon by an internal pressure p (Fig. 8.8.1). We

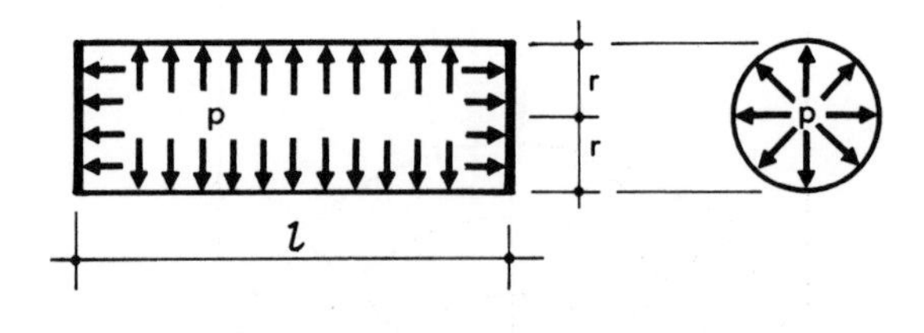

Fig. 8.8.1

wish to determine its *longitudinal stress* f_1 and *circumferential* or *hoop stress* f_2. The force P_1 exerted by the pressure p on the end diaphragms, $P_1 = p(\pi r^2)$, must be equilibrated by the resultant T_1 of the longitudinal tensile stress f_1 on any cross section of the cylinder:

$$T_1 = f_1 \times (2\pi r) \times t.$$

Hence:

$$2\pi rt\, f_1 = \pi pr^2 \quad \therefore \quad f_1 = \frac{1}{2}\left(\frac{r}{t}\right)p. \tag{8.8.1}$$

To evaluate the circumferential or hoop stress f_2, let us cut out of the membrane a ring of unit width and consider the equilibrium of a free body consisting of half such a ring (Fig. 8.8.2a, b). The resultants $T_2 = f_2 \times 1 \times t$ of the circumferential tension f_2 must equilibrate the resultant P_2 of the pressure p applied to half the ring. P_2 may be computed by taking the radial force $p(\Delta s \times 1)$ on a small element of area $\Delta s \times 1$ of the ring (Fig. 8.8.2c), multiplying $p\Delta s$ by $\cos\theta$ to obtain its vertical component and by adding up all these components:

$$P_2 = \sum p\Delta s \cos\theta.$$

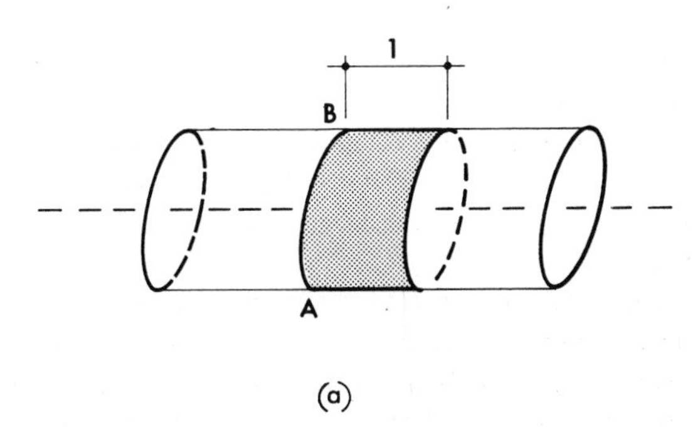

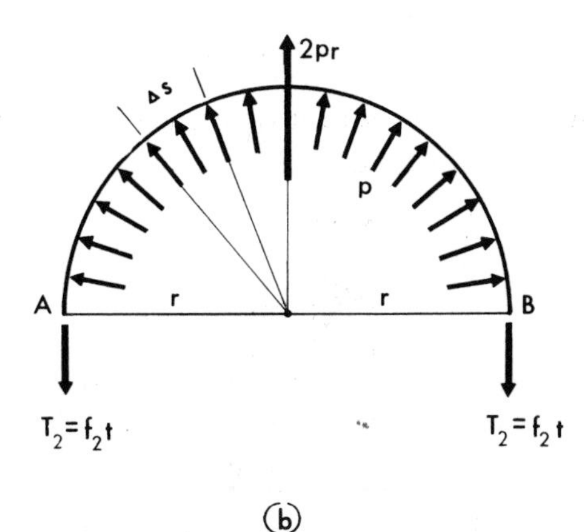

Fig. 8.8.2a–b

But $\Delta s \cos \theta$ is the horizontal component Δr of Δs, and since p is constant, P_2 is also the product of p times the sum of the projections Δr, i.e., times the diameter $2r$ of the membrane:

$$P_2 = p\sum \Delta s \cos \theta = p\sum \Delta r = p \times 2r.$$

For vertical equilibrium of the half ring, $P_2 = 2T_2$ or:

$$2pr = 2f_2 t \quad \therefore \quad f_2 = p\left(\frac{r}{t}\right). \tag{8.8.2}$$

Equation (8.8.2) shows that, for a given internal pressure p, f_2 is small when r is small and large when r is large. On the other hand, solving (8.8.2) for p and indicating by p_c the pressure carried by the cylindrical membrane, we find that:

$$p_c = f_2\left(\frac{t}{r}\right), \tag{8.8.3}$$

which shows that, for a given allowable stress f_2 and a given thickness, the pressure p_c varies inversely with r, so that if r becomes very large the membrane can carry a very small pressure. Introducing the concept of *curvature*, which is the reciprocal $1/r$ of the radius, we can say that *the membrane owes its pressure carrying capacity to its curvature*: the larger the curvature, the larger the pressure carrying capacity.

To evaluate the tensile stress f in a spherical membrane of radius r and thickness t under an internal pressure p, we notice that, by symmetry, f must have the same value in all directions at all points of the membrane. Considering one half of the spherical membrane as a free body (Fig. 8.8.3), we see that the resultant T of the tensile stress around its boundary is:

$$T = f \times 2\pi r \times t,$$

while the resultant P_2 of the pressure at right angles to the boundary plane is

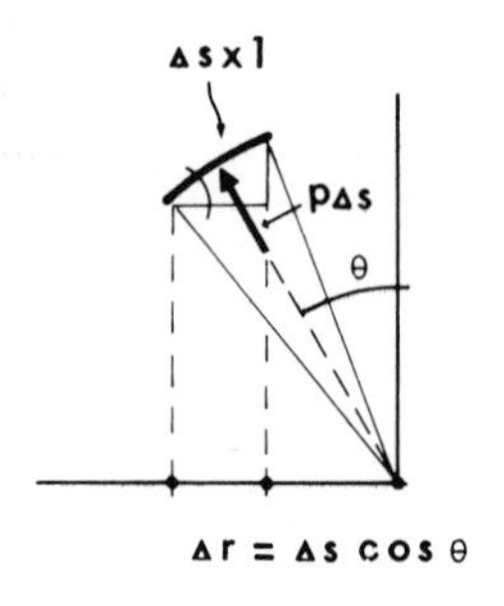

Fig. 8.8.2c

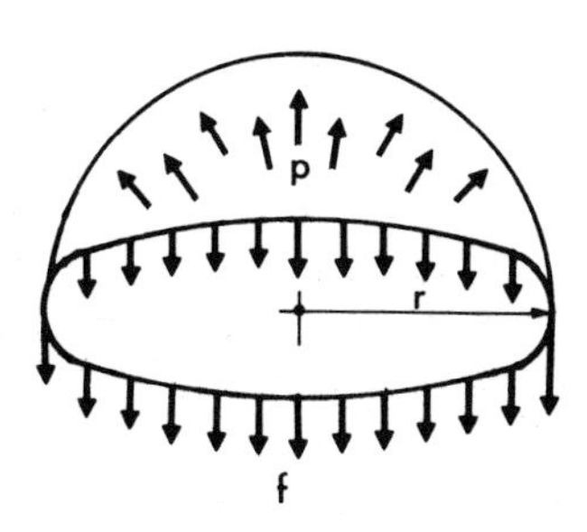

Fig. 8.8.3

equal to the pressure times the projection of the half-sphere's area on the boundary plane. This projection is the area πr^2 of the boundary circle, so that:

$$P_2 = p(\pi r^2).$$

For equilibrium in a direction perpendicular to the boundary plane, T must equal P_2, so that:

$$2\pi frt = \pi pr^2 \quad \therefore \quad f = \frac{1}{2}\left(\frac{r}{t}\right)p, \tag{8.8.4}$$

or calling p_s the pressure carried by a spherical membrane:

$$p_s = 2\left(\frac{t}{r}\right)f. \tag{8.8.5}$$

Equations (8.8.5) and (8.8.3) show that, if a spherical and a cylindrical membrane have the same thickness, radius and allowable stress, the spherical membrane carries twice as much pressure as the cylindrical membrane. This is due to the fact that the cylinder is curved in only one direction, while the sphere has curvature in two orthogonal directions, so that the sphere develops "cylinder action" in two directions, each "cylinder" carrying a pressure $p_c = (t/r)f$.

PROBLEMS

8.8.1 A cylindrical membrane 2 ft in diameter, closed by rigid diaphragms, is inflated with a pressure p and then used as a vertical column to carry a compressive load $C = 10$ k. Determine the internal pressure p so that the longitudinal stress f_1 due to p is twice the compressive stress due to C. Determine the thickness t of the membrane for a material with an allowable tensile stress of 6,000 psi.

8.8.2 A cylindrical membrane of thickness t, 2 ft in diameter, is used as a simply supported beam to carry a uniform load $w = 400$ lb/ft over a span of 10 ft. Determine the value of the internal pressure p for which the longitudinal tensile stress due to p is twice the compressive stress due to bending. Does the maximum longitudinal tensile stress due to the combined action of w and p, or the circumferential stress due to p, govern the determination of the membrane thickness? (*Note:* The moment of inertia of a thin circular section is $I_x = \pi r^3 t$.)

8.8.3 A spherical balloon of radius $r = 5$ ft and thickness $t = 0.01$ in. is inflated with a pressure p psi at sea level. The tension in the membrane under this pressure is equal to 2/3 the ultimate tension $f_u = 6{,}000$ psi in the material of the membrane. If air is assumed to weigh 0.08 lb/cu ft, at what height will the balloon burst?

8.8.4 A spherical balloon of radius 4 ft and thickness 0.1 in. develops a stress $f =$ 6,000 psi under a pressure p. At what depth in water will the stress be reduced to 2,000 psi? At what depth will the balloon collapse under compression? (*Note:* Water weighs 62.4 lb/cu ft.)

8.9 Axisymmetric Spherical Domes

Consider an axisymmetric thin shell, made out of concrete or some other material, with a thickness small enough not to allow the development of appreciable bending stresses over most of its surface, but large enough to allow the development of substantial compressive stresses without danger of buckling. Such a shell can support, by means of tensile and compressive stresses, a variety of axisymmetrical loads without changing shape, i.e., it is a stable structure. Because axisymmetrical thin shells, like membranes, develop minor bending stresses over most of their surface, their compressive and tensile stresses are referred to as *membrane stresses*. While in a cylinder we considered longitudinal and circumferential (or hoop) stresses f_1 and f_2, in a sphere we shall consider the *meridional stress* f_ϕ acting in the direction of the meridian on a section defined by the *co-latitude* angle ϕ in Fig. 8.9.1, and the *parallel stress* f_θ, acting in the direction of the parallel at the level defined by the same angle ϕ. (The stress f_ϕ is analogous to the longitudinal stress f_1 and the stress f_θ to the hoop stress f_2 in the cylinder.) The stresses f_ϕ and f_θ will be considered positive when tensile.

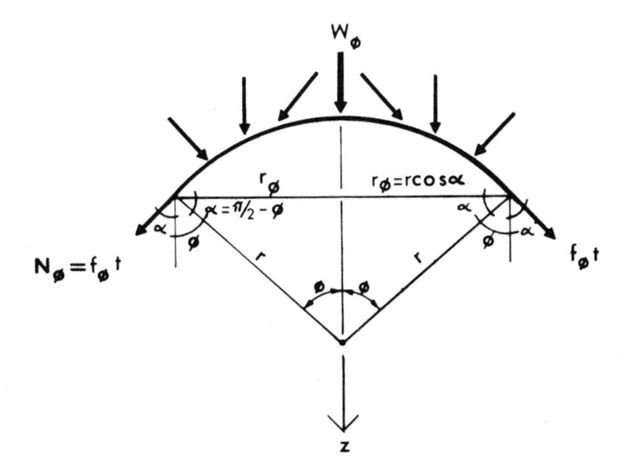

Fig. 8.9.1

To determine the meridional stress f_ϕ at the level ϕ in an axisymmetric *spherical* shell of radius r and thickness t, we consider the vertical equilibrium of a free body cut from it by means of a horizontal plane at the level ϕ (Fig. 8.9.1). Because of the assumed symmetry of the loads, the resultant W_ϕ of all the loads applied to this free body is vertical and acts along the shell axis. The force *per unit of boundary length* applied to the circular boundary, whose radius is $r_\phi = r \cos \alpha$, is $N_\phi = f_\phi t$, and its vertical component (Fig. 8.9.1) is $f_\phi t \cos \alpha$. Since f_ϕ, by symmetry, is constant along the boundary, the total vertical force applied to the boundary is $(f_\phi t \cos \alpha)(2\pi r_\phi) = (f_\phi t \cos \alpha)(2\pi r \cos \alpha)$. For vertical equilibrium of the free body:

$$W_\phi + (f_\phi t \cos \alpha)(2\pi r \cos \alpha) = 0,$$

or, since $\alpha = \pi/2 - \phi$, and $\cos \alpha = \sin \phi$:

$$W_\phi + (f_\phi t \sin \phi)(2\pi r \sin \phi) = 0,$$

from which:

$$f_\phi = -\frac{W_\phi}{2\pi r t \sin^2 \phi}. \tag{8.9.1}$$

To evaluate the parallel or hoop stress f_θ, let us indicate by w the *distributed load per unit of shell area* carried by the shell *at the level* ϕ, and by w_n its component in the direction of the normal *into* the shell (Fig. 8.9.2). Notice that w_n acts like an external pressure applied to the spherical shell. We have seen in Section 8.8 that a spherical membrane of radius r acts like two cylinders at right angles to each other, and that a cylinder carries an internal pressure $p_c = f(t/r)$ by developing a tensile stress f, and, hence, an *external* pressure $p_c = -f(t/r)$ by developing a stress $-f$. Therefore, the sphere carries an ex-

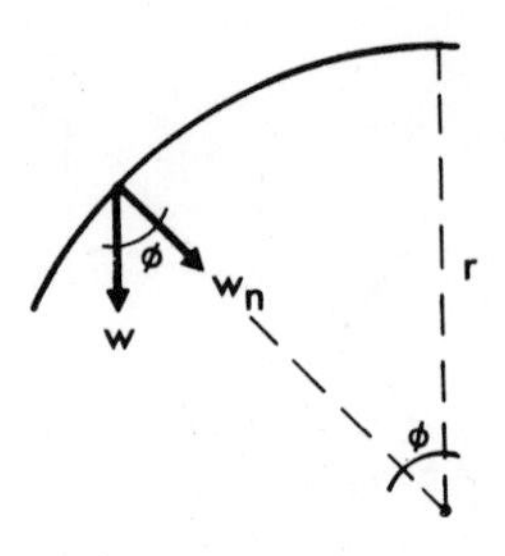

Fig. 8.9.2

ternal pressure $p_\phi = -f_\phi(t/r)$ by cylinder action in the meridional plane and an external pressure $p_\theta = -f_\theta(t/r)$ by cylinder action at right angles to the meridional plane.* The total external pressure w_n carried by the sphere through the stresses f_ϕ and f_θ is thus:

$$w_n = p_\phi + p_\theta = -f_\phi\left(\frac{t}{r}\right) - f_\theta\left(\frac{t}{r}\right),$$

from which, as soon as w_n is given and f_ϕ is known by (8.9.1):

$$f_\theta = -w_n\left(\frac{r}{t}\right) - f_\phi. \tag{8.9.2}$$

Equations (8.9.1) and (8.9.2) determine the membrane stresses in any spherical shell axisymmetrically loaded and supported.

Let us evaluate, for example, the stresses f_ϕ and f_θ at the boundary $\phi = 90°$ of a full spherical dome under the action of its dead load w per unit area. The total weight $W_{90°}$ of the dome is $2(\pi r^2)w$ [since the area of a half sphere of radius r is twice the area πr^2 of the circle of radius r] and by (8.9.1), with $\phi = 90°$:

$$f_\phi\Big]_{\phi=90°} = -\frac{2\pi r^2 w}{2\pi rt(\sin^2 90°)} = -w\left(\frac{r}{t}\right).$$

Thus, f_ϕ is compressive as shown by its negative sign. Since for $\phi = 90°$ the direction n of the perpendicular to the shell is horizontal, the component w_n of the vertical dead load w is zero at the boundary and (8.9.2) gives:

$$f_\theta\Big]_{\theta=90°} = 0 - f_\phi = +w\left(\frac{r}{t}\right).$$

Hence, f_θ is tensile at the boundary, as indicated by its positive sign.

*The parallel stress f_θ is identical with the hoop stress in a circle at right angles to the meridional plane because the tangent to the horizontal parallel is also the tangent to this inclined circle.

For a concrete shell with $r = 100$ ft, $t = 4$ in., and a weight of 150 lb/cu ft, for which $w = 150(4/12) = 50$ psf $= 50/144$ psi:

$$f_\phi \Big]_{90°} = -\frac{50}{144}\left(\frac{100 \times 12}{4}\right) = -104 \text{ psi}, \qquad f_\theta = -f_\phi = 104 \text{ psi}.$$

f_ϕ is a very low compressive stress for concrete. The tensile hoop force *per foot of shell meridian* at the boundary is $f_\theta \times t \times 12 = +104 \times 4 \times 12 = 5{,}000$ lb/ft and requires 0.25 sq in. of steel per foot of meridian for $F_t = 20{,}000$ psi.

PROBLEMS

8.9.1 Determine f_ϕ and f_θ at the boundary $\phi = 90°$ of a spherical shell of radius r and thickness t due to a uniform load q psf in horizontal projection (a so-called *snow load*).

8.9.2 Determine f_ϕ at a level ϕ in a spherical shell of radius r and thickness t due to a uniform load q in horizontal projection.

8.9.3 At which point of a spherical dome acted upon by its dead load w or a snow load q is $f_\phi = f_\theta$? What are the values of f_ϕ and f_θ at this point due: a) to the dead load w or b) to the snow load q? Can you explain the result on physical grounds?

8.9.4 The normal component of the dead load w at the level of the parallel ϕ in a spherical shell is $w_n = w \cos \phi$. Determine f_ϕ and f_θ at this level. (*Note:* The weight of a spherical sector above the level ϕ is $W_\phi = 2\pi w r^2(1 - \cos \phi)$.)

8.9.5 A spherical dome of radius r has a circular opening of radius a at the top and supports a lantern of total weight W at the boundary of this opening. Determine the values of f_ϕ and f_θ at any level ϕ due to the lantern weight W, noticing that for this loading condition the uniform load w in (8.9.2) is zero. Are the hoop stresses compressive or tensile?

8.9.6 The dead load stresses f_θ in a spherical dome are tensile at the boundary $\phi = 90°$ and compressive at the top $\phi = 0°$. [The general expression for f_θ (see Problem 8.9.4) is:

$$f_\theta = w\left(\frac{r}{t}\right)\left(\frac{1}{1 + \cos \phi} - \cos \phi\right).$$

At what level ϕ does f_θ go from positive to negative values?

8.9.7 Two spherical shells span 200 ft, one with a rise $h_1 = 60$ ft, the other with a rise $h_2 = 20$ ft. The two shells are made out of concrete weighing 150 lb/cu ft and are 4 in. thick. After determining the radius r and the opening angle ϕ_0 of each sphere from the geometry of Fig. 8.9.3, evaluate the ratio of the dead load stresses f_ϕ at $\phi = \phi_0$ in the two shells. Which of the two shells, if any, develops a tensile stress f_θ at its boundary? (See note of Problem 8.9.4.)

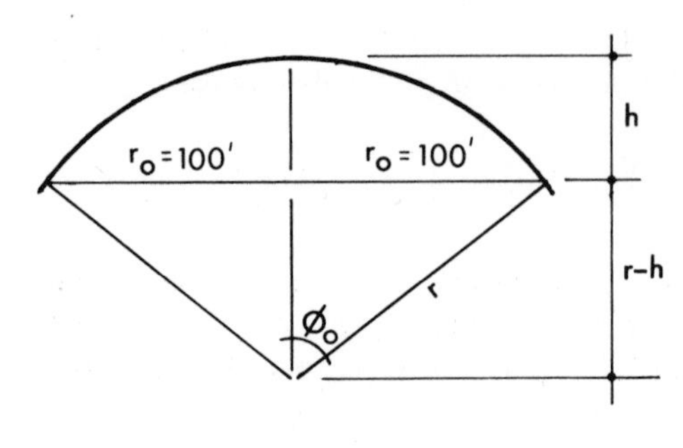

Fig. 8.9.3

8.9.8 A spherical shell of reinforced concrete carries a concentrated load W at its top. Which parallels require tensile reinforcement in this shell? Does the tensile reinforcement per foot of shell increase or decrease as one moves from the top to the bottom of the shell? (*Note:* f_ϕ and f_θ approach infinity at $\phi = 0$, because a thin shell cannot carry concentrated loads by membrane stresses only.)

8.9.9 A spherical shell carries a vertical line load of Q lb/ft uniformly distributed on its parallel $\phi = 45°$. What are the values of f_ϕ and of f_θ at $\phi = 90°$ and $\phi = 30°$?

8.10 Hyperbolic Paraboloids

A *hyperbolic paraboloid element* is a thin two-dimensional resisting element whose middle surface may be obtained by connecting with straight lines the corresponding points of two straight line segments skew in space (Fig. 8.10.1). If the two straight line segments lie in two orthogonal vertical planes, and one of them is horizontal while the other is inclined, the element is called a "twisted rectangle." With reference to the x-, y-, z-axes of Fig. 8.10.2, its sides a and b lie in vertical planes parallel to x and y and its *rise* c is measured along the z-axis. When c is small in comparison with a and b, the paraboloid is said to be *shallow*. A thin shell in the shape of a shallow twisted rectangle is often supported on its boundaries by vertical trusses or *stiffeners*, which are vertically stiff but flexible in the horizontal direction. Such a hyperbolic paraboloid or *hypar* element, because of its small thickness, does not develop appreciable bending stresses under distributed loads; it carries such loads by means of membrane stresses, i.e., tensile, compressive and *shear stresses acting in the surface of the element*. The membrane stresses in a shallow "twisted rectangle" can be determined by statics on the basis of its geometry and its support conditions.

Notice first that, since the support stiffeners do not react horizontally, any strip parallel to x or y, like $AA' - BB'$ or $CC' - DD'$, cannot be under tension

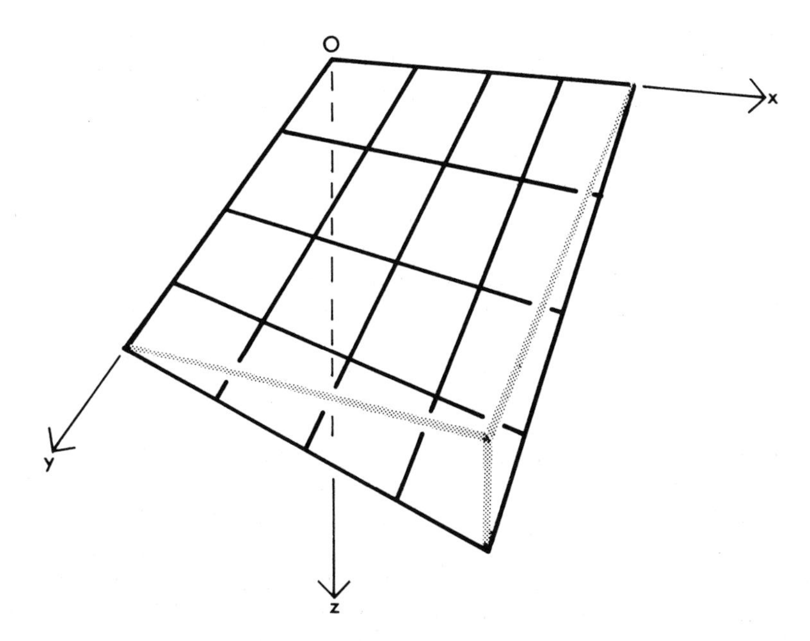

Fig. 8.10.1

or compression. Moreover, since bending stresses are bound to be negligible because the shell is thin, the load on an area with sides parallel to the x- and y-axes (such as the area shaded in Fig. 8.10.2) *can only be supported by shears*

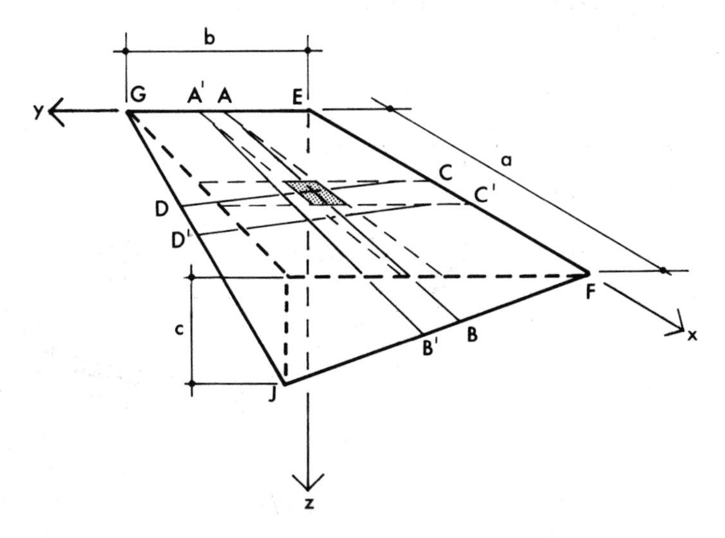

Fig. 8.10.2

on its sides. Notice next that the slope s_x of a line, like AB, lying in a vertical plane parallel to x, varies linearly from zero along the side EF to c/a along the side GJ. The change t_{xy} in the slope s_x for a unit displacement of the line in the y-direction is thus:

$$t_{xy} = \frac{c/a - 0}{b} = \frac{c}{ab}. \tag{a}$$

Similarly, the change in the slope s_y of a line, like CD, lying in a vertical plane parallel to y, for a unit displacement of the line in the x-direction is:

$$t_{yx} = \frac{c/b - 0}{a} = \frac{c}{ab} = t_{xy}. \tag{b}$$

The quantity $t_{xy} = t_{yx}$ is called the *twist* of the hyperbolic paraboloid.

Let w be the load on the shell per unit of *horizontally* projected area. This load is a so-called *snow* load, but for a *shallow* paraboloid it may also include its dead load, since the area of the horizontal projection of the shallow hypar element is for all practical purposes equal to the area of the element itself.

To determine the stresses in the hypar element, we cut from it a "free body" in the shape of a rectangle $MNPQ$ with sides in vertical planes parallel to x and y, whose projections along the x- and y-axes are Δa and Δb (Fig. 8.10.3). Calling s_x the slope of the side MN, the slope of the side PQ is s_x plus the change $t_x \Delta b$ in s_x due to a displacement Δb along y, i. e., $s_x + t_{xy}\Delta b$. Similarly, the slope of the side NQ is the slope s_y of the side MP plus the change $t_{yx}\Delta a$ in s_y due to a displacement Δa along x, i. e., $s_y + t_{yx}\Delta a$. The stresses along the sides of $MNPQ$ were seen to be shear stresses. The value f_s of these stresses must

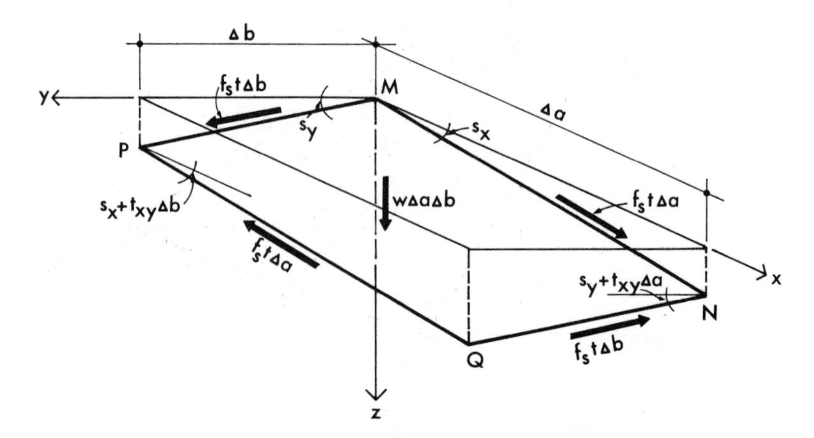

Fig. 8.10.3

be the same on all 4 sides, as may be checked by the equation for rotational equilibrium around the z-axis, in which the forces $f_s t\,\Delta a$ and $f_s t\,\Delta b$ are to all practical purposes horizontal:

$$f_s t\,\Delta b \times \Delta a - f_s t\,\Delta a \times \Delta b = 0.$$

Therefore, we can determine the value of f_s by stating that the element $MNPQ$ is in vertical equilibrium under the action of the load $w\,\Delta a\,\Delta b$ and the vertical components of the shears (i.e., the shears times the corresponding slopes) on its 4 sides:

$$w\,\Delta a\,\Delta b + (f_s t\,\Delta a)s_x - f_s t\,\Delta a(s_x + t_{xy}\,\Delta b)$$
$$+ (f_s t\,\Delta b)s_y - f_s t\,\Delta b(s_y + t_{yx}\,\Delta a) = 0,$$

from which, dividing by $\Delta a\,\Delta b$ and by equations (a) and (b):

$$w - f_s t(t_{xy} + t_{yx}) = w - f_s t\left(\frac{2c}{ab}\right) = 0 \quad \therefore \quad f_s = \frac{wab}{2ct}. \tag{8.10.1}$$

The shear stress is seen to be *constant throughout the hypar element and inversely proportional to the rise c and to the thickness t.*

For example, a concrete hypar 4 in. thick, with $a = 20$ ft, $b = 10$ ft and $c = 4$ ft, has a dead load of $\frac{4}{12}150 = 50$ psf. If it carries a maximum live load of 50 psf, its total w is 100 psf, and its constant shear stress is:

$$f_s = \frac{100 \times 20 \times 10}{2 \times 4 \times 4/12} = 7{,}500 \text{ psf} = 52 \text{ psi}.$$

Remembering that when equal shear stresses develop on the sides of a rectangular element, tensile and compressive stresses equal in value to the shear stresses develop at 45° to the element sides (see Section 5.7), we find that compressive stresses:

$$f_c = -\frac{wab}{2ct} \tag{8.10.2}$$

develop in the direction of the line MQ bisecting the positive x- and y-axes (Fig. 8.10.4) and tensile stresses:

$$f_t = \frac{wab}{2ct} \tag{8.10.3}$$

develop in the direction of the line *PN* bisecting the $+x$- and $-y$-axes (Fig. 8.10.4). It is thus seen (Fig. 8.10.5) that the shell develops *compressive funicular arch action* along the downward curved diagonal *BD* of a rectangular hypar element and *tensile cable action* along its upward curved diagonal *AC*.

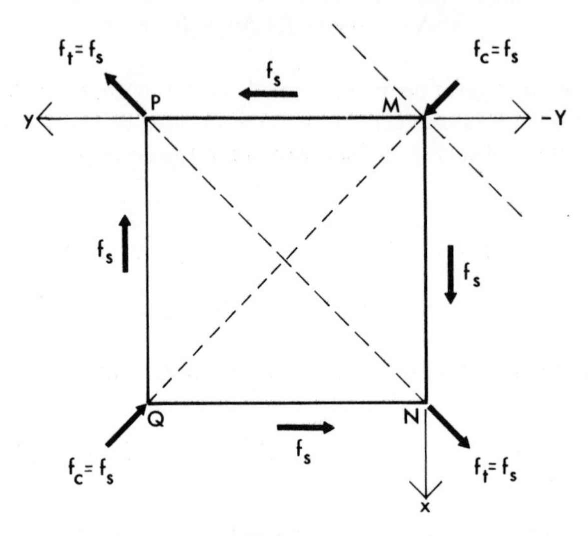

Fig. 8.10.4

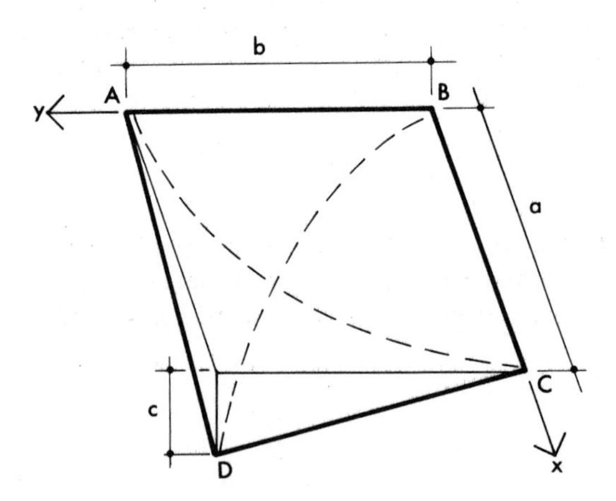

Fig. 8.10.5

In the previous example, the 4 in. thick concrete shell develops a concrete compressive stress $f_c = 52$ psi in the *BD* direction and a tensile force *per foot width of shell* in the *AC* direction equal to $52 \times 4 \times 12 = 2{,}496$ lb, requiring for $F_t = 20$ ksi a steel area $A_s = 2{,}496/20{,}000 = 0.125$ in.^{2} per foot width of shell.

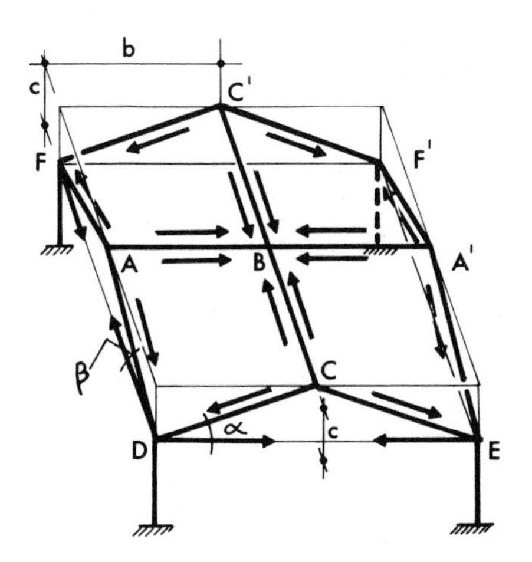

Fig. 8.10.6

To complete the shell design, consider a roof consisting of 4 twisted rectangles supported on its boundary by triangular trusses resting on 4 columns (Fig. 8.10.6). The shears exerted by the twisted rectangles on the inclined struts of the boundary trusses accumulate from a crown point like C to a support point like D, where the compression at D in the strut of length $CD \doteq b$ is:

$$C_{CD} = (f_s t)b = \frac{wab^2}{2c}. \tag{8.10.4}$$

Similarly, the maximum compression in the strut AD occurs at D and is:

$$C_{AD}(f_s t)a = \frac{wa^2 b}{2c}. \tag{8.10.5}$$

A tie rod DE is required to absorb the horizontal component of C_{CD}; the tension in the tie rod is:

$$T_{DE} = C_{CD} \cos \alpha = \left(\frac{wab^2}{2c}\right) \frac{b}{\sqrt{b^2 + c^2}} \doteq \frac{wab^2}{2c}. \tag{8.10.6}$$

Similarly, the tension in the tie rod FD is:

$$T_{FD} = C_{AD} \cos \beta = \frac{wa^2 b}{2c} \frac{a}{\sqrt{b^2 + c^2}} \doteq \frac{wa^2 b}{2c}.$$

In the previous example:

$$C_{CD} = T_{DE} = \frac{100 \times 20(10)^2}{2 \times 4} = 25{,}000 \text{ lb} = 25 \text{ k},$$

$$C_{AD} = T_{FD} = \frac{100 \times (20)^2 \times 10}{2 \times 4} = 50{,}000 \text{ lb} = 50 \text{ k}.$$

For an allowable compressive stress in the concrete of $F_c = 1$ ksi, the boundary struts require areas:

$$A_{CD} = 25 \text{ in.}^2, \qquad A_{AD} = 50 \text{ in.}^2,$$

and the tie rods, for an $F_t = 20$ ksi, require steel areas:

$$A_{S,DE} = 1.25 \text{ in.}^2, \qquad A_{S,FD} = 2.5 \text{ in.}^2.$$

The struts AB and $A'B$ are compressed by the accumulated shears of the 2 adjoining elements (like $ABC'F$ and $ABCD$); hence:

$$C_{AB} = 2C_{CD} = \frac{wab^2}{c}. \tag{8.10.7}$$

Similarly, the struts CB and $C'B$ are acted on by a maximum compressive force:

$$C_{CB} = 2C_{AD} = \frac{wa^2b}{c}. \tag{8.10.8}$$

In our example, the areas of these struts, for $F_c = 1$ ksi, are 50 in.^{2} and 100 in.^{2}, respectively. The arrangement of Fig. 8.10.6 is equilibrated because the compressive forces in CB and $C'B$ are equal and opposite, as are those in AB and $A'B$.

PROBLEMS

8.10.1 Design the reinforcement, the boundary trusses and the internal struts for a hyperbolic paraboloid, "twisted rectangle" roof with $a = 20$ ft, $b = 30$ ft, $c = 6$ ft and $t = 5$ in., carrying a live load of 50 psf and supported at its corners (Fig. 8.10.6). Assume $F_c = 1$ ksi, $F_s = 20$ ksi.

8.10.2 A square hyperbolic paraboloid *umbrella* roof is made out of concrete and supported on a central column. Figure 8.10.7 indicates the forces exerted by the shell shears on its supporting beams and shows that the accumulated forces are tensile in the boundary beams, which act as tie rods, and compressive in the inclined struts. Design the thin shell, the boundary beams and the inclined struts for $a = 10$ ft, $c = 4$ ft, $t = 4$ in. and a live load of 40 psf. Which diagonal directions are in tension? Assume $F_c = 1$ ksi and $F_s = 20$ ksi.

8.10.3 A square hyperbolic paraboloid roof with $a = 30$ ft made out of concrete carries a negligible live load. If we call ρ the weight of its concrete per unit volume and t its thickness, its dead load is $w = \rho t$. What is its smallest allowable rise c if $\rho = 120$ lb/cu ft (lightweight concrete) and $F_c = 100$ psi.

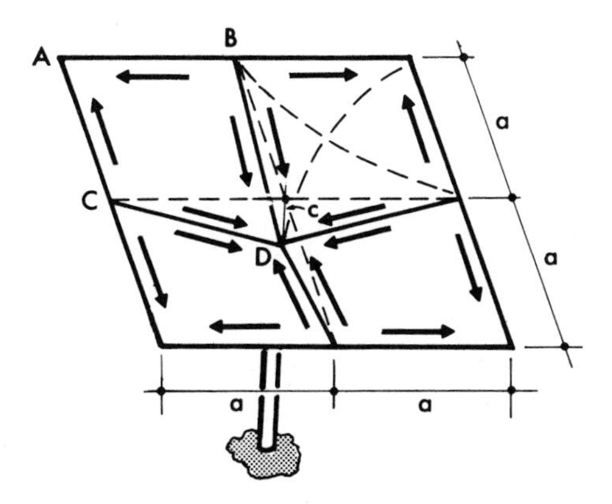

Fig. 8.10.7

8.10.4 Two hyperbolic paraboloid roofs of the type shown in Fig. 8.10.6 cover the same area A and have the same rise. One is square of side $a' = \sqrt{A}$; the other is rectangular with sides a and $b = 2a$, so that $a'^2 = ab = 2a^2$. Which roof requires a larger amount of steel for the 4 tie rods if the load w is the same for both roofs?

Appendix

A.1 Centroids

The centroid of a plane figure is the point on which the figure could be balanced if it were cut out of a sheet of material of constant thickness.* The plane figure may represent an actual area (like a contributory floor area or the cross section of a beam) or a diagram (like a load or a bending moment diagram). If a figure has a line of symmetry, its centroid C lies on it, since the figure can be balanced on an edge set along this line (Fig. A.1.1). If a figure has 2 lines of symmetry, its centroid must lie on both lines, and hence, it is the point where the two lines intersect (Fig. A.1.2).

From its definition, the centroid of any plane figure may be located, with respect to an arbitrary set of x-, y-axes in the plane of the figure, by means of 2 equations of rotational equilibrium. If the figure is cut out of a sheet of thickness t of a material of weight ρ per unit volume (Fig. A.1.3), a small area ΔA of the figure has a weight $\rho t\,\Delta A$. Indicating by x_C and y_C the coordinates of

*In this context the "plane figure" may consist of many separate plane figures. In this case the separate figures may be imagined rigidly connected by weightless wires lying in the plane of the figures.

Section Properties

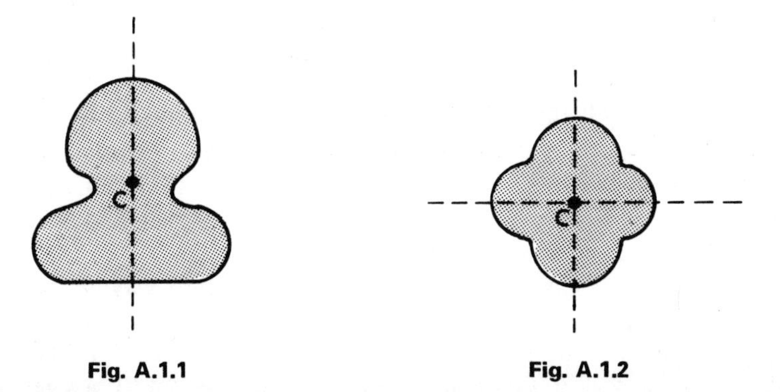

Fig. A.1.1 **Fig. A.1.2**

the figure's centroid C and by x and y the coordinates of the center of a small area ΔA, rotational equilibrium about the centroidal axis A–A parallel to y requires that the sum of the moments about the axis A–A of the weights of all the areas ΔA be equal to zero, i.e., that:

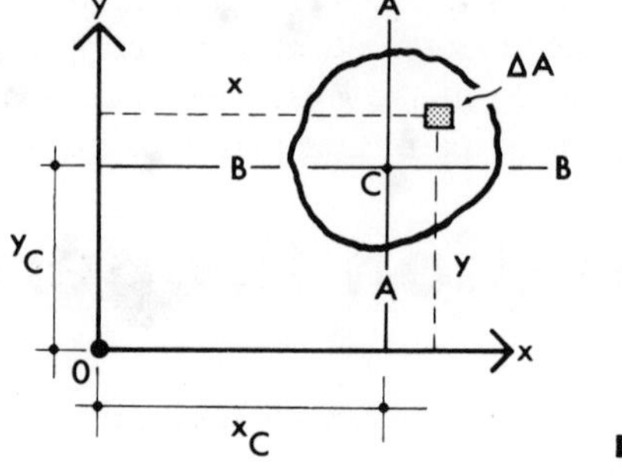

Fig. A.1.3

$$\sum_A pt\, \Delta A(x - x_C) = 0, \tag{a}$$

where the symbol $\sum_A$ ("sum extended to the entire area A") indicates that we must add the products of the weights $pt\Delta A$ times their lever arms $x - x_C$ about the A–A axis for all the small areas ΔA in the figure of area A. Let equation (a) be rewritten as:

$$\sum_A (pt\Delta A\, x - pt\Delta A\, x_C) = \sum_A t\Delta A\, x - \sum_A pt\Delta A\, x_C = 0,$$

or:

$$\sum_A ptx\Delta A = \sum_A pt\Delta A\, x_C.$$

Noticing that pt can be deleted on both sides of this equation and that x varies with each ΔA, while x_C is a constant, we may factor out x_C from the sum on the right side of the equation and write the equation in the form:

$$\sum_A x\Delta A = x_C \sum_A \Delta A. \tag{b}$$

But the sum of all the partial areas ΔA, extended to the entire area A, is the area A of the entire figure, so that solving (b) for the x-coordinate x_C of the centroid, we obtain:

$$x_C = \frac{\sum_A x\Delta A}{A}. \tag{A.1.1}$$

Writing a rotational equilibrium equation about the centroidal axis B–B parallel to x we find, similarly, that:

$$y_C = \frac{\sum_A y\Delta A}{A}. \tag{A.1.2}$$

Notice that any set of x-, y-axes may be used to determine x_C and y_C.

The numerators of equations (A.1.1), (A.1.2), i.e., the sum of the products of the small areas ΔA times their distances x or y from the y- or x-axis, are called the *static moments* of the areas about y or x and are indicated by S_y or S_x.* The centroidal coordinates may thus be written in terms of static moments as:

$$x_C = \frac{S_y}{A}, \qquad y_C = \frac{S_x}{A}. \tag{A.1.3}$$

The evaluation of static moments is obtained mathematically by the process of integration:

$$S_x = \int_A y\,dA, \qquad S_y = \int_A x\,dA. \tag{A.1.4}$$

For example, for the triangle of Fig. A.1.4a, S_y may be computed by the taking as elementary areas dA, the areas of infinitesimal rectangles of width dx and height $y = (b/a)x$ like that shaded in Fig. A.1.4a:

$$S_y = \int_0^a x\left(\frac{b}{a}x\right) dx = \frac{b}{a}\int_0^a x^2\,dx = \frac{b}{a}\frac{x^3}{3}\bigg]_0^a = \frac{ba^2}{3}.$$

Since $A = ba/2$, we obtain from the first of equations (A.1.3):

$$x_C = \frac{ba^2/3}{ba/2} = \frac{2}{3}a.$$

To evaluate S_x, we may take as elementary areas, rectangles of height dy and width $a - x = a - \frac{a}{b}y$, like that shaded in Fig. A.1.4b:

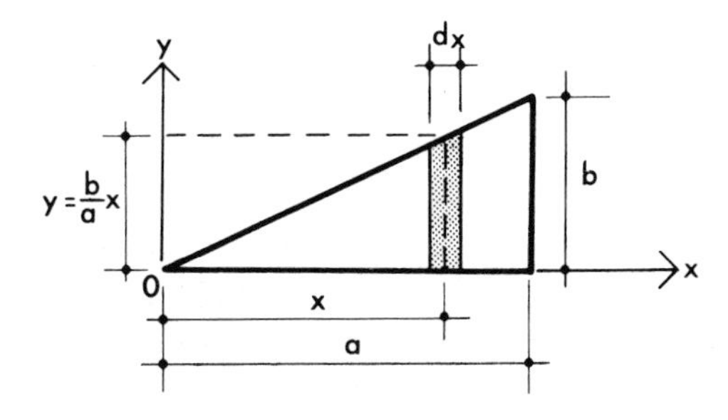

Fig. A.1.4a

*S_x and S_y must not be confused with the section moduli (see Section 5.8).

$$S_x = \int_0^b y\left(a - \frac{a}{b}y\right) dy = \int_0^b \left(ay - \frac{a}{b}y^2\right) dy = a\frac{y^2}{2} - \left(\frac{a}{b}\right)\frac{y^3}{3}\Big]_0^b$$

$$= \frac{ab^2}{2} - \frac{ab^2}{3} = \frac{ab^2}{6}.$$

With this value of S_x the second of equations (A.1.3) gives:

$$y_C = \frac{ab^2/6}{ab/2} = \frac{1}{3}b.$$

Table A.1 gives the centroidal coordinates for some of the most commonly encountered nonsymmetrical figures.

Handbooks, in which the properties of steel rolled sections are given, also locate the centroids of these sections.

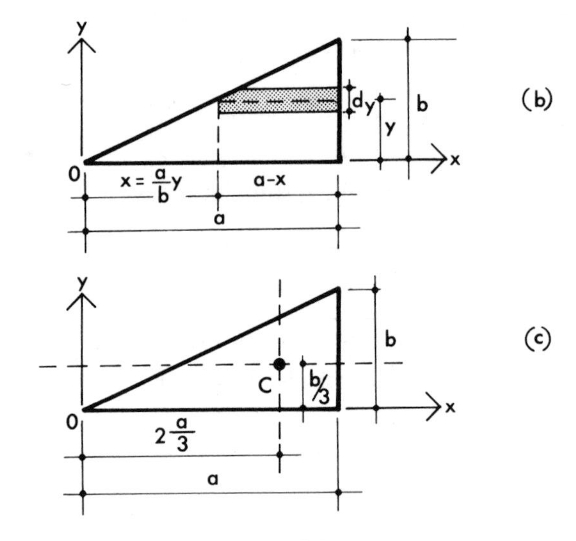

Fig. A.1.4b-c

A.2 Moments of Inertia

The *moment of intertia* of a plane figure about an axis lying in the plane of the figure is the sum of the products of its small areas ΔA times the *square* of the distance of their center from the axis (Fig. A.2.1):

$$I_B = \sum_A d^2 \Delta A. \tag{A.2.1}$$

When the figure considered is the cross section of a beam and the axis a

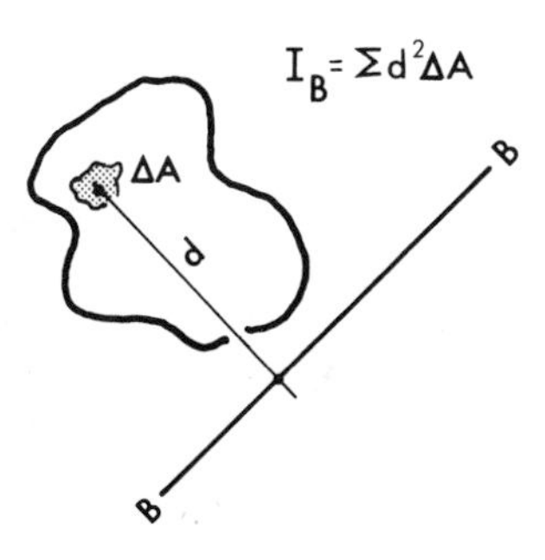

Fig. A.2.1

centroidal axis, the moment of inertia acquires an important physical meaning: it is *a measure of the stiffness of the beam in bending when the chosen axis is free of stress or neutral* (see Section 5.8). By (A.2.1), the moments of inertia I_x and I_y of a plane figure about 2 orthogonal axes x, y are given by:

$$I_x = \sum_A y^2 \Delta A, \qquad I_y = \sum_A x^2 \Delta A, \tag{A.2.2}$$

or, using the mathematical process of integration to obtain the sums, by:

$$I_x = \int_A y^2 \, dA, \qquad I_y = \int_A x^2 \, dA. \tag{A.2.3}$$

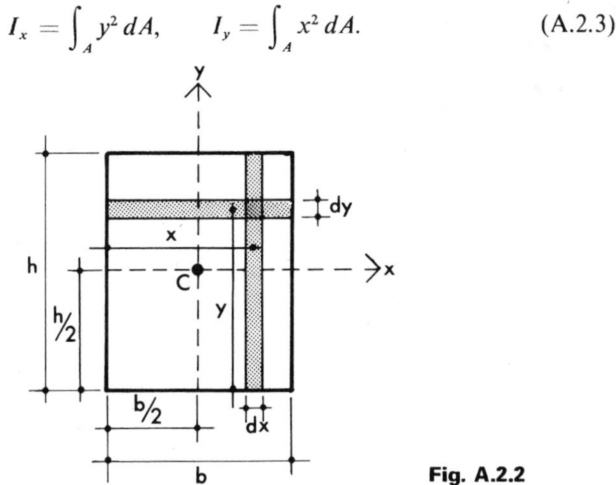

Fig. A.2.2

For example, for the centroidal x-, y-axes of the rectangle of Fig. A.2.2, taking as elementary areas ΔA, the areas of rectangles of width b and height dy, one obtains:

$$I_x = \int_{-h/2}^{h/2} y^2(bdy) = b\frac{y^3}{3}\Big]_{-h/2}^{h/2} = \frac{b}{3}\left[\left(\frac{h}{2}\right)^3 - \left(-\frac{h}{2}\right)^3\right] = \frac{bh^3}{12}, \tag{a}$$

a result already used in Section 5.8. Similarly, taking as elementary areas ΔA, the areas of rectangles of height h and width dx, we get:

$$I_y = \int_{-b/2}^{b/2} x^2(h\,dx) = h\frac{x^3}{3}\Big]_{-b/2}^{b/2} = \frac{h}{3}\left[\left(\frac{b}{2}\right)^3 - \left(-\frac{b}{2}\right)^3\right] = \frac{hb^3}{12}. \tag{b}$$

Table A.1 gives the moments of inertia about the centroidal axes for the figures most commonly used as beam cross sections.

Two additional section properties, related to its moments of inertia, play an important role in the stress-analysis of beams. The first is encountered in the determination of the extreme fiber stress f_b, a distance c from the neutral axis in a beam of moment of inertia I, due to a bending moment M:

$$f_b = \frac{Mc}{I} \tag{c}$$

(see Section 5.8). It is called the *section modulus S* and is defined by:

$$S = \frac{I}{c}. \tag{A.2.4}$$

For example, in a rectangular cross section $b \times h$, $c = \pm h/2$ and by (a) and (A.2.4):

$$S_x = \frac{I_x}{c} = \frac{bh^3/12}{h/2} = \frac{bh^2}{6}, \tag{d}$$

by means of which:

$$f_b = \pm\frac{6M}{bh^2}. \tag{e}$$

For unsymmetrical sections (Fig. A.2.3), the distances c_1 and c_2 of the extreme fibers from the neutral axis are different, and one needs to define two moduli:

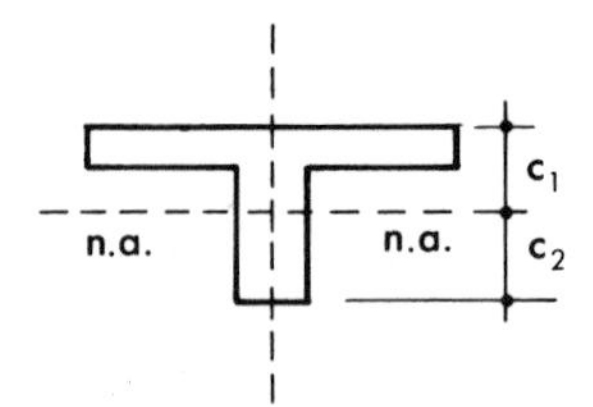

Fig. A.2.3

$$S_1 = \frac{I}{c_1}, \qquad S_2 = \frac{I}{c_2}. \tag{A.2.5}$$

The values of S, or S_1 and S_2, are also given in Table A.1 for the most commonly encountered beam cross sections.

The second section property related to the moment of inertia is called the *radius of gyration* of the section and is defined as:

$$r = \sqrt{\frac{I}{A}}, \tag{A.2.6}$$

where I is the moment of inertia and A the area of the section. The radius of gyration gives a measure of the beam capacity to resist axial compressive loads without bending out or "buckling." If l is the beam length free to buckle (because unsupported), the larger the ratio r/l (i.e., the smaller the *slenderness ratio* l/r), the larger the beam capacity against buckling. By (A.2.6), the radius of gyration r_x of a rectangular cross section $b \times h$ with respect to a centroidal x-axis parallel to its side b is:

$$r_x = \sqrt{\frac{I_x}{A}} = \sqrt{\frac{bh^3/12}{bh}} = \sqrt{\frac{h^2}{12}} = \frac{h}{2\sqrt{3}} = 0.29h, \tag{f}$$

while the radius of gyration with respect to a centroidal axis parallel to its side h is:

$$r_y = \sqrt{\frac{I_y}{A}} = \sqrt{\frac{hb^3/12}{bh}} = \sqrt{\frac{b^2}{12}} = \frac{b}{2\sqrt{3}} = 0.29b. \tag{g}$$

The sum of the products of the elementary areas ΔA of a plane figure of area A by the square of the distance of their centers from a point 0 is called the *polar moment of inertia* I_p of the figure about 0 (Fig. A.2.4a):

$$I_p = \sum_A r^2 \Delta A = \int_A r^2 \, dA. \tag{A.2.7}$$

The polar moment of inertia of a symmetrical cross section about its centroid

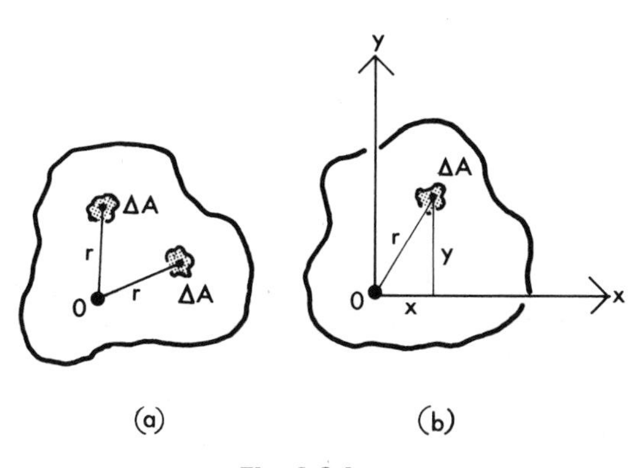

Fig. A.2.4

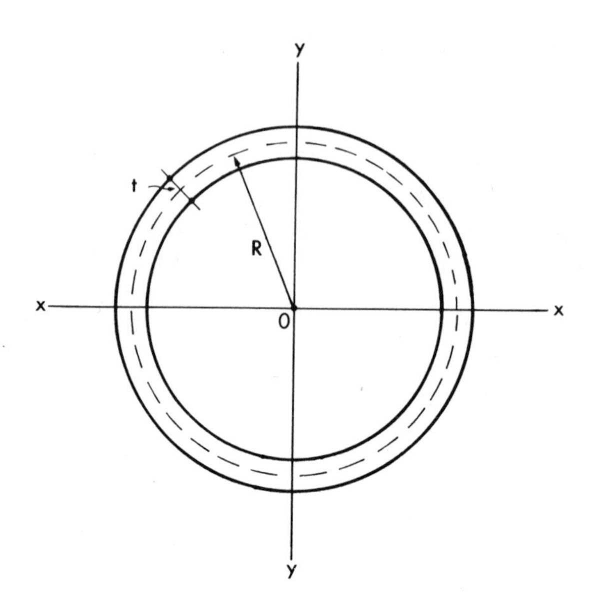

Fig. A.2.5

is a measure of the beam stiffness in torsion, i.e., against twisting deformations. If we refer the plane figure to 2 orthogonal x-, y-axes passing through 0 (Fig. A.2.4b), $r^2 = x^2 + y^2$ and I_p becomes:

$$I_p = \sum_A (x^2 + y^2)\Delta A = \sum_A x^2 \Delta A + \sum_A y^2 \Delta A = I_y + I_x. \qquad \text{(A.2.8)}$$

By (A.2.8), it is seen that the polar moment of inertia about 0 is the sum of the moments of inertia about *any* 2 orthogonal x-, y-axes through 0. For example, the polar moment of inertia of a rectangle $b \times h$ about its centroid is:

$$I_p = I_x + I_y = \frac{bh^3}{12} + \frac{hb^3}{12} = \frac{bh}{12}(h^2 + b^2). \qquad \text{(h)}$$

Equations (A.2.7) and (A.2.8) may be used to evaluate the moment af inertia I_x of a hollow circular section of radius R and small thickness t about its diametral axis x–x (Fig. A.2.5), by noticing that, because of symmetry, $I_x = I_y$, so that:

$$I_p = (2\pi Rt)(R)^2 = I_x + I_y = 2I_x \quad \therefore \quad I_x = I_y = \pi R^3 t. \qquad \text{(i)}$$

Similarly, for a full circular section of radius R, taking as elementary area ΔA, the area of a ring of radius r and thickness dr (Fig. A.2.6), we obtain:

$$I_p = \int_0^R (2\pi r dr) r^2 = 2\pi \int_0^R r^3\, dr = 2\pi \frac{R^4}{4} = \frac{\pi R^4}{2}$$

$$\therefore \quad I_x = I_y = \frac{\pi}{4} R^4. \tag{j}$$

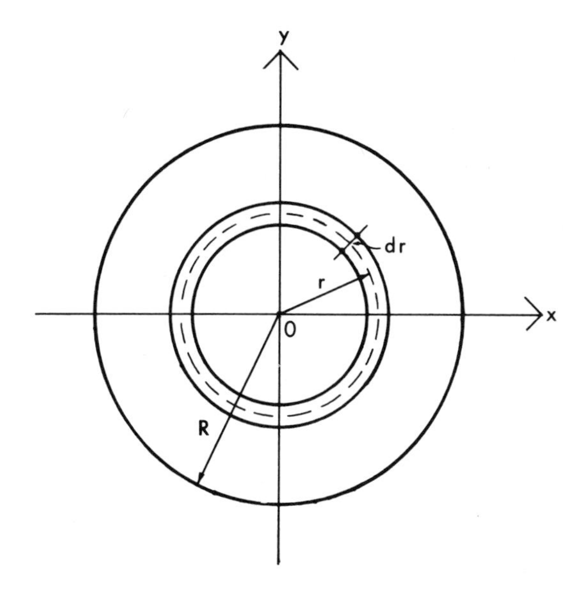

Fig. A.2.6

Table A.1

No.	Section	A	C_x	I_x	S_x
1	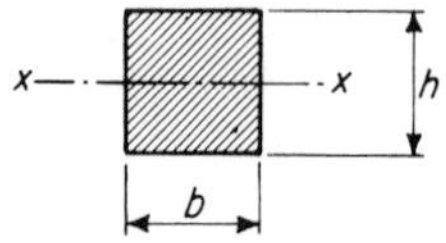	bh	$\frac{h}{2}$	$\frac{bh^3}{12}$	$\frac{bh^2}{6}$
2	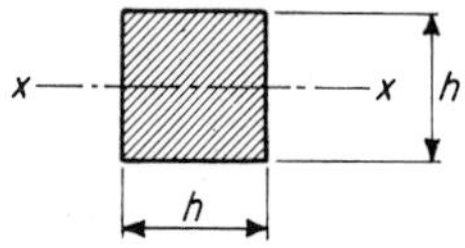	h^2	$\frac{h}{2}$	$\frac{h^4}{12}$	$\frac{h^3}{6}$
3	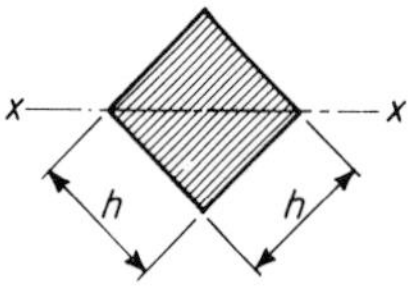	h^2	$\frac{h}{\sqrt{2}}$	$\frac{h^4}{12}$	$\frac{\sqrt{2}}{12}h^3 = 0.12h^3$
4	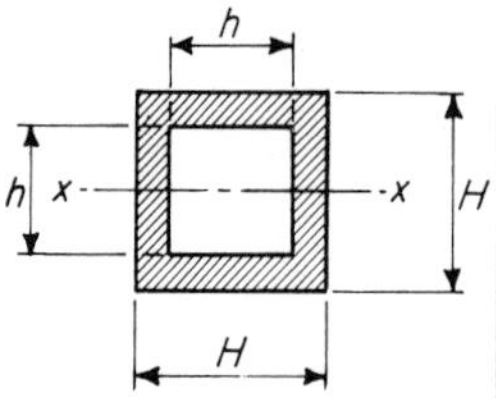	$H^2 - h^2$	$\frac{H}{2}$	$\frac{H^4 - h^4}{12}$	$\frac{H^4 - h^4}{6H}$
5	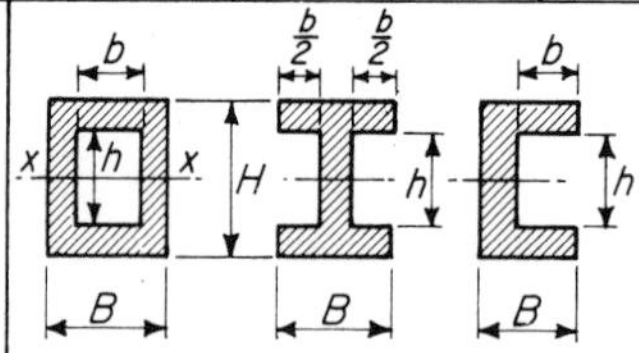	$BH - bh$	$\frac{H}{2}$	$\frac{BH^3 - bh^3}{12}$	$\frac{BH^3 - bh^3}{6H}$

Table A.1 (Continued)

No.	Section	A	C_x	I_x	S_x
6	t, h, x, x, H, b	$b(H-h)$ $= 2bt$	$\frac{H}{2}$	$\frac{b}{12}(H^3-h^3)$; for $t \ll H$ $\frac{1}{2}bth^2 =$ $\frac{1}{4}Ah^2$	$\frac{b}{6}\frac{H^3-h^3}{H}$; for $t \ll H$ $bth =$ $\frac{1}{2}Ah$
7	$\frac{b}{2}$, $\frac{b}{2}$, b, b, x, x, H, h, h, h, B, B, $\frac{B}{2}$, $\frac{B}{2}$	BH $+$ bh	$\frac{H}{2}$	$\frac{BH^3+bh^3}{12}$	$\frac{BH^3+bh^3}{6H}$
8	C_2, x, C_1, x, h, b	$\frac{bh}{2}$	$C_2 = \frac{2}{3}h$ $C_1 = \frac{1}{3}h$	$\frac{bh^3}{36}$	$S_2 = \frac{bh^2}{24}$ $S_1 = \frac{bh^2}{12}$
9	R, D	$\frac{\pi}{4}D^2 =$ $0.79D^2 =$ $3.14R^2$	$\frac{D}{2} = R$	$\frac{\pi D^4}{64} \approx$ $0.05D^4 \approx$ $0.79R^4$	$\frac{\pi D^3}{32} \approx$ $0.1D^3 \approx$ $0.79R^3$
10	$(t \ll D)$, D	$\pi Dt =$ $6.28Rt$	$\frac{D}{2} = R$	$\frac{\pi}{8}D^3t =$ $0.39D^3t =$ $3.14R^3t$	$\frac{\pi}{4}D^2t =$ $0.79D^2t =$ $3.14R^2t$

Table A.1 (Continued)

No.	Section	A	C_x	I_x	S_x
11	C_2, C_1, R	$\frac{\pi}{2}R^2 = 1.57R^2$	$C_2 = 0.58R$ $C_1 = 0.42R$	$0.11R^4$	$S_2 = 0.19R^3$ $S_1 = 0.26R^3$
12	C_2, C_1, $t \ll R$, R	πRt	$C_2 = 0.36R$ $C_1 = 0.64R$	$0.30R^3t$	$S_2 = 0.83R^2t$ $S_1 = 0.47R^2t$

Answers to Problems

Chapter One

1.2.1 $d_y = 0, d_z = 0, r_x = 0, r_y = 0, r_z = 0.$
1.2.2 $r_y = 0.$
1.2.3 $d_y = 0, r_x = 0, r_z = 0.$
1.2.4 $d_z = 0.$
1.2.5 $d_z = 0.$
1.2.6 $d_x = 0, d_y = 0, r_x = 0, r_y = 0, r_z = 0.$
1.2.7 $d_y = 0, r_x = 0, r_y = 0, r_z = 0.$
1.3.1 $R_z = 65$ k.
1.3.2 $R_z = 25$ k.
1.3.3 $R_z = 0.$
1.3.4 $R_{z,b} = 1{,}600$ k, $R_{z,12} = 640$ k.
1.3.5 $p = 48$ psf.
1.3.6 $b = \frac{32}{75} h = 0.427 h.$
1.4.1 $R_1 = 14.6$ k, $R_2 = 15.4$ k.
1.4.2 $R_1 = 0$, $R_2 = 20$ k.
1.4.3 $R_1 = 43$ k, $R_2 = 27$ k.
1.4.4 $R_1 = 2$ k (up), $R_2 = -2$ k (down).

1.4.5 $b = 0.38\,h$.
1.4.6 $p = 57.6$ psf.
1.4.7 $T = 388$ k, $C = 3{,}988$ k.
1.4.8 $R_1 = 1.29$ k.
1.4.9 $T = 50$ lb, $W = 100$ lb.
1.4.10 No.
1.4.11 $T = 250$ lb, $R_1 = 250$ lb, $R_2 = 100$ lb.
1.4.12 $R_C = \frac{x}{h} P$, $R_A = R_B = \left(1 - \frac{x}{h}\right) \frac{P}{2}$
1.4.13 *Note:* Up is plus. Load at A': $R_A = \frac{3}{5} P$, $R_B = \frac{11}{15} P$, $R_C = -\frac{1}{3} P$; Load at B': $R_A = R_C = -\frac{1}{6} P$, $R_B = \frac{4}{3} P$; Load at C': $R_A = -\frac{1}{3} P$, $R_B = \frac{11}{15} P$, $R_C = \frac{3}{5} P$.

Chapter Two

2.2.1 10 lb arrow to right, 2′ below x-axis.
2.2.2 50 lb arrow down.
2.2.3 10 lb arrow to the right.
2.2.4 1 oz arrow up.
2.2.5 $F = +104$ k.
2.2.6 (a) $+1$ lb; (b) -2 lb; (c) $+2$ lb; (d) 0.
2.2.7 $R = +200$ lb; up.
2.2.8 $p = -810$ psf; yes.
2.2.9 $p = +2{,}940$ psf.
2.2.10 $T = W/2$, $R = 4T = 2W$.
2.2.11 3 times over the upper sheave and twice under the lower sheave.
2.3.1 $R = 67$ k, 19.8 ft to the left of A.
2.3.2 $R = 55$ k, 9.45 ft to the left of A.
2.3.3 $R = 205$ k, 23.5 ft to the left of B.
2.3.4 $C = 18$ k, $M_B = -8$ k ft.
2.3.5 $R = 1{,}200$ k, 31.7 ft to the left of B.
2.3.6 $F = 25$ lb; $F_h = 25$ lb, $F_v = 50$ lb.
2.3.7 $R = 0$, $M = 10$ lb ft.
2.3.8 $R = 1{,}020$ lb. Otherwise part of the 510 lb force is used to accelerate the elevator.
2.3.9 $R = 4{,}500$ lb, 30.47 ft above the ground; $M_A = 137{,}500$ lb ft.
2.3.10 $R = 250$ k, $M_F = -7{,}500$ k ft; clockwise torsional motion.
2.3.11 $R = 210$ k, $M_A = -5{,}220$ k ft, 24.85 ft above the ground.
2.3.12 $F = 50$ lb.
2.3.13 $R = 0$, $M = 0$.
2.4.1 $R_A = 7.55$ k, $R_B = 5.45$ k.
2.4.2 $R_A = R_B = 12$ lb.
2.4.3 $R_A = R_B = 25$ k.
2.4.4 $R = 900$ k, $M = 180{,}000$ k ft.

2.4.5 $R = 28.8$ k, $M = 288$ k ft.
2.4.6 $R_A = +3.33$ lb, $R_B = -3.33$ lb.
2.4.7 $R = 2{,}000$ lb, $M = +13{,}333$ lb ft.
2.4.8 $R_A = R_B = 37.5$ k.
2.4.9 $W = 700$ lb.
2.4.10 $l = 100$ ft, $a = 6$ ft.
2.4.11 $R_A = 6$ k, $R_B = 3$ k; $R_C = 6$ k, $M_C = +18$ k ft, $R_D = 3$ k, $M_D = -18$ k ft.
2.4.12 $P_A = 150\left(1 - \frac{a}{25}\right)$, $P_B = \frac{150}{25}a$.
$P_{A\,max} = 150$ lb for $a = 0$, $a = 0$, $P_{B\,max} = 150$ lb for $a = 25$ ft.
2.4.13 6.46 ft.
2.4.14 $P = 20$ lb.
2.5.1 $R_A = 1.125 + 0.533 = 1.658$ k, $R_B = 1.875 + 1.067 = 2.942$ k.
2.5.2 $R_A = 5 + \frac{5}{3} = 6.67$ k, $R_B = 5 + \frac{10}{3} = 8.33$ k.
2.5.3 $R_A = 0$, $R_B = 20$ k. Beam is balanced on B.
2.5.4 $R_A = 6 + 2.75 + 13.75 = 22.50$ k (up), $R_B = 6 - 2.75 - 13.75 = -10.5$ k (down).
2.5.5 $R_A = 9.2 + 12.5 - 0.833 = 20.867$ k,
$R_B = 7.8 - 2.5 + 5.833 = 11.133$ k.
2.5.6 $R_A = R_B = 18.75 + 11.25 = 30$ k.
2.6.1 (a) $F_x = +14.14$ lb, $F_y = +14.14$ lb; (b) $F_x = +28.28$ lb, $F_\alpha = 20$ lb;
(c) $F_y = +28.28$ lb, $F_\beta = +20$ lb;
2.6.2 (a) $V_1 = V_2 = 50$ lb, $H_1 = H_2 = 50$ lb, $T_1 = T_2 = 70.71$ lb;
(b) $V_1 = V_2 = 50$ lb, $H_1 = H_2 = 100$ lb, $T_1 = T_2 = 112$ lb.
2.6.3 $V_1 = 1.6$ k, $V_2 = 0.4$ k, $H_1 = H_2 = 1.07$ k, $T_1 = 1.92$ k, $T_2 = 1.14$ k.
2.6.4 $H = 1.21$ k, $V = 4.85$ k, $C = 19.40$ k.
2.6.5 $H_{max} = (Wl)/(4f)$ with W at mid-span,
$H_{min} = 0$ with W at ends, $T_{max} = \frac{W}{2}\sqrt{1 + (l/2f)^2}$.
2.6.6 Yes, because the slopes of the cable are the same.
2.6.7 $R = 101$ k, $\theta = 8°32'$, $M = 750$ k ft.
2.6.8 $\theta = 26°37'$ to the left.
2.6.9 $\theta = 30°58'$, $H = 120$ lb, $V = 200$ lb.
2.6.10 $H = 7.5$ lb.
2.6.11 $T = 50$ lb, $R = 92.5$ lb.
2.6.12 (a) $AB = 57.7$ lb(t), $BC = -115.5$ lb(c);
(b) $AB = -57.7$ lb(c), $BC = +115.5$ lb(t).
2.6.13 $AB = -84.6$ lb(c), $BC = 98.5$ lb(t).

Chapter Three

3.1.1 $n_b = 21$, $n_j = 12$, $21 = 2 \times 12 - 3$; determinate.
3.1.2 $n_b = 26$, $n_j = 14$, $26 > 2 \times 14 - 3 = 25$; indeterminate.
3.1.3 Because the hinged rectangle $FGIH$ collapses under vertical loads.

3.1.4 $n_b = 21 = 2n_j - 3$, statically determinate internally; 4 reactions V_A, H_A, V_B, H_B, statically indeterminate externally under a general set of plane forces.

3.1.5 Hinge *A* has reaction V_A, M_A, hinge *B* only H_B, equal and opposite to the force in bar *BC*.

3.1.6 The truss carrying the pressure loads has only the diagonals inclined to the right (like *AC*); the truss carrying the suction loads has only the diagonals inclined to the left (like *BD*).

3.1.7 Load W_3. Because joint *C* will be in equilibrium under the action of the equal and opposite forces F_{EC}, F_{CF}.

3.1.8 $n_b = 15$, $n_j = 9$; yes.

3.2.1 $AC = +21.5$ k, $BD = -43.5$ k, $AD = +24.6$ k.

3.2.2 $CE = -40$ k, $DE = +33.3$ k, $EF = +10$ k.

3.2.3 $FG = +60$ k.

3.2.4 $V_A = -V_B = 1.22$ k, $H_A = +10$ k, $FG = -10.7$ k.

3.2.5 $EG = -3.33$ k, $GF = +1.04$ k, $FH = -0.5$ k, $GH = 0$

3.2.6 $AD = -14$ k, $DB = +12.64$ k, $BC = +10$ k.

3.2.7 $AB = +36$ k, $AC = BC = -37$ k.

3.2.8 $AC = +160$ k, $AD = +224$ k, $BD = -360$ k.

3.2.9 $EG = -120$ k.

3.2.10 $FG = +93.75$ k.

3.3.1 $Ba = -70.7$ k, $cb = +42.4$ k.

3.3.2 $FG = +60$ k.

3.3.3 $ij = +14.5$ k.

3.3.4 $cd = +11.2$ k.

3.3.5 $Ed = +640$ lb.

3.3.6 $Ed = +9$ k.

3.5.1 $f_t = 23.7$ ksi, yes.

3.5.2 $4 \times 4/25.6$ angles; $f_t = 13.3$ ksi.

3.5.3 $8WF\ 5\frac{1}{4}/17$, $f_c = 20$ ksi.

3.5.4 $l = 59.2$ ft.

3.5.5 $A_c = 0.67$ in.$^2 > A_t = 0.59$ in.^{2}.

3.5.6 $1\frac{1}{2} \times 1\frac{1}{2}/\frac{3}{16}$ angles; $C = 2.4$ k.

3.5.7 $4 \times 3/\frac{5}{16}$ angles.

3.5.8 $3 \times 2\frac{1}{2}$ angles.

3.5.9 (a) $21WF\ 8\frac{1}{4}$; (b) $14WF\ 10$; (c) practically the same.

3.5.10 Two $3\frac{1}{2} \times 3\frac{1}{2}/\frac{7}{16}$ angles. $C_1 = 82.5$ k, $C_2 = 80.4$ k.

Chapter Four

4.2.1 $V_A = V_B = 150$ k, $H = \text{DE} = 229$ k, $AC = BF = 274$ k, $CD = EF = 234$ k.

4.2.2 $V_A = V_B = 150$ k, $H = 250$ k, $AC = EB = 292$ k, $CD = DE = 255$ k.

4.2.3 $l_1 = 13$ ft, $l_2 = 19$ ft, $l_3 = 25$ ft, $l_4 = 31$ ft, $l_5 = 37$ ft;
$W_1 = 39$ k, $W_2 = 57$ k, $W_3 = 75$ k, $W_4 = 93$ k, $W_5 = 111$ k;
$V_A = V_B = 375$ k, $H = 413$ k, $AC = 558$ k, $CD = 490$ k, $DE = 447$ k,

$EF = 424$ k, $FG = 415$ k.

4.2.4 Because the level of point C is unknown and, hence, M_A and H cannot be evaluated. The problem is determined if the length of the cable is also given.

4.2.5 A regular hexagon, 1 ft by the side; $T = 5.77$ lb.

4.2.6 $T_{22} = 11.22$ k, $T_{28} = 7.14$ k.

4.2.7 An ellipse with semi-axes $a = 29.15$ ft and $b = 15$ ft of equation $(x/29.15)^2 + (y/15)^2 = 1$.

4.2.8 $f_2\sqrt{\frac{2}{3}}f_1$, $T_1 > T_2$ for $f/l < 1/\sqrt{6}$.

4.3.1 $H = \dfrac{w_0 l^2}{24f} = 500$ k, $T = 584$ k.

4.3.2 $y = f(1 \mp 8x^3/l^3)$ for $x \lesseqgtr 0$.

4.3.3 $H = 750$ k, $T = 828$ k.

4.3.4 A circle of radius $r = \dfrac{l}{2\pi}$, $T = pr$.

4.3.5 $H = \dfrac{w_0 l^2}{12f} = 8{,}333$ k, $T = 8{,}700$ k.

4.3.6 $H = 333$ k, $T = 520$ k.

4.4.1 $V_A = 61.7$ k, $V_B = 48.3$k, $H = 123$ k, $AC = 138$ k, $CD = 125$ k, $DE = 129$ k, $EB = 132$ k.

4.4.2 $V_A = -V_B = 40$ k, $H = 80$ k, $AC = DB = 89.4$ k, $CD = 100$ k.

4.4.3 $V_A = 74.5$ k, $V_B = 62.3$ k, $H_A = H_B = 31.0$ k.
$H_A = H_B$ because the horizontal components of the 100 lb and the 71 lb forces are equal and opposite.

4.4.4 $a = 0.53l$, $H = 1.51\dfrac{w_0 l^2}{8f}$, $T_B = 1.51\dfrac{w_0 l^2}{8f}\sqrt{1 + 19.5\left(\dfrac{f}{l}\right)^2}$.

4.4.5 $a = \dfrac{7}{16}l$; $H = 1.53\dfrac{w_0 l^2}{8f}$, $T_A = H\sqrt{1 + \left(\dfrac{32}{7}\right)^2\left(\dfrac{f}{l}\right)^2}$.

4.4.6 No: $T_{1/3} = \dfrac{2}{3}w_0 l\sqrt{1 + \left(\dfrac{l}{3f}\right)^2} > T_{\text{unif}} = \dfrac{1}{2}w_0 l\sqrt{1 + \left(\dfrac{l}{4f}\right)^2}$.

4.5.1 $d_1 = 1.85$ in, $d_2 = 2.55$ in.

4.5.2 $d = 0.94$ in. for two 60 k loads.

4.5.3 $l_{u,1} = 90.4$ ft, $l_{u,2} = 47.8$ ft.

4.5.4 $w = 0.15$ k/ft.

4.5.5 $d = 16.3$ in.

4.5.6 $f = 0.76$ in.

4.5.7 $d = 2.77$ in.

4.5.8 $n = 10$.

Chapter Five

5.2.1 Simple support.

5.2.2 (a) Simple support; (b) fixed-ends.

5.2.3 Fixed ends.

5.2.4 Fixed at the core end, movable built-in support at the column end.

5.2.5 Movable built-in support conditions.
5.2.6 5.2*d*, fixed-end conditions.
5.2.7 (a) Fixed-end; (b) fixed hinge.
5.2.8 One fixed, one movable hinge. To allow horizontal expansion of the girder.
5.2.9 Statically indeterminate once.
5.2.10 Determinate in all cases.
5.2.11 Once statically indeterminate.
5.2.12 Yes, because the mid-span section does not deflect vertically under anti-symmetrical loads. No, because the mid-span section deflects vertically under symmetrical loads.
5.3.1 $V_A = \frac{7}{8}wl,\ V_B = \frac{5}{8}wl.$
5.3.2 $V_A = \frac{wl}{4},\ M_A = \frac{5}{24}wl^2.$ **5.3.3** $V_A = \frac{47}{144}wl,\ V_B = \frac{73}{144}wl.$
5.3.4 $V_A = 0,\ H_A = W,\ M_A = -wl/2.$
5.3.5 (a) $V_A = V_B = W/2$; (b) $V_A = \frac{5}{8}W,\ H_A = 0.216W,\ R_B = 0.433W$; (c) $V_A = W,\ H_A = R_B = 0.866W.$
5.3.6 (a) $V_A = -V_B = -P\frac{a}{l},\ H_A = 0$; (b) $V_A = -V_B = \frac{Pa}{l},\ H_A = P.$ Because the applied forces are a couple.
5.3.7 For $0 < x \leq a : V_A = \frac{2}{3}W\left(1 - \frac{x}{l}\right)$; for $a < x < l : V_A = \frac{5}{3}W\left[\left(1 - \frac{x}{l}\right) + \frac{3}{5}\frac{a}{l}\right]$; for $l \leq x \leq l + a:\ V_A = W\left(1 - \frac{x-a}{l}\right).$
5.3.8 $V_A = 1 - \frac{x}{l}$. For load at C, $V_A = -\frac{1}{3}.$
5.3.9 $x = l/3,\ V_A = V_B = \frac{3W}{2}.$
5.3.10 $x = 0,\ V_A = \frac{5}{2}W;\ x = \frac{3l}{4},\ V_B = \frac{11}{4}W.$
5.4.1 $DC)\ V = 3\text{ k};\ CB)\ V = 5\text{ k},\ BA)\ V = 6\text{ k}.$
5.4.2 $V_x = \frac{wl}{2}(1 - 2x/l)$
5.4.3 $CB)\ V = wx',\ BA)\ V = -wl/8.$
5.4.4 $AC)\ V = 9.87\text{ k},\ CD) + 5.87\text{ k},\ V_B = -14{,}13\text{ k}.$
5.4.5 $CA)\ V_x = -\frac{3}{10}x'^2,\ BD) = \frac{3}{10}x'^2,\ AB)\ V_x = 30 - 3x.$
5.4.6 $CA)\ V = -10\text{ k},\ AD)\ V = +4\text{ k},\ DE)\ V = -6\text{ k},\ EB)\ V = +4\text{ k},\ BF)\ V = +10\text{ k}.$
5.4.7 $W_1 = 12\text{ k},\ W_2 = 11.14\text{ k};\ AC)\ V = +6\text{ k},\ N = +10.39\text{ k};\ CB)\ V = -4\text{ k},\ N = +10.39\text{ k}.$
5.4.8 $AC)\ V = \frac{w_0 l}{4}\left(1 - 4\frac{x^2}{l^2}\right)$, antisymmetrical.
5.4.9 $V_{max} = W$ for $x = 0$, $V_{min} = -W$ for $x = l$.
5.4.10 $V_{max} = V_A = w_0 l/3$ for beam (*b*); $V_{min} = V_A = V_B = w_0 l/4$ for beams (*a*) and (*c*).
5.4.11 $x = 0.53l.$
5.4.12 (a) $x = l/2$; (b) $x = l/4$ and $x = 3l/4$; (c) shear crosses axis at $x = a$, $x = a + b$; (d) $x = \frac{3}{8}l.$

5.4.13 $a = 0.423l$.

5.4.14 $AC)$ $V = +124.4$ lb, $N = 0$; $CD)$ $V = +24.4$ lb, $N = +100$ lb; $DB)$ $V = -148.8$ lb, $N = 0$.

5.4.15 $AC)$ $V = 86.6$ lb, $N = -100$ lb; $CD)$ $V = 0$, $N = -50$ lb; $DB)$ $V = 86.6$ lb, $N = -100$ lb.

5.4.16 $AC)$ $V = 35$ lb, $N = -141$ lb; $CB)$ $V = -35$ lb, $N = 20$ lb.

5.5.1 $M_C = -12$ k ft, $M_B = -27$ k ft, $M_A = -39$ k ft.

5.5.2 $M = \frac{w}{2}x(l - x)$.

5.5.3 $BC)$ $M = wx'^2/2$, $AB)$ $M = \frac{wl^2}{8}\left(\frac{x}{l}\right)$.

5.5.4 $M_C = 29.61$ k ft, $M_D = 41.35$ k ft.

5.5.5 $M_A = M_B = -12.5$ k ft, $M_E = +137.5$ k ft.

5.5.6 $M_A = -30$ k ft, $M_D = -18$ k ft, $M_E = -42$ k ft, $M_B = -30$ k ft.

5.5.7 $M_C = 24$ k ft.

5.5.8 $M_C = w_0 l^2/12$.

5.5.9 (a) $M_{l/2} = w_0 l^2/12$; (b) $M_{l/\sqrt{3}} = w_0 l^2/15.6$; (c) $M_{l/2} = w_0 l^2/16$.

5.5.10 $M = 0.19 w_0 l^2$ at $x = 0.53l$.

5.5.11 (a) $M_{l/2} = w_0 l^2/8$; (b) $M_{l/4} = \frac{w_0 l^2}{32} = -M_{3l/4}$; (c) $M_c = \frac{Wab}{b + 2a} = -M_D$

(d) $M_{3l/8} = \frac{9}{128} w_0 l^2$.

5.5.12 $0 \leq x \leq a$, $M = \frac{Wx}{3}$; $a \leq x \leq l/2$, $M = \frac{W}{6}(5x - 3a)$;

$\frac{l}{2} < x \leq \frac{l}{2} + a$, $M = \frac{W}{6}(2l + x - 3a)$;

$\frac{l}{2} + a < x < l$, $M = \frac{W}{6}[5(l - x) + 3a]$;

$l < x < l + a$, $M = \frac{W}{2}(l + a - x)$.

5.5.13 $M_A = -28.67$ k ft, $M_E = -13.34$ k ft, $M_D = -50.67$ k ft, $M_F = -16.67$ k ft, $M_G = +18.8$ k ft.

5.5.14 $AC)$ $M = 0$; $CB)$ $M = -W(l/2 - x)$; $BD)$ $M = -W(l/2 - x)$.

5.5.15 $a = l/\sqrt{6} = 0.41l$.

5.5.16 $a = \frac{l}{2\sqrt{2}} = \frac{L}{2(1 + \sqrt{2})} = 0.36.\ 36l = 0.21L$; $a = \frac{L}{1 + 1/\sqrt{2}} = 0.59L$.

5.5.17 $a = l/\sqrt{6}$; $M_A = M_B = -wl^2/12$, $M_C = wl^2/24$.

5.5.18 $a = 1.98l$.

5.5.19 $M_1 = \frac{wl^2}{4}$, $M_2 = \frac{wl^2}{6}$; $M_3 = \frac{wl^2}{6}$; $M_4 = \frac{3wl^2}{20} = \frac{wl^2}{6.67}$.

For an increasing number n of loads M_n approaches $wl^2/8$.

5.6.1 See Prob. 5.5.1.

5.6.2 See Prob. 5.5.2.

5.6.3 See Prob. 5.5.4.

5.6.4 See Prob. 5.5.6.

5.6.5 See Prob. 5.5.19.

5.6.6 $M_C = -3.33$ k ft, $M_D = -21.67$ k ft, $M_B = -50$ k ft.

5.6.7 $M_A = 15.00$ k ft, $M_B = 10.31$ k ft, $M_C = 6.25$ k ft, $M_D = 2.81$ k ft.
5.6.8 $M_C = M_G = 72$ k ft, $M_E = M_F = 108$ k ft.
5.7.1 $V = 15$ k, $V = 60$ k.
5.7.2 $V = 309$ k.
5.7.3 $V = 638$ k.
5.7.4 $V = 393$ lb.
5.7.5 $V = 237$ k.
5.7.6 $V = 244$ k.
5.7.7 $V = 159.5$ k.
5.7.8 No, $V = 50.6$ k.
5.7.9 $V = 202.5$ k.
5.7.10 14 WF 202.
5.7.11 $V = 43.2$ k.
5.7.12 Yes, $v = 3.96$ ksi.
5.7.13 $V = 155$ k.
5.8.1 (a) 16 WF 36; (b) 18 WF 55; (c) 24 WF 76; (d) 24 WF 100; (e) 36 WF 300.
5.8.2 (a) 1.02 k ft; (b) 0.30 k ft.
5.8.3 (a) 78.3 k ft; (b) 35.7 k ft; (c) 12.1 k ft.
5.8.4 (a) 329 k ft; (b) 63.0 k ft; (c) 2.83 k ft.
5.8.5 $h = 4.55$ in., 6 in. nominal.
5.8.6 $b = 3.49$ in., 4 in. nominal.
5.8.7 $M_1/M_2 = h/b$
5.8.8 $M_x/M_y = 3h^2/b^2$
5.8.9 $f_{\max} = 1{,}391$ psi (c), $f_{\min} = 131$ psi (c).
5.8.10 $f_b = 6.48$ ksi.
5.8.11 $l = \frac{4}{3}\left(\frac{F_b}{\rho}\right)\left(\frac{h}{l}\right)$; $l]_{l/h=10} = 557$ ft, $l]_{l/h=20} = 279$ ft.
5.8.12 $l_{\text{cont}} = \frac{1}{3}\left(\frac{F_b}{\rho}\right)\left(\frac{h}{l}\right)$; $l]_{l/h=10} = 139$ ft; $l]_{l/h=20} = 69.7$ ft.
5.8.13 $l_{s.s.} = 4\left(\frac{F_b}{\rho}\right)\left(\frac{h}{l}\right)$; $l_c = \left(\frac{F_b}{\rho}\right)\left(\frac{h}{l}\right)$.
5.8.14 $b/h = \frac{3r^2}{4}\frac{w}{F_b h}$.
5.8.15 $w_1 = \frac{4}{3}\left(\frac{h}{l}\right)^2 F_b b - cl^2$.

l(ft)	83	80	60	40	20	0
w_1(k/ft)	0	0.51	3.31	5.31	6.51	6.91

5.8.16 $w_1 l = A\left[8F_b\left(\frac{h}{l}\right) - \rho l\right]$
5.8.17 $c = 2.05$ ft $\simeq 2$ ft.
5.8.18 $w = 41$ psf, $l = \sqrt{\frac{2}{3}}\,10 = 8.17$ ft, 18.3%; by adding brackets under joists ends.
5.8.19 $l_a/l_s = \sqrt{3} = 1.73$; no.
5.8.20 100%.
5.8.21 $W_c/W_{ss} = 4$.

5.8.22 $W_1 = \frac{1}{2}wl$, $W_2 = \frac{3}{8}wl$.

5.8.23 $c = 6.90$ ft $\simeq 7$ ft; 2×6 joists.

5.8.24 $A = 22.75$ in.^{2} Because $S = Ah$ decreases with h and M decreases towards the supports.

5.8.25 $A_1 = 2.96$ ft^2 $= 426$ in.^{2}; 72.5 tons.

5.9.1 $d = 18$ in.

5.9.2 $d_5 = 19.1$ in., $d_6 = 17.4$ in., $d_7 = 16.1$ in., $d_8 = 15.1$ in.

5.9.3 $d = 28$ in.

5.9.4 21 WF 62, $372; 18 in. × 24 in. r.c. beam, $333.

5.9.5 $A_s = 6.26$ in.^{2}; 8 #8 bars = 6.32 in.^{2}.

5.9.6 $A_s = 1.91$ in.^{2}/ft; #6 at $2\frac{3}{4}$ in. = 1.92 in.^{2}/ft.

5.9.7 $w_{LL} = 436$ psf.

5.9.8 $h = 28$ in., $A_s = 4.92$ in.^{2} (3 #9 + 3 #8 = 5.37 in.^{2}.)

5.9.9 $d = 20$ in., $D = 23$ in.

5.9.10 $b = 20.9$ in. $= 21$ in., $h = 2b + c = 2 \times 21 + 2 = 44$ in.

5.9.11 $A_s = 14.76$ in.^{2}, $p = 1.46\%$.

Chapter Six

6.2.1 $H = 2.5$ k, $M_D = 45.8$ k ft, $N_{\max} = N_A = 8.7$ k, $N_{\min} = H = 2.5$ k, $V_C = V_B = 1.67$ k.

6.2.2 $H = 20$ k, $M_D = 100$ k ft, $N_{\max} = 28.3$ k, $N_{\min} = H = 20$ k.

6.2.3 $H = 11$ k, $M_D = 155$ k ft, $M_E = -15$ k ft, $N_{\max} = 27.15$ k, $V_{\max} = V_C = -5$ k.

6.2.4 $H = 41.67$ k, $M_D = 25$ k ft, $M_E = 267$ k ft, $M_F = 308$ k ft, $M_G = 233$ k ft, $M_C = 0$ k ft, $M_{G'} = -167$ k ft, $M_{F'} = -292$ k ft, $M_{E'} = -333$ k ft, $M_{D'} = -375$ k ft.

6.2.5 $H_2/H_1 = 2$, $M_2/M_1 = 3$.

6.2.6 $H = w_0 r/6$

x/r	0	0.2	0.4	0.6	0.8	1.0
M_x(k ft)	0	5.4	8.55	−7.20	−50.4	0

6.2.7 $H_a = 2.5$ k, $H_b = 7.5$ k, $M = +79.25$ k ft.

6.3.1 (a) $M_{\min} = -31.1$ k ft, $M_{\max} = 47.5$ k ft; (b) $M_{\min} = -165$ k ft, $M_{\max} = 50.4$ k ft; (c) $M_{\min} = -173$ k ft, $M_{\max} = 140$ k ft; (d) $M_{\min} = -125$ k ft, $M_{\max} = 125$ k ft,

6.3.2 $V_a = \dfrac{a}{2f}W$, $V_b = \dfrac{2f-a}{2f}W$; $V_{a'} = \dfrac{a}{2f-c}W$, $V_{b'} = \dfrac{2f-a-c}{2f-c}W$;
$H = V_a$, $H' = V_{a'} > V_a$; $R_a = \sqrt{2}\,V_a$, $R_{a'} = \sqrt{2}\,V_{a'} > R_a$; $M_D = R_a e$; $M_{D'} = R_{a'}e > M_D$.

6.3.3 $V_{a'} = \left(1 + \dfrac{ac}{f(2f-c)}\right)W = 112.5$ k;

$V_{b'} = \left(1 - \dfrac{ac}{f(2f-c)}\right)W = 87.5$ k; $H' = \dfrac{2a}{2f-c}W = 62.5$ k;

Corners of polygon; $x = 0, y = 0$; $x = 25$ ft, $y = 45$ ft; $x = 75$ ft, $y = 55$ ft; $x = 100$ ft, $y = 0$.

6.4.1 $h_s = 33.3$ in.; $h_c = 26.0$ in.

6.4.2 $\Delta W = 2.03$ k/ft.

6.4.3 $h = 28$ in.

6.4.4 $A_s = 6.25$ in.^{2}.

6.4.5 $A-C)\ y = 2f\frac{x}{l}\left[3 - 4\left(\frac{x}{l}\right)\right]$;

$C-B)\ y = 2f\left(1 - \frac{x}{l}\right)$

6.4.6 A circle.

6.4.7 $C = 1{,}911$ k, $A_C = 7.33$ sq ft.

6.4.8 $t = 0.0267$ in.

6.4.9 Because the circular arch is not funicular for vertical loads.

6.4.10 To channel the compressive forces inside the buttresses.

6.4.11 Because the eccentricities are large.

6.4.12 $e = 13.4$ ft, $M = 25{,}607$ k ft.

6.5.1 $d = 1.68$ ft, $A_s = 4.55$ in.^{2}.

6.5.2 $l_{0.2} = 2{,}160$ ft, $l_{0.1} = 1{,}284$ ft.

6.5.3 $l_u = 13{,}224$ ft.

6.5.4 $W = 107$ k.

6.5.5 10 WF 60; 60 lb/ft $\ll$ 2.5 k/ft.

6.5.6 12 WF 45, $f_c = 9.06$ ksi.

Chapter Seven

7.1.1 $M_{\max} = 225$ k ft, $V_{\max} = 30$ k, 18 WF 96.

7.1.2 $M_{\max} = 75$ k ft, $V_{\max} = 5$ k; $f_w = 8$ ksi, $f_{\text{tot}} = 28$ ksi,

$\frac{f_{\text{tot}}}{f_{u.l.}} = \frac{28}{24} = 1.17 < 1.33.$

7.1.3 $M_{\max} = 225$ k ft, $V_{\max} = 30$ k, 18 WF 96.

7.1.4 $f_w = 8$ ksi, $f_{\text{tot}} = 28$ ksi, $f_{\text{tot}}/f_{u.l.} = 1.17 < 1.33$.

7.1.5 36 WF 230, 12 WF 99, $f = 15.30$ ksi < 26.6 ksi.

7.1.6 $V_d = -\frac{a}{l}W,\ V_a = \left(1 + \frac{a}{l}\right)W,\ M_{\max} = -Wa.$

Columns are straight and inclined to the left. Beam is bent downward.

7.1.7 $V_d = -\frac{a}{l}W,\ V_a = \left(1 + \frac{a}{l}\right)W,\ M_{\max} = -Wa.$

Columns are straight and at right angles to beam bent downward.

7.1.8 $M_{\max} = -225$ k ft, 12 WF 92; $V_d = 67.5$ k, 8 WF 17.

7.1.9 $V_d = \frac{x}{l}W.$

7.1.10 $V_d = \frac{x}{l}W,\ M_x = \frac{x}{l}\left(1 - \frac{x}{l}\right)Wl.$

7.2.1 $M_E = 320$ k ft, $H = 18$ k; $V = 100$ k, $M_B = 180$ k ft, 18 WF 105, 10 WF 33.

7.2.2 18 WF 105, 10 WF 33.
7.2.3 Beam 10 WF 29; column 10 WF 33.
7.2.4 Beam 10 WF 54; column 10 WF 60.
7.2.5 *CD*) 10 WF 45; *BE*) 12 WF 106; *CB*) 8 WF 35, *BA*) 12 WF 58.
7.2.6 $M_C = 12$ k ft, $M_B = 36$ k ft,
$f_{CD} = 2.93$ ksi, $f_{BE} = 2.99$ ksi, $f_{BC} = 4.79$ ksi, $f_{AB} = 5.89$ ksi.
7.2.7 Beam: $b \times h = 8$ in. $\times$ 28 in., $A_s = 3.37$ in.^{2}; Column: $b \times h = 8$ in. $\times$ 6 in.
$A_{s,\text{top}} = 10.6$ in.^{2}, $A_{s,\text{bott}} = 5.3$ in.^{2}
7.2.8 Beam: $A_s' = 0.2$ in.^{2}; Column: $A_s' = 1.23$ in.^{2} top and bottom.
7.2.9 Beams 10 WF 39; exterior columns 10 WF 39, interior columns 10 WF 72.
7.2.10 Exterior columns: $M = \pm 30$ k ft;
interior columns: $M = 60$ k ft;
beams: $M = \pm 30$ k ft.
7.3.1 $V_1 = 2$ k, $V_2 = 12$ k, $H_1 = 3$ k, $H_2 = 8$ k; $V_1' = 2$ k, $V_2' = 10$ k.
7.3.2 $M_A = 10.125$ k ft.
7.3.3 $M_C = 8.33$ k ft.
7.3.4 $M_{EA} = 6.0$ k ft.
7.3.5 $M_{EF} = 23.3$ k ft.

Chapter Eight

8.2.1 *AB*) $V = W$, $M = -W(a - y)$, $M_t = 0$; *BC*) $V = W$, $M = -W(l - x)$,
$M_t = Wa$.
8.2.2 *AB*) $V = W$, $M = -Wx$, $M_t = 0$; *BC*) $V = W$, $M = -Wy$, $M_t = Wa$;
CD) $V = W$, $M = -Wx$, $M_t = Wa$; *DE*) $V = W$, $M = -Wy$, $M_t = 2Wa$;
EF) $V = W$, $M = -Wx$, $M_t = 0$.
8.2.3 *AB*) $V = W$, $M = -W(c - y)$, $M_t = 0$; *BD*) $V = W/2$, $M = Wx/2$,
$M_t = -Wc/2$; *BC*) $V = -W/2$, $M = (W/2)(2a - x)$, $M_t = -Wc/2$.
8.2.4 *AB*) $V = W$, $M = -W(b - y)$, $M_t = 0$; *CD*) $V = W$, $M = -W(b + y)$,
$M_t = 0$. *FB*) $V = W$, $M = Wx$, $M_t = 0$; *BD*) $V = 0$, $M = Wa$,
$M_t = 2Wb\left(\frac{3}{2} - \frac{x}{a}\right)$; *DE*) $V = -W$, $M = W(3a - x)$, $M_t = 0$.
8.2.5 Load $\sqrt{2}\,W$ at $-45°$ to z − axis. *DA*) $V = \frac{\sqrt{2}}{2}W$, $M = \frac{\sqrt{2}}{2}Wx$;
AC) $V = -\frac{\sqrt{2}}{2}W$, $M = \frac{\sqrt{2}}{2}W(2a - x)$.
8.2.6 *BC*) $V = 180y$ lb, $M = 90y^2$ lb ft, $M_t = 270y$ lb ft *CA*) $V = 1{,}800$ lb,
$M = 1{,}800(y - 5)$ lb ft, $M_t = 2{,}700$ lb ft.
8.2.7 $t_{\text{beam}} = 0.325$ in. $= \frac{3}{8}$ in., $t_{\text{post}} = 0.088 \simeq \frac{1}{8}$ in.
8.2.8 $e/h = 1/6$.
8.2.9 $e/b = 1/10$; $f_{\max} = 2\frac{W}{bh}$.
8.2.10 $f_c = 3$ ksi, 300%; $f_t = 1$ ksi.
8.3.1 $M_t = 480$ k ft.

8.3.2 $v_t = 0.85$ ksi.

8.3.3 $BD)\ f_b = 843$ psi, $v_s = 13$ psi, $v_t = 717$ psi, $v_{max} = 730$ psi;
$AB)\ f_b = 1{,}010$ psi, $v_s = 25.4$ psi.

8.3.4 $D = 1.13a$, $W_{sq}/W_{cir} = 4/3.55$.

8.4.1 $F_1 = 0$, $F_2 = 0.575W(t)$, $F_3 = 0.813W(c)$, $F_4 = 0.333W(c)$;
$F_5 = 0.333W(c)$, $F_6 = 0.417W(t)$.

8.4.2 $F_1 = 0$, $F_2 = 0.575W(t)$, $F_3 = 0.813W(c)$, $F_4 = 0.333W(c)$, $F_5 = 0.333W(c)$,
$F_6 = 0.417W(t)$.

8.4.3 (a) $F_1 = \frac{2}{3}W(c)$, $F_2 = \frac{1}{3}W(t)$; (b) $F_1 = \frac{4}{3\sqrt{3}}H(t)$, $F_2 = \frac{2}{3\sqrt{3}}H(c)$,
$F_3 = \frac{2}{3\sqrt{3}}H(c)$, $F_4 = \frac{5}{6\sqrt{3}}W(t)$.

8.4.4 $H = \frac{\sqrt{3}}{2}W$.

8.4.5 $F_1 = 11.2$ lb(c), $F_2 = 46.8$ lb(c), $F_3 = 46.4$ lb(c), $F_4 = 7.9$ lb(t),
$F_5 = 35.2$ lb(t), $F_6 = 7.1$ lb(t).

8.4.6 $d = 8$ in.

8.5.1 $F_1 = \frac{1}{2\sqrt{2}}W(c)$, $F_2 = \frac{1}{\sqrt{2}}W(t)$, $F_3 = 0$. $F_4 = \frac{1}{2}W(t)$

8.5.2 By symmetry, analogous bars in 4 quadrants have equal forces.
(a) Bars 1 at A by $\sum F_x = 0$, at A' by $\sum F_y = 0$; (b) Bars 1 at U by $\sum F_x = 0$;
(c) Bars 2 at B by $\sum F_x = 0$; (d) Bars 3 at A and A' by $\sum F_z = 0$.

8.5.3 $F_1/\sqrt{2} = -\frac{11}{18}W$, $F_2/\sqrt{2} = -\frac{19}{18}W$, $F_3/\sqrt{2} = \frac{22}{18}W$, $F_4/\sqrt{2} = -\frac{26}{18}W$,
$F_5/\sqrt{2} = -\frac{10}{18}W$, $F_6/\sqrt{2} = \frac{38}{18}W$, $F_7/\sqrt{2} = -\frac{9}{18}W$,
$F_8/\sqrt{2} = -\frac{9}{18}W$, $F_9 = \frac{40}{18}W$, $F_{10} = \frac{48}{18}W$, $F_{11} = \frac{56}{18}W$.

8.5.4 $t_1 = 0.093$ in. $\doteq \frac{1}{8}$ in.; $t_2 = 0.056$ in. $\doteq \frac{1}{16}$ in.;
$t_4 = 0.040$ in. $\doteq \frac{6}{64}$ in.

8.5.5 $t_{11} = 0.247$ in. $= \frac{1}{4}$ in., $t_4 = 0.541$ in. $= \frac{9}{16}$ in.

8.5.6 $F_1/\sqrt{2} = -\frac{5}{18}W$, $F_2/\sqrt{2} = -\frac{7}{18}W$, $F_3/\sqrt{2} = \frac{10}{18}W$,
$F_4/\sqrt{2} = -\frac{2}{18}W$, $F_5/\sqrt{2} = \frac{2}{18}W$, $F_6/\sqrt{2} = \frac{14}{18}W$, $F_7/\sqrt{2} = 0$,
$F_8/\sqrt{2} = 0$, $F_9 = \frac{10}{18}W$, $F_{10} = \frac{12}{18}W$, $F_{11} = \frac{14}{18}W$.

8.6.1 Bars 1, 7, 8, 13, 18, 19, 24, 25, 26, 30, 31, 32, 36.

8.6.2 $F_1 = W(c)$, $F_2 = 0$, $F_3 = \sqrt{3}\,W(c)$, $F_4 = 0$, $F_5 = \sqrt{3}\,W(c)$;
$R_z = W$, $R_x = R_y = 0$.

8.6.3 (a) 1 — 10 — 5 — 9 — 8, 16 — 21 — 20 — 24 — 19, 13 — 22 — 17
(—21 — 20), 14 — 23 — 18 — (22 — 17); (b), $F_1 = F_2 = F_3 = F_4 = -W(c)$,
$F_5 = F_6 = F_7 = F_8 = -\sqrt{3}\,W(c)$, $F_9 = F_{10} = F_{11} = F_{12} = 0 = F_{21} = F_{22} =$
$F_{23} = F_{24}$, $F_{13} = F_{14} = F_{15} = F_{16} = 0$, $F_{17} = F_{18} = F_{19} = F_{20} = -\sqrt{3}\,W(c)$.

8.6.4 $F_1 = F_2 = -W(c)$, $F_5 = -\sqrt{3}\,W(c)$, $F_6 = F_8 = -\frac{\sqrt{3}}{3}W(c)$,
$F_9 = F_{12} = \frac{\sqrt{6}}{3}W(t)$.

8.6.5 $F_9 = F_{10} = F_{11} = F_{12} = 0$; $F_1 = F_2 = F_3 = F_4 = -W(c)$;
$F_5 = F_6 = F_7 = F_8 = -\sqrt{3}\,W(c)$.

8.7.1 $P_1 = 58.7$ k(t), $P_2 = 117.5$ k(t), $N_1 = -54.0$ k(c), $N_2 = -162$ k(c).

8.7.2 $P_1 = 383$ k(t), $P_2 = 305$ k(t), $P_3 = -331$ k(c), $N_1 = -179$ k(c), $N_2 = -481$ k(c), $N_3 = -714$ k(c).

8.7.3 $P_1 = 1{,}915$ k(t), $P_2 = -1{,}056$ k(c), $P_3 = -605$ k(c); $N_1 \doteq -899$ k(c), $N_2 = -602$ k(c), $N_3 = -510$ k(c).

8.7.4 $P_0 = 48.2$ k(t), $P_1 = 90.4$ k(t), $P_2 = 55.3$ k(t), $P_3 = 1.28$ k(t), $P_4 = 34.00$ k(t), $N_0 = -19.1$ k(c), $N_1 = -38.2$ k(c), $N_2 = -56.7$ k(c), $N_3 = -71.2$ k(c), $N_4 = -68.1$ k(c).

8.7.5 $N_{\max} = -97.1$ k(c), $P_4 = 28.8$ k(t).

8.7.6 $N = -226$ k(c), $A_s = 11.3$ in.^{2}.

8.8.1 $P = 44.2$ psi, $t = 0.09$ in.

8.8.2 $P = 44.3$ psi, $f_{\text{circ}} = \dfrac{552}{t} > f_{\text{long}} = \dfrac{399}{t}$.

8.8.3 $h = 1{,}200$ ft.

8.8.4 $h = 38.5$ in., $h_{\text{coll}} = 57.7$ in.

8.9.1 $f_\phi = -\dfrac{qr}{2t}$, $f_\theta = +\dfrac{qr}{2t}$.

8.9.2 $f_\phi = -\dfrac{qr}{2t}$.

8.9.3 At top ($\phi = 0$), $f_\phi = f_\theta = -\dfrac{qr}{2t}$.

8.9.4 $f_\phi = -\dfrac{wr}{t}\dfrac{1}{1 + \cos\phi}$, $f_\theta = -\dfrac{wr}{t}\left(\cos\phi - \dfrac{1}{1 + \cos\phi}\right)$.

8.9.5 $f_\phi = -W/2\pi rt \sin^2\phi(c)$, $f_\theta = W/2\pi rt \sin^2\phi(t)$

8.9.6 $\phi = 51°50'$.

8.9.7 $f_{\phi,1}/f_{\phi,2} = 79/141$; the 60 ft rise shell.

8.9.8 All parallels; decreases with increasing ϕ.

8.9.9 $f_\phi]_{90} = -f_\theta]_{90°} = -\dfrac{Q}{2\pi rt}$; $f_\phi]_{30°} = f_\theta]_{30°} = 0$.

8.10.1 $f_s = f_t = -f_c = 94$ psi, $A_s = 0.28$ in.^{2}/ft (3 # 3 at 6 in. $\doteq 0.33$ in.^{2}/ft) $A_{CD} = 169$ in.$^2 \doteq 18$ in. $\times$ 10 in. $= 180$ in.^{2}, $A_{AD} = 113$ in.$^2 \doteq 18$ in. $\times$ 7 in. $= 126$ in.^{2}; $A_{s,DE} = 8.45$ in.^{2} ($d = 3\frac{1}{4}$ in). $A_{s,FD} = 5.65$ in.^{2} ($d = 2\frac{3}{4}$ in.) $A_{AB} = 2A_{CD} = 388$ in.$^2 \doteq 18$ in. $\times$ 19 in. $= 342$ in.^{2}; $A_{BC} = 2A_{AD} = 226$ in.^{2} $\doteq 18 \times 13 = 234$ in.^{2}.

8.10.2 $f_s = f_t = -f_c = 94$ psi, $A_s = 0.225$ in.^{2}/ft (2#3 at 6 in. $= 0.22$ in.^{2}/ft.) $A_{CD} = A_{BC} = 180$ in.$^2 = 18$ in. $\times$ 10 in., $A_s = 4.5$ in.^{2} (4 # 10 $= 4.88$ in.^{2}). Diagonal *BC* is in tension.

8.10.3 $c = 3.75$ ft.

8.10.4 $2T' = 2\sqrt{2}\, wa^3/c = 2.83\dfrac{wa^3}{c}$, $T_1 + T_2 = 2\dfrac{wa^3}{c} + \dfrac{wa^3}{c} = 3\dfrac{wa^3}{c}$.

The rectangular hyperbolic paraboloid requires more steel for the tie-rods.

Index

Index